SELECTED SOLUTIONS FOR

CHEMICAL PRINCIPLES
Second Edition

Kenneth C. Brooks
New Mexico State University, Las Cruces

Thomas J. Hummel
University of Illinois, Urbana-Champaign

Steven S. Zumdahl
University of Illinois, Urbana-Champaign

D.C. Heath and Company
Lexington, Massachusetts   Toronto

Address editorial correspondence to:

D. C. Heath and Company
125 Spring Street
Lexington, MA 02173

Published simultaneously in Canada.

Printed in the United States of America.

International Standard Book Number: 0-669-39322-3

10 9 8 7 6 5 4 3 2

TO THE STUDENT: HOW TO USE THIS GUIDE

Chemistry is an applied science. It is valuable because a collection of facts about chemical behavior can be dealt with in a systematic way and applied to solving the new problems that chemists encounter daily. In your study of chemistry you should give priority to solving problems so that you gain a true understanding of chemical concepts.

Solutions to approximately half of the end-of-chapter exercises are in this manual. This Selected Solutions Guide can be very valuable if you use it properly. The way *not* to use it is to look at an exercise in the book and then check the solution, often saying to yourself, "That's easy, I can do it." Chemistry can be easy once you get the hang of it, but it takes work. Don't look up a solution to a problem until you have tried to work the problem on your own. If you try and cannot solve a problem, see if you can find a similar problem in the Examples in the chapter, then work the problem again. Only as a last resort should you look at the solution before you completely solve a problem. If you do get stuck on a problem and must look up a solution, find a similar problem in the end-of-chapter exercises and try working it. The more problems you do, the easier chemistry becomes. It is also in your best interest to try to work as many problems as possible. Most exams that you will take in chemistry will involve a lot of problem solving. You will do much better if you have worked several problems similar to the ones on an exam than if you try to solve a particular type of problem for the first time on the exam. No matter how much you read and study the text, or how well you think you understand the material, you don't really understand it until you use the information to solve problems.

In this Selected Solutions Guide we've worked problems as in the textbook. We have shown intermediate answers to the correct number of significant figures and used that rounded answer in later calculations. Thus, some of your answers may differ slightly from ours. When we have not followed this convention, we have noted this.

We are grateful to Delores Wyatt for her outstanding effort in preparing this guide. We also wish to thank Beverly Foote and Susan Gibson for their careful accuracy review of the entire Selected Solutions Guide.

A Study Guide (ISBN 0-669-39457-2) is also available for student purchase. It provides alternate strategies for solving various types of problems, supplemental explanations for the most difficult material, and self-tests with answers. There are hundreds of worked examples and practice problems to help you master the material. Look for this supplement in your bookstore. If you don't find it, check with your bookstore manager or call D. C. Heath toll free at 1-800-334-3284. In Canada, call toll free at 1-800-268-2472. Tell the operator you are placing a #1-PREFER order.

K. C. B.
T. J. H.
S. S. Z.

TABLE OF CONTENTS

CHAPTER TWO

ATOMS, MOLECULES AND IONS

Development of the Atomic Theory

1. $\dfrac{1.188}{1.188} = 1.000$; $\dfrac{2.375}{1.188} = 1.999$; $\dfrac{3.563}{1.188} = 2.999$

   The masses of fluorine are simple ratios of whole numbers to each other, 1:2:3.

2. From Avogadro's hypothesis, volume ratios are equal to molecule ratios at constant temperature and pressure. Therefore, $Cl_2 + 3 F_2 \rightarrow 2 X$. Two molecules of X contain 6 atoms of F and two atoms of Cl. Therefore, the formula of X is ClF_3.

3.   a. The composition of a substance depends on the numbers of atoms of each element making up the compound (i.e. the formula of the compound) and not on the composition of the mixture from which it was formed.

   b. $H_2 + Cl_2 \rightarrow 2$ HCl. The volume of HCl produced is twice the volume of H_2 (or Cl_2) used.

4. To get the atomic mass of H to be 1.00, we divide the mass that reacts with 1.00 g of oxygen by 0.126. $\dfrac{0.126}{0.126} = 1.00$

   To get Na, Mg, and O on the same scale, we do the same division.

   Na: $\dfrac{2.875}{0.126} = 22.8$; Mg: $\dfrac{1.500}{0.126} = 11.9$; O: $\dfrac{1.00}{0.1260} = 7.94$

	H	O	Na	Mg
Scale	1.00	7.94	22.8	11.9
Accepted Value	1.01 (1.0079)	15.999	22.99	24.31

   The atomic masses of O and Mg are incorrect. The atomic masses of H and Na are close. Something must be wrong about the assumed formulas of the compounds. It turns out the correct formulas are H_2O, Na_2O, and MgO. The smaller discrepancies result from the error in the atomic mass of H.

5.   a.   Atoms have mass and are neither destroyed nor created by chemical reactions. Therefore, mass is neither created nor destroyed by chemical reactions. Mass is conserved.

      b.   The composition of a substance depends on the number and kinds of atoms that form it.

      c.   Compounds of the same elements differ only in numbers of atoms of the elements forming them, i.e., NO, N_2O, NO_2.

6.   Some elements exist as molecular substances. That is, hydrogen normally exists as H_2 molecules, not single hydrogen atoms. The same is true for N_2, O_2, F_2, Cl_2, etc.

7.   Yes, many questions can be raised from Dalton's theory. For example: What are the masses of atoms? Are the atoms really structureless? What forces hold atoms together in compounds?, etc.

8.   We now know that some atoms of the same element have different masses. We have had to include the existence of isotopes in our models.

The Nature of the Atom

11.   Density of hydrogen nucleus:

$$V_{nucleus} = \frac{4}{3}\pi r^3 = \frac{4}{3}(3.14)(5 \times 10^{-14}\text{ cm})^3 = 5 \times 10^{-40}\text{ cm}^3$$

$$d = \frac{1.67 \times 10^{-24}\text{ g}}{5 \times 10^{-40}\text{ cm}^3} = 3 \times 10^{15}\text{ g/cm}^3$$

Density of H-atom:

$$V_{atom} = \frac{4}{3}(3.14)(1 \times 10^{-8}\text{ cm})^3 = 4 \times 10^{-24}\text{ cm}^3$$

$$d = \frac{1.67 \times 10^{-24} + 9 \times 10^{-28}\text{ g}}{4 \times 10^{-24}\text{ cm}^3} = 0.4\text{ g/cm}^3$$

Elements and the Periodic Table

15.   promethium (Pm) and technetium (Tc); Elements with atomic masses in parentheses have no stable isotopes.

16.   a.   Eight, Li to Ne   b.   Eight, Na to Ar

       c.   Eighteen, K to Kr   d.   Four, Fe, Ru, Os, and Uno (#108)

       e.   Five, O, S, Se, Te, Po   f.   Three, Ni, Pd, Pt

17.   a.   P   b.   I

18.   a. $^{24}_{12}$Mg: 12 protons, 12 neutrons, 12 electrons

b. $^{24}_{12}$Mg^{2+}: 12 p, 12 n, 10 e   c. $^{59}_{27}$Co^{2+}: 27 p, 32 n, 25 e

19.

Symbol	Number of protons	Number of neutrons	Number of electrons	Net charge
$^{75}_{33}$As^{3+}	33	42	30	3+
$^{32}_{16}$S^{2-}	16	16	18	2-
$^{204}_{81}$Tl^{+}	81	123	80	1+
$^{197}_{79}$Au	79	118	79	0
$^{197}_{79}$Au^{3+}	79	118	76	3+

21.   Carbon is a nonmetal. Silicon and germanium are metalloids. Tin and lead are metals. Thus, metallic character increases as one goes down a family in the periodic table.

Nomenclature

23.   a. sodium perchlorate   b. magnesium phosphate

c. aluminum sulfate   d. sulfur difluoride

24.   i. dinitrogen tetroxide   j. nitrogen trifluoride

k. dinitrogen tetrafluoride   l. iron(II) sulfate

26.   a. SO_2 b. SO_3 c. Na_2SO_3 d. $KHSO_3$

e. Li_3N f. $Cr_2(CO_3)_3$

Additional Exercises

29.   There should be no difference. The composition of insulin from both sources will be the same
       and therefore, it will have the same activity regardless of the source. As a practical note, trace
       contaminants in the two types of insulin may be different. These trace components may be
       important.

32.   In the case of sulfur, SO_4^{2-} is sulfate and SO_3^{2-} is sulfite. By analogy:

       SeO_4^{2-}: selenate; SeO_3^{2-}: selenite; TeO_4^{2-} tellurate; TeO_3^{2-}: tellurite

34.   If the formula was Be_2O_3, then 2 times the atomic mass of Be would combine with three times
       the atomic mass of oxygen, or:

$$\frac{2 A}{3(15.999)} = \frac{0.5633}{1.000}$$ Solving, A = atomic mass Be = 13.52.

37.   a.   Atomic number is 36. Kr   b.   Atomic number is 52. Te

       c.   Atomic number is 20. Ca   d.   Atomic number is 47. Ag

       e.   Atomic number is 94. Pu

CHAPTER THREE

STOICHIOMETRY

Atomic Masses and the Mass Spectrometer

3. $186.207 = 0.6260 \,(186.956) + 0.3740(A), \ 186.207 - 117.0 = 0.3740(A)$

$$A = \frac{69.2}{0.3740} = 185 \text{ amu}$$

5. $A = 0.0140(203.973) + 0.2410(205.9745) + 0.2210(206.9759) + 0.5240(207.9766)$

$A = 2.86 + 49.64 + 45.74 + 109.0 = 207.2$ amu; The element is Pb.

Moles and Molar Masses

8.   a. 3.00×10^{20} molecules HF $\times \dfrac{1 \text{ mol HF}}{6.022 \times 10^{23} \text{ molecules}} \times \dfrac{20.01 \text{ g HF}}{\text{mol HF}} = 9.97 \times 10^{-3}$ g HF

b. 3.00×10^{-3} mol HF $\times \dfrac{20.01 \text{ g HF}}{\text{mol HF}} = 6.00 \times 10^{-2}$ g HF

c. 1.5×10^{2} mol HF $\times \dfrac{20.01 \text{ g HF}}{\text{mol HF}} = 3.0 \times 10^{3}$ g HF

d.   1 molecule HF $\times \dfrac{1 \text{ mol HF}}{6.022 \times 10^{23} \text{ molecules HF}} \times \dfrac{20.01 \text{ g HF}}{\text{mol HF}} = 3.323 \times 10^{-23}$ g HF

e. 2.00×10^{-15} mol HF $\times \dfrac{20.01 \text{ g HF}}{\text{mol HF}} = 4.00 \times 10^{-14}$ g HF $= 40.0$ fg HF

f.   18.0 pmol HF $\times \dfrac{1 \text{ mol HF}}{10^{12} \text{ pmol}} \times \dfrac{20.01 \text{ g HF}}{\text{mol HF}} = 3.60 \times 10^{-10}$ g HF $= 360.$ pg HF

g.   5.0 nmol HF $\times \dfrac{1 \text{ mol HF}}{10^{9} \text{ nmol}} \times \dfrac{20.01 \text{ g HF}}{\text{mol HF}} = 1.0 \times 10^{-7}$ g HF $= 1.0 \times 10^{2}$ ng

9.   a. $100 \text{ molecules } H_2O \times \dfrac{1 \text{ mol } H_2O}{6.022 \times 10^{23} \text{ molecules } H_2O} = 1.661 \times 10^{-22} \text{ mol } H_2O$

    b. $100.0 \text{ g } H_2O \times \dfrac{1 \text{ mol } H_2O}{18.015 \text{ g } H_2O} = 5.551 \text{ mol } H_2O$

    c. $500 \text{ atoms Fe} \times \dfrac{1 \text{ mol Fe}}{6.022 \times 10^{23} \text{ atoms}} = 8.303 \times 10^{-22} \text{ mol Fe}$

    d. $500.0 \text{ g Fe} \times \dfrac{1 \text{ mol Fe}}{55.85 \text{ g Fe}} = 8.953 \text{ mol Fe}$

    e. $150 \text{ molecules } N_2 \times \dfrac{1 \text{ mol } N_2}{6.022 \times 10^{23} \text{ molecules } N_2} = 2.491 \times 10^{-22} \text{ mol } N_2$

    f. $150.0 \text{ g } Fe_2O_3 \times \dfrac{1 \text{ mol}}{159.70 \text{ g}} = 0.9393 \text{ mol } Fe_2O_3$

    g. $10.0 \text{ mg } NO_2 \times \dfrac{1 \text{ g}}{10^3 \text{ mg}} \times \dfrac{1 \text{ mol}}{46.01 \text{ g}} = 2.17 \times 10^{-4} \text{ mol } NO_2$

    h. $1.0 \text{ fmol } NO_2 \times \dfrac{1 \text{ mol}}{10^{15} \text{ fmol}} = 1.0 \times 10^{-15} \text{ mol } NO_2$

    i. $1.5 \times 10^{16} \text{ molecules } BF_3 \times \dfrac{1 \text{ mol}}{6.02 \times 10^{23} \text{ molecules}} = 2.5 \times 10^{-8} \text{ mol } BF_3$

    j. $2.6 \text{ mg } BF_3 \times \dfrac{1 \text{ g}}{10^3 \text{ mg}} \times \dfrac{1 \text{ mol}}{67.8 \text{ g}} = 3.8 \times 10^{-5} \text{ mol } BF_3$

12. $1.0 \text{ lb flour} \times \dfrac{454 \text{ g flour}}{\text{lb flour}} \times \dfrac{30.0 \times 10^{-9} \text{ g EDB}}{\text{g flour}} \times \dfrac{1 \text{ mol EDB}}{187.9 \text{ g}} \times \dfrac{6.02 \times 10^{23} \text{ molecules}}{\text{mol EDB}}$

$$= 4.4 \times 10^{16} \text{ molecules of EDB}$$

Percent Composition

13.   In 1 mole of $YBa_2Cu_3O_7$ there are 1 mole of Y, 2 moles of Ba, 3 moles of Cu, and 7 moles of O.

$$\text{Molar mass} = 1 \text{ mol Y} \left(\dfrac{88.91 \text{ g Y}}{\text{mol Y}} \right) + 2 \text{ mol Ba} \left(\dfrac{137.3 \text{ g Ba}}{\text{mol Ba}} \right)$$

$$+ 3 \text{ mol Cu} \left(\dfrac{63.55 \text{ g Cu}}{\text{mol Cu}} \right) + 7 \text{ mol O} \left(\dfrac{16.00 \text{ g O}}{\text{mol O}} \right)$$

Molar mass = 88.91 + 274.6 + 190.65 + 112.00 = 666.2 g/mol

$\% \ Y = \dfrac{88.91 \ g}{666.2 \ g} \times 100 = 13.35\% \ Y; \quad \% \ Ba = \dfrac{274.6 \ g}{666.2 \ g} \times 100 = 41.22\% \ Ba$

$\% \ Cu = \dfrac{190.65 \ g}{666.2 \ g} \times 100 = 28.62\% \ Cu; \quad \% \ O = \dfrac{112.0 \ g}{666.2 \ g} \times 100 = 16.81\% \ O$

or % O = 100.00 - (13.35 + 41.22 + 28.62) = 100.00 - (83.19) = 16.81% O

14.   a. PF_3: molar mass = 31.0 + 3(19.0) = 88.0 g/mol

mass % P = $\dfrac{31.0 \ g}{88.0 \ g} \times 100 = 35.2\%$

b. P_4O_{10}: molar mass = 4(31.0) + 10(16.0) = 284.0 g/mol

mass % P = $\dfrac{124 \ g}{284.0 \ g} \times 100 = 43.7\%$

c. $(NPCl_2)_3$: molar mass = 3(14.0) + 3(31.0) + 6(35.45) = 347.7 g/mol

mass % P = $\dfrac{93.0 \ g}{347.7 \ g} \times 100 = 26.7\%$

d.   InP: molar mass = 114.8 + 31.0 = 145.8 g/mol

mass % P = $\dfrac{31.0 \ g}{145.8 \ g} \times 100 = 21.3\%$

The order from lowest to highest percentage of phosphorus is:

$InP < (NPCl_2)_3 < PF_3 < P_4O_{10}$

16.   % Co = 4.34 = $\dfrac{58.95 \ g \ Co}{molar \ mass} \times 100$, molar mass = 1360 g/mol

Empirical and Molecular Formulas

20.   First, get composition in mass percent. We assume all of the carbon in 0.213 g CO_2 came from the 0.157 g of the compound and that all of the hydrogen in the 0.0310 g H_2O came from the 0.157 g of the compound.

$0.213 \ g \ CO_2 \times \dfrac{12.01 \ g \ C}{44.01 \ g \ CO_2} = 0.0581 \ g \ C$

$\% \ C = \dfrac{0.0581 \ g \ C}{0.157 \ g \ compound} \times 100 = 37.0\% \ C$

$0.0310 \ g \ H_2O \times \dfrac{2.016 \ g \ H}{18.02 \ g \ H_2O} = 3.47 \times 10^{-3} \ g \ H$

$$\% \text{ H} = \frac{3.47 \times 10^{-3} \text{ g}}{0.157 \text{ g}} = 2.21\% \text{ H}$$

We get % N from the second experiment:

$$0.0230 \text{ g NH}_3 \times \frac{14.01 \text{ g N}}{17.03 \text{ g NH}_3} = 1.89 \times 10^{-2} \text{ g N}$$

$$\% \text{ N} = \frac{1.89 \times 10^{-2} \text{ g}}{0.103 \text{ g}} \times 100 = 18.3\% \text{ N}$$

The mass percent of oxygen is obtained by difference:

$$\% \text{ O} = 100.0 - (37.0 + 2.21 + 18.3) = 42.5\%$$

So, out of 100.0 g of compound, there are:

$$37.0 \text{ g C} \times \frac{1 \text{ mol}}{12.01 \text{ g}} = 3.08 \text{ mol C}$$

$$2.21 \text{ g H} \times \frac{1 \text{ mol H}}{1.008 \text{ g H}} = 2.19 \text{ mol H}$$

$$18.3 \text{ g N} \times \frac{1 \text{ mol N}}{14.01 \text{ g N}} = 1.31 \text{ mol N}$$

$$42.5 \text{ g O} \times \frac{1 \text{ mol O}}{16.00 \text{ g O}} = 2.66 \text{ mol O}$$

Lastly, and often the hardest part, we need to find simple whole number ratios. We do this by trial and error.

$$\frac{2.19}{1.31} = 1.67 = 1\frac{2}{3} = \frac{5}{3}$$

So, we try $\dfrac{1.31}{3} = 0.437$ as lowest common denominator.

$$\frac{3.08}{0.437} \approx 7 \qquad \frac{2.19}{0.437} \approx 5 \qquad \frac{1.31}{0.437} = 3 \qquad \frac{2.66}{0.437} \approx 6$$

Empirical formula is $C_7H_5N_3O_6$.

22. $$0.979 \text{ g Na} \times \frac{1 \text{ mol Na}}{22.99 \text{ g Na}} = 4.26 \times 10^{-2} \text{ mol Na}$$

$$1.365 \text{ g S} \times \frac{1 \text{ mol S}}{32.07 \text{ g S}} = 4.256 \times 10^{-2} \text{ mol S}$$

$$1.021 \text{ g O} \times \frac{1 \text{ mol O}}{15.999 \text{ g O}} = 6.382 \times 10^{-2} \text{ mol O}$$

$$\frac{6.382 \times 10^{-2} \text{ mol O}}{4.256 \times 10^{-2} \text{ mol S}} = 1.500 = \frac{1.5 \text{ mol O}}{\text{mol S}} = \frac{3 \text{ mol O}}{2 \text{ mol S}}, \frac{\text{mol Na}}{\text{mol S}} \approx 1$$

Empirical formula: $Na_2S_2O_3$

23.   Out of 100.0 g of the pigment, there are:

$$59.9 \text{ g Ti} \times \frac{1 \text{ mol Ti}}{47.88 \text{ g Ti}} = 1.25 \text{ mol Ti}$$

$$40.1 \text{ g O} \times \frac{1 \text{ mol O}}{16.00 \text{ g O}} = 2.51 \text{ mol O}$$

Empirical formula: TiO_2

25. $156.8 \text{ mg CO}_2 \times \dfrac{12.011 \text{ mg C}}{44.009 \text{ mg CO}_2} = 42.79 \text{ mg C}$

$42.8 \text{ mg H}_2\text{O} \times \dfrac{2.016 \text{ mg H}}{18.02 \text{ mg H}_2\text{O}} = 4.79 \text{ mg H}$

$\% \text{ C} = \dfrac{42.79 \text{ mg}}{47.6 \text{ mg}} \times 100 = 89.9\% \text{ C}; \ \% \text{ H} = 100.0 - 89.9 = 10.1\% \text{ H}$

Out of 100.0 g Cumene, we have:

$$89.9 \text{ g C} \times \frac{1 \text{ mol C}}{12.01 \text{ g C}} = 7.49 \text{ mol C}; \ 10.1 \text{ g H} \times \frac{1 \text{ mol H}}{1.008 \text{ g H}} = 10.0 \text{ mol H}$$

$\dfrac{7.49}{10.0} = 0.749 \approx 0.75$ which is a 3:4 ratio. Empirical formula: C_3H_4

Mass of one empirical formula $\approx 3(12) + 4(1) = 40$

So molecular formula is $(C_3H_4)_3$ or C_9H_{12}.

Balancing Chemical Equations

28.   a. $Fe + O_2 \rightarrow Fe_2O_3$

$2 \text{ Fe(s)} + 3/2 \text{ O}_2\text{(g)} \rightarrow Fe_2O_3\text{(s)}$

Multiply all coefficients by 2 to convert the fraction coefficient of oxygen to a whole number.

$4 \text{ Fe(s)} + 3 \text{ O}_2\text{(g)} \rightarrow 2 \text{ Fe}_2\text{O}_3\text{(s)}$

b. $C_6H_{12}O_6 \rightarrow C_2H_5OH + CO_2$

Balance C-atoms first.   6-C on left, 3-C on right.
First, try multiplying both products by 2:

$C_6H_{12}O_6 \rightarrow 2\ C_2H_5OH + 2\ CO_2$

O and H are also balanced, and the balanced equation is:

$C_6H_{12}O_6(aq) \rightarrow 2\ C_2H_5OH(aq) + 2\ CO_2(g)$

c. $Ca(s) + 2\ H_2O(l) \rightarrow Ca(OH)_2(aq) + H_2(g)$

d. $Ba(OH)_2(aq) + H_2SO_4(aq) \rightarrow BaSO_4(s) + 2\ H_2O(l)$

Reaction Stoichiometry

31. $1.000 \text{ kg Al} \times \dfrac{1000 \text{ g Al}}{\text{kg Al}} \times \dfrac{1 \text{ mol Al}}{26.98 \text{ g Al}} \times \dfrac{3 \text{ mol NH}_4\text{ClO}_4}{3 \text{ mol Al}} \times \dfrac{117.49 \text{ g NH}_4\text{ClO}_4}{\text{mol NH}_4\text{ClO}_4} = 4355 \text{ g}$

33. $1.0 \times 10^2 \text{ g Ca}_3(\text{PO}_4)_2 \times \dfrac{1 \text{ mol Ca}_3(\text{PO}_4)_2}{310.2 \text{ g Ca}_3(\text{PO}_4)_2} \times \dfrac{3 \text{ mol H}_2\text{SO}_4}{\text{mol Ca}_3(\text{PO}_4)_2}$

$\times \dfrac{98.09 \text{ g H}_2\text{SO}_4}{\text{mol H}_2\text{SO}_4} = 95 \text{ g H}_2\text{SO}_4 \text{ are needed}$

$95 \text{ g H}_2\text{SO}_4 \times \dfrac{100 \text{ g concentrated reagent}}{98 \text{ g H}_2\text{SO}_4} = 97 \text{ g of concentrated sulfuric acid}$

35. a. $C_8H_{18}(l) + \dfrac{25}{2}\ O_2(g) \rightarrow 8\ CO_2(g) + 9\ H_2O(g)$

or $2\ C_8H_{18}(l) + 25\ O_2(g) \rightarrow 16\ CO_2(g) + 18\ H_2O(g)$

b. $1.2 \times 10^{10} \text{ gallon} \times \dfrac{4 \text{ qt}}{\text{gal}} \times \dfrac{946 \text{ mL}}{\text{qt}} \times \dfrac{0.692 \text{ g}}{\text{mL}} = 3.1 \times 10^{13} \text{ g of gasoline}$

$3.1 \times 10^{13} \text{ g C}_8\text{H}_{18} \times \dfrac{1 \text{ mol C}_8\text{H}_{18}}{114.2 \text{ g C}_8\text{H}_{18}} \times \dfrac{16 \text{ mol CO}_2}{2 \text{ mol C}_8\text{H}_{18}} \times \dfrac{44.0 \text{ g CO}_2}{\text{mol CO}_2} = 9.6 \times 10^{13} \text{ g CO}_2$

Limiting Reactants and Percent Yield

38. $2\ Cu(s) + S(s) \rightarrow Cu_2S(s)$ or $16\ Cu(s) + S_8(s) \rightarrow 8\ Cu_2S(s)$

$2.00 \text{ g Cu} \times \dfrac{1 \text{ mol Cu}}{63.55 \text{ g Cu}} \times \dfrac{1 \text{ mol Cu}_2\text{S}}{2 \text{ mol Cu}} \times \dfrac{159.2 \text{ g Cu}_2\text{S}}{\text{mol Cu}_2\text{S}} = 2.51 \text{ g Cu}_2\text{S is theoretical yield.}$

$$\% \text{ yield} = \frac{\text{Actual yield}}{\text{Theoretical yield}} \times 100 = \frac{2.31 \text{ g}}{2.51 \text{ g}} \times 100 = 92.0\%$$

40.   a. $1.00 \text{ g Ag} \times \dfrac{1 \text{ mol Ag}}{107.9 \text{ g Ag}} \times \dfrac{8 \text{ mol Ag}_2\text{S}}{16 \text{ mol Ag}} = 4.63 \times 10^{-3} \text{ mol Ag}_2\text{S}$

$2.00 \text{ g S}_8 \times \dfrac{1 \text{ mol S}_8}{256.6 \text{ g S}_8} \times \dfrac{8 \text{ mol Ag}_2\text{S}}{\text{mol S}_8} = 6.24 \times 10^{-2} \text{ mol Ag}_2\text{S}$

When 4.63×10^{-3} mol Ag_2S is formed, all of the Ag will be consumed.

Ag is limiting. 4.63×10^{-3} mol $Ag_2S \times 247.9$ g/mol = 1.15 g Ag_2S

b. S_8 is left unreacted. 0.15 g sulfur (1.15 g Ag_2S - 1.00 g Ag) is required to make 1.15 g of Ag_2S. Therefore, 1.85 g S_8 remains.

43. $C_6H_{10}O_4 + 2 NH_3 + 4 H_2 \rightarrow C_6H_{16}N_2 + 4 H_2O$

Adip (Adipic acid)   HMD

a. $1.00 \times 10^3 \text{ g Adip} \times \dfrac{1 \text{ mol Adip}}{146.1 \text{ g Adip}} \times \dfrac{1 \text{ mol HMD}}{\text{mol Adip}} \times \dfrac{116.2 \text{ g HMD}}{\text{mol HMD}} = 795 \text{ g HMD}$

b. $\% \text{ Yield} = \dfrac{765 \text{ g}}{795 \text{ g}} \times 100 = 96.2\%$

Additional Exercises

45. $\dfrac{9.123 \times 10^{-23} \text{ g}}{\text{atom}} \times \dfrac{6.022 \times 10^{23} \text{ atom}}{\text{mol}} = \dfrac{54.94 \text{ g}}{\text{mol}}$

The atomic mass is 54.94. The element is manganese (Mn).

47.   a.   M = 195.1 + 2(14.01) + 6(1.008) + 2(35.45) = 300.1 g/mol

$\% \text{ Pt} = \dfrac{195.1 \text{ g}}{300.1 \text{ g}} \times 100 = 65.01\% \text{ Pt}; \quad \% \text{ N} = \dfrac{28.02 \text{ g}}{300.1 \text{ g}} \times 100 = 9.335\% \text{ N};$

$\% \text{ H} = \dfrac{6.048 \text{ g}}{300.1 \text{ g}} \times 100 = 2.015\% \text{ H}; \quad \% \text{ Cl} = \dfrac{70.90 \text{ g}}{300.1 \text{ g}} \times 100 = 23.63\% \text{ Cl}$

65.01% Pt; 9.335% N; 2.015% H; 23.63% Cl

b. $100. \text{ g K}_2\text{PtCl}_4 \times \dfrac{1 \text{ mol K}_2\text{PtCl}_4}{415.1 \text{ g K}_2\text{PtCl}_4} \times \dfrac{1 \text{ mol cisplatin}}{\text{mol K}_2\text{PtCl}_4} \times \dfrac{300.1 \text{ g cisplatin}}{\text{mol cisplatin}} = 72.3 \text{ g cisplatin}$

$100. \text{ g K}_2\text{PtCl}_4 \times \dfrac{1 \text{ mol K}_2\text{PtCl}_4}{415.1 \text{ g K}_2\text{PtCl}_4} \times \dfrac{2 \text{ mol KCl}}{\text{mol K}_2\text{PtCl}_4} \times \dfrac{74.55 \text{ g KCl}}{\text{mol KCl}} = 35.9 \text{ g KCl}$

49.   Out of 100.00 g of compound there are:

$$83.53 \text{ g Sb} \times \frac{1 \text{ mol Sb}}{121.8 \text{ g Sb}} = 0.6858 \text{ mol Sb}$$

$$16.47 \text{ g O} \times \frac{1 \text{ mol O}}{15.599 \text{ g O}} = 1.029 \text{ mol O}$$

$$\frac{0.6858}{1.029} = 0.6665 \approx \frac{2}{3} \qquad \text{Empirical formula: } Sb_2O_3$$

Mass of Sb_2O_3 unit is $2(121.8) + 3(16.0) = 291.6$

Mass of Sb_4O_6 is 583.2, which is in the correct range. Therefore the molecular formula is Sb_4O_6.

51.   Consider the case of aluminum plus oxygen. Aluminum forms Al^{3+} ions; oxygen forms O^{2-} anions. The simplest compound of the two elements is Al_2O_3. Similarly we would expect the formula of any group VI element with Al to be Al_2X_3. Assuming this, out of 100.00 g of compound there are 18.56 g Al and 81.44 g of the unknown element.

$$18.56 \text{ g Al} \times \frac{1 \text{ mol Al}}{26.98 \text{ g Al}} \times \frac{3 \text{ mol X}}{2 \text{ mol Al}} = 1.032 \text{ mol X}$$

100.00 g of the compound must contain 1.032 mol of X, if the formula is Al_2X_3. Therefore:

$$\text{Atomic mass X} = \frac{81.44 \text{ g X}}{1.032 \text{ mol X}} = 78.91 \text{ g X/mol}$$

The unknown element is selenium, Se, and the formula is Al_2Se_3.

53. $$41.98 \text{ mg CO}_2 \times \frac{12.01 \text{ mg C}}{44.01 \text{ mg CO}_2} = 11.46 \text{ mg C}; \quad \% \text{ C} = \frac{11.46 \text{ mg}}{19.81 \text{ mg}} \times 100 = 57.85\% \text{ C}$$

$$6.45 \text{ mg H}_2O \times \frac{2.016 \text{ mg H}}{18.02 \text{ mg H}_2O} = 0.722 \text{ mg H}; \quad \% \text{ H} = \frac{0.722 \text{ mg}}{19.81 \text{ mg}} \times 100 = 3.64\% \text{ H}$$

$\% \text{ O} = 100.00 - (57.85 + 3.64) = 38.51\% \text{ O}$

Out of 100.00 g terephthalic acid, there are:

$$57.85 \text{ g C} \times \frac{1 \text{ mol C}}{12.011 \text{ g C}} = 4.816 \text{ mol C}; \quad 3.64 \text{ g H} \times \frac{1 \text{ mol H}}{1.008 \text{ g H}} = 3.61 \text{ mol H};$$

$$38.51 \text{ g O} \times \frac{1 \text{ mol O}}{15.999 \text{ g O}} = 2.407 \text{ mol O}$$

$$\frac{4.816}{2.407} \approx 2, \quad \frac{3.61}{2.407} = 1.5, \quad \frac{2.407}{2.407} = 1$$

C:H:O ratio is 2:1.5:1 or 4:3:2. Empirical formula: $C_4H_3O_2$

Mass of $C_4H_3O_2 \approx 4(12) + 3(1) + 2(16) = 83$

$\dfrac{166}{83} = 2$; Molecular formula: $C_8H_6O_4$

55. $Ca_3(PO_4)_2 + 3\ H_2SO_4 \rightarrow 3\ CaSO_4 + 2\ H_3PO_4$

1.0×10^3 g $Ca_3(PO_4)_2 \times \dfrac{1\ mol\ Ca_3(PO_4)_2}{310.2\ g\ Ca_3(PO_4)_2} \times \dfrac{3\ mol\ CaSO_4}{mol\ Ca_3(PO_4)_2} = 9.7\ mol\ CaSO_4$

1.0×10^3 g con $H_2SO_4 \times \dfrac{98\ g\ H_2SO_4}{100\ g\ con\ H_2SO_4} = 980\ g\ H_2SO_4$

$980\ g\ H_2SO_4 \times \dfrac{1\ mol\ H_2SO_4}{98.1\ g\ H_2SO_4} \times \dfrac{3\ mol\ CaSO_4}{3\ mol\ H_2SO_4} = 10.\ mol\ CaSO_4$

The calcium phosphate is the limiting reagent.

$9.7\ mol\ CaSO_4 \times \dfrac{136.2\ g\ CaSO_4}{mol\ CaSO_4} = 1300\ g\ CaSO_4$

$9.7\ mol\ CaSO_4 \times \dfrac{2\ mol\ H_3PO_4}{3\ mol\ CaSO_4} \times \dfrac{98.0\ g\ H_3PO_4}{mol\ H_3PO_4} = 630\ g\ H_3PO_4$

57. $Hg + Br_2 \rightarrow HgBr_2$

a. $10.0\ g\ Hg \times \dfrac{1\ mol\ Hg}{200.6\ g\ Hg} \times \dfrac{1\ mol\ HgBr_2}{mol\ Hg} = 4.99 \times 10^{-2}\ mol\ HgBr_2$

$10.0\ g\ Br_2 \times \dfrac{1\ mol\ Br_2}{159.8\ Br_2} \times \dfrac{1\ mol\ HgBr_2}{mol\ Br_2} = 6.26 \times 10^{-2}\ mol\ HgBr_2$

Hg is limiting. $HgBr_2$ produced is:

$4.99 \times 10^{-2}\ mol\ HgBr_2 \times \dfrac{360.4\ g\ HgBr_2}{mol\ HgBr_2} = 17.98\ g \approx 18.0\ g\ HgBr_2$

18.0 g $HgBr_2$ with 2.0 g Br_2 left unreacted.

b. $5.00\ mL\ Hg \times \dfrac{13.5\ g\ Hg}{mL} = 67.5\ g\ Hg$; $5.00\ ml\ Br_2 \times \dfrac{3.12\ g\ Br_2}{mL\ Br_2} = 15.6\ g\ Br_2$

$67.5\ g\ Hg \times \dfrac{1\ mol\ Hg}{200.6\ g\ Hg} \times \dfrac{1\ mol\ HgBr_2}{mol\ Hg} = 0.336\ mol\ HgBr_2$

$15.6\ g\ Br_2 \times \dfrac{1\ mol\ Br_2}{159.8\ g\ Br_2} \times \dfrac{1\ mol\ HgBr_2}{mol\ Br_2} = 0.0976\ mol\ HgBr_2$

Br$_2$ is limiting.

$$0.0976 \text{ mol HgBr}_2 \times \frac{360.4 \text{ g HgBr}_2}{\text{mol HgBr}_2} = 35.2 \text{ g HgBr}_2$$

59. $^{12}C_2\,^1H_6$: $2(12.000000) + 6(1.007825) = 30.046950$ amu

$^{12}C^1H_2\,^{16}O$: $1(12.000000) + 2(1.007825) + 1(15.994915) = 30.010565$ amu

$^{14}N^{16}O$: $1(14.003074) + 1(15.994915) = 29.997989$ amu

The peak results from $^{12}C^1H_2\,^{16}O$.

62.   The volume of a gas is proportional to the number of molecules of gas. Thus the formulas are:

I: H_3N,   II: H_4N_2,   III: HN_3

The mass ratios are:

I: $\dfrac{4.634 \text{ g N}}{\text{g H}}$,   II: $\dfrac{6.949 \text{ g N}}{\text{g H}}$, III: $\dfrac{41.7 \text{ g N}}{\text{g H}}$

If we set the atomic mass of H equal to 1.008, then the atomic mass for nitrogen is:

I: 14.01,   II: 14.01,   III. 14.0

For example for Compound I: $\dfrac{A}{3(1.008)} = \dfrac{4.634}{1}$, $A = 14.01$

64. $PaO_2 + O_2 \rightarrow Pa_xO_y$ (unbalanced)

$$0.200 \text{ g PaO}_2 \times \frac{231 \text{ g Pa}}{263 \text{ g PaO}_2} = 0.1757 \text{ g Pa} \quad \text{(We will carry an extra S.F.)}$$

0.2081 g Pa$_x$O$_y$ - 0.1757 g Pa = 0.0324 g O

$$0.1757 \text{ g Pa} \times \frac{1 \text{ mol Pa}}{231 \text{ g Pa}} = 7.61 \times 10^{-4} \text{ mol Pa}$$

$$0.0324 \text{ g O} \times \frac{1 \text{ mol O}}{16.00 \text{ g O}} = 2.025 \times 10^{-3} \text{ mol O}$$

$$\frac{\text{mol O}}{\text{mol Pa}} = \frac{2.025 \times 10^{-3} \text{ mol O}}{7.61 \times 10^{-4} \text{ mol Pa}} = 2.66 \approx 2\frac{2}{3} = \frac{8 \text{ mol O}}{3 \text{ mol Pa}}$$

Empirical formula: Pa_3O_8

66. $1.375 \text{ g AgI} \times \dfrac{1 \text{ mol AgI}}{234.8 \text{ g AgI}} = 5.856 \times 10^{-3} \text{ mol AgI} = 5.856 \times 10^{-3} \text{ mol I}$

$1.375 \text{ g AgI} \times \dfrac{126.9 \text{ g I}}{234.8 \text{ g AgI}} = 0.7431 \text{ g I}$

XI_2 contains 0.7431 g I and 0.257 g X.

$5.856 \times 10^{-3} \text{ mol I} \times \dfrac{1 \text{ mol X}}{2 \text{ mol I}} = 2.928 \times 10^{-3} \text{ mol X}$

$\dfrac{0.257 \text{ g X}}{2.928 \times 10^{-3} \text{ mol X}} = \dfrac{87.8 \text{ g}}{\text{mol}}$ (X is Sr.)

69. $4.000 \text{ g M}_2S_3 \rightarrow 3.723 \text{ g MO}_2$

There are twice as many moles of MO_2 as of M_2S_3.

$2\left(\dfrac{4.000 \text{ g}}{2\,A + 3(32.07)}\right) = \dfrac{3.723 \text{ g}}{A + 2(16.00)}, \quad \dfrac{8.000}{2\,A + 96.21} = \dfrac{3.723}{A + 32.00}$

$8.000\,A + 256.0 = 7.446\,A + 358.2, \;\; 0.554\,A = 102.2$

$A = \dfrac{184 \text{ g}}{\text{mol}};$ The metal is W.

70. X_2Z: 40.0% X and 60.0% Z by mass

$\dfrac{\text{mol X}}{\text{mol Z}} = 2 = \dfrac{40.0/A_x}{60.0/A_z} = \dfrac{40.0\,A_z}{60.0\,A_x}$ or $A_z = 3\,A_x$

For XZ_2, molar mass $= A_x + 2\,A_z = A_x + 2(3\,A_x) = 7\,A_x$

$\% X = \dfrac{A_x}{7A_x} \times 100 = 14.3\% \text{ X}$ $\% Z = 100.0 - \% X = 85.7\% \text{ Z}$

72. $10{,}000 \text{ kg waste} \times \dfrac{3.0 \text{ kg NH}_4^+}{100 \text{ kg waste}} \times \dfrac{1000 \text{ g}}{\text{kg}} \times \dfrac{1 \text{ mol NH}_4^+}{18.04 \text{ g NH}_4^+} \times \dfrac{1 \text{ mol C}_5H_7O_2N}{55 \text{ mol NH}_4^+}$

$\times \dfrac{113.12 \text{ g C}_5H_7O_2N}{\text{mol C}_5H_7O_2N} = 3.4 \times 10^4 \text{ g tissue if all NH}_4^+ \text{ converted}$

Since only 95% of the NH_4^+ ions react:

mass of tissue $= (0.95)(3.4 \times 10^4 \text{ g}) = 3.2 \times 10^4$ g or 32 kg

75. $MCO_3(s) + 2 H^+(aq) \rightarrow M^{2+}(aq) + H_2O(l) + CO_2(g)$

$$0.421 \text{ g CO}_2 \times \frac{1 \text{ mol CO}_2}{44.01 \text{ g CO}_2} \times \frac{1 \text{ mol MCO}_2}{1 \text{ mol CO}_2} = 9.57 \times 10^{-3} \text{ mol of MCO}_3 \text{ present}$$

Let x = g $SrCO_3$ and y = g $BaCO_3$:

   Mass balance: $x + y = 1.60$ g

   Mole balance: $\dfrac{x}{147.6} + \dfrac{y}{197.3} = 9.57 \times 10^{-3}$ total mol or $1.337 x + y = 1.89$

Solving:

$$1.337 x + y = 1.89$$
$$\underline{-x - y = -1.60}$$
$$0.337 x \quad = 0.29$$

$x = 0.86$ g $SrCO_3$ and $y = 0.74$ g $BaCO_3$

% $SrCO_3 = \dfrac{0.86 \text{ g}}{1.60 \text{ g}} \times 100 = 54\%$ by mass; % $BaCO_3 = 46\%$

Note: with no rounding, % $SrCO_3 = 53.4\%$; % $BaCO_3 = 46.6\%$

78. $a \text{ C}_8\text{H}_{18} \text{ (l)} + b \text{ O}_2 \text{ (g)} \rightarrow c \text{ CO}_2 \text{ (g)} + d \text{ CO (g)} + e \text{ CH}_4 \text{ (g)} + f \text{ H}_2 \text{ (g)} + g \text{ H}_2\text{O (g)}$

Volume ratios are proportional to mole ratios. Volume percent of O_2 reacted is:

$$\frac{21 \text{ mol \% O}_2}{78 \text{ mol \% N}_2} = \frac{x}{82.1 \text{ vol \% N}_2}, \quad x = 22 \text{ vol \% O}_2 = \text{volume percent of O}_2 \text{ reacted}$$

Determining mole ratios in balanced equation:

$\dfrac{b}{c} = \dfrac{22}{11.5} = 1.9,\ c = 0.52 \text{ b};\quad \dfrac{b}{d} = \dfrac{22}{4.4} = 5.0,\ d = 0.20 \text{ b};$

$\dfrac{b}{e} = \dfrac{22}{0.5} = 44 \approx 40,\ e = 0.02 \text{ b};\quad \dfrac{b}{f} = \dfrac{22}{1.5} = 15,\ f = 0.068 \text{ b}$

Balancing the carbon atoms: $8a = c + d + e$

Let's assume $a = 1$, so 1 mol of gasoline consumed:

$8 = 0.52 \text{ b} + 0.20 \text{ b} + 0.02 \text{ b} = 0.74 \text{ b},\ b = 11$

Using b to determine c, d, e, and f:

c = 5.7; d = 2.2; e = 0.2; f = 0.75

Balancing the hydrogen atoms: 18 a = 4 e + 2 f + 2 g, 18 = 4(0.2) + 2(0.75) + 2 g, g = 7.9

$C_8H_{18} + 11 O_2 \rightarrow 5.7 CO_2 + 2.2 CO + 0.2 CH_4 + 0.75 H_2 + 7.9 H_2O$

CHAPTER FOUR

TYPES OF CHEMICAL REACTIONS AND SOLUTION STOICHIOMETRY

Aqueous Solutions: Strong and Weak Electrolytes

1.   "Slightly soluble" refers to substances that dissolve only to a small extent. A slightly soluble salt may still dissociate completely to ions and, hence, be a strong electrolyte. An example of such a substance is $Mg(OH)_2$. It is a strong electrolyte, but not very soluble. A weak electrolyte is a substance that doesn't dissociate completely to produce ions. A weak electrolyte may be very soluble in water, or it may not be very soluble.   Acetic acid is an example of a weak electrolyte that is very soluble in water.

Solution Concentration: Molarity

5.   a. $4.592 \text{ g NaHCO}_3 \times \dfrac{1 \text{ mol NaHCO}_3}{84.01 \text{ g NaHCO}_3} = 5.466 \times 10^{-2} \text{ mol}$

$$M = \dfrac{5.466 \times 10^{-2} \text{ mol}}{250.0 \text{ mL}} \times \dfrac{1000 \text{ mL}}{L} = 0.2186 \text{ mol/L}$$

   b. $0.2759 \text{ g K}_2\text{Cr}_2\text{O}_7 \times \dfrac{1 \text{ mol K}_2\text{Cr}_2\text{O}_7}{294.20 \text{ g K}_2\text{Cr}_2\text{O}_7} = 9.378 \times 10^{-4} \text{ mol}$

$$M = \dfrac{9.378 \times 10^{-4} \text{ mol}}{500.0 \times 10^{-3} \text{ L}} = 1.876 \times 10^{-3} \text{ mol/L}$$

   c. $0.1025 \text{ g Cu} \times \dfrac{1 \text{ mol Cu}}{63.55 \text{ g Cu}} = 1.613 \times 10^{-3} \text{ mol Cu} = 1.613 \times 10^{-3} \text{ mol Cu}^{2+}$

$$M = \dfrac{1.613 \times 10^{-3} \text{ mol Cu}^{2+}}{200.0 \text{ mL}} \times \dfrac{1000 \text{ mL}}{L} = 8.065 \times 10^{-3} \text{ mol/L}$$

6. $\dfrac{50.0 \times 10^{-3} \text{ g Myocrisin}}{0.500 \times 10^{-3} \text{ L}} \times \dfrac{1 \text{ mol Myocrisin}}{390.1 \text{ g}} = 0.256 \ M$

$\dfrac{300.0 \times 10^{-6} \text{ g Au}}{100.0 \text{ mL}} \times \dfrac{1 \text{ mol Au}}{197.0 \text{ g Au}} \times \dfrac{1 \text{ mol Myocrisin}}{\text{mol Au}} \times \dfrac{1000 \text{ mL}}{L} = 1.523 \times 10^{-5} \ M$

9.   a.   5.0 ppb Hg in water = $\dfrac{5.0 \text{ ng Hg}}{\text{mL } H_2O} = \dfrac{5.0 \times 10^{-9} \text{ g Hg}}{\text{mL } H_2O}$

$$\dfrac{5.0 \times 10^{-9} \text{ g Hg}}{\text{mL}} \times \dfrac{1 \text{ mol Hg}}{200.6 \text{ g Hg}} \times \dfrac{1000 \text{ mL}}{L} = 2.5 \times 10^{-8} \ M$$

   b. $\dfrac{1.0 \times 10^{-9} \text{ g CHCl}_3}{\text{mL}} \times \dfrac{1 \text{ mol CHCl}_3}{119.4 \text{ g CHCl}_3} \times \dfrac{1000 \text{ mL}}{L} = 8.4 \times 10^{-9} \ M$

   c.   10.0 ppm As = $\dfrac{10.0 \ \mu\text{g As}}{\text{mL}} = \dfrac{10.0 \times 10^{-6} \text{ g As}}{\text{mL}}$

$$\dfrac{10.0 \times 10^{-6} \text{ g As}}{\text{mL}} \times \dfrac{1 \text{ mol As}}{74.92 \text{ g As}} \times \dfrac{1000 \text{ mL}}{L} = 1.33 \times 10^{-4} \ M$$

   d. $\dfrac{0.10 \times 10^{-6} \text{ g DDT}}{\text{mL}} \times \dfrac{1 \text{ mol DDT}}{354.5 \text{ g DDT}} \times \dfrac{1000 \text{ mL}}{L} = 2.8 \times 10^{-7} \ M$

11.   Stock solution = $\dfrac{10.0 \text{ mg}}{500.0 \text{ mL}} = \dfrac{10.0 \times 10^{-3} \text{ g}}{500.0 \text{ mL}} = \dfrac{2.00 \times 10^{-5} \text{ g}}{\text{mL}}$

$$100.0 \times 10^{-6} \text{ L stock} \times \dfrac{1000 \text{ mL}}{L} \times \dfrac{2.00 \times 10^{-5} \text{ g steroid}}{\text{mL}} = 2.00 \times 10^{-6} \text{ g steroid}$$

This is diluted to a final volume of 100.0 mL.

$$\text{ppb steroid} = \dfrac{\text{g steroid}}{\text{g solution}} \times 10^9 = \dfrac{\text{ng steroid}}{\text{mL aqueous solution}}$$

$$\text{ppb steroid} = \dfrac{2.00 \times 10^{-6} \text{ g}}{100.0 \text{ mL}} = \dfrac{2.00 \times 10^{-8} \text{ g}}{\text{mL}} = \dfrac{20.0 \times 10^{-9} \text{ g}}{\text{mL}} = 20.0 \text{ ppb}$$

$$\dfrac{20.0 \times 10^{-9} \text{ g steroid}}{\text{mL}} \times \dfrac{1000 \text{ mL}}{L} \times \dfrac{1 \text{ mol steroid}}{336.4 \text{ g steroid}} = 5.95 \times 10^{-8} \ M$$

13.   1 ppm = $\dfrac{1 \ \mu\text{g}}{\text{mL}} = \dfrac{1 \text{ mg}}{L}$

$$\dfrac{1 \times 10^{-3} \text{ g F}^-}{L} \times \dfrac{1 \text{ mol F}^-}{19.0 \text{ g F}^-} = \dfrac{5 \times 10^{-5} \text{ mol}}{L}$$

$$2 \text{ ppm F}^- = \dfrac{1 \times 10^{-4} \text{ mol}}{L}; \ 3 \text{ ppm F}^- = \dfrac{1.6 \times 10^{-4} \text{ mol}}{L} = \dfrac{2 \times 10^{-4} \text{ mol}}{L}$$

$$\dfrac{50. \times 10^{-3} \text{ g}}{L} \times \dfrac{1 \text{ mol F}^-}{19.0 \text{ g F}^-} = \dfrac{2.6 \times 10^{-3} \text{ mol}}{L}$$

15.   Stock solution:

$$1.584 \text{ g Mn} \times \dfrac{1 \text{ mol Mn}}{54.94 \text{ g Mn}} = 2.883 \times 10^{-2} \text{ mol Mn}; \ M = \dfrac{2.883 \times 10^{-2} \text{ mol}}{L}$$

Solution A contains:

$$50.00 \text{ mL} \times \frac{1 \text{ L}}{1000 \text{ mL}} \times \frac{2.883 \times 10^{-2} \text{ mol}}{\text{L}} = 1.442 \times 10^{-3} \text{ mol}$$

$$\text{molarity} = \frac{1.442 \times 10^{-3} \text{ mol}}{1000.0 \text{ mL}} \times \frac{1000 \text{ mL}}{\text{L}} = 1.442 \times 10^{-3} \ M$$

Solution B contains:

$$10.0 \text{ mL} \times \frac{1 \text{ L}}{1000 \text{ mL}} \times \frac{1.442 \times 10^{-3} \text{ mol}}{\text{L}} = 1.442 \times 10^{-5} \text{ mol}$$

$$\text{molarity} = \frac{1.442 \times 10^{-5} \text{ mol}}{0.250 \text{ L}} = 5.768 \times 10^{-5} \ M$$

Solution C contains:

$$10.00 \times 10^{-3} \text{ L} \times \frac{5.768 \times 10^{-5} \text{ mol}}{\text{L}} = 5.768 \times 10^{-7} \text{ mol}$$

$$\text{molarity} = \frac{5.768 \times 10^{-7} \text{ mol}}{0.500 \text{ L}} = 1.154 \times 10^{-6} \ M$$

Precipitation Reactions

18.

a.

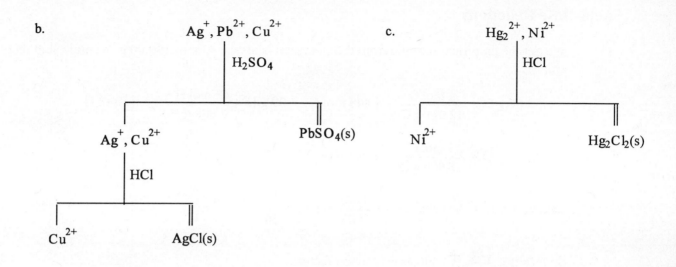

b.

c.

21.   The reaction is: $Ni(NO_3)_2(aq) + 2\ NaOH(aq) \rightarrow Ni(OH)_2(s) + 2\ NaNO_3(aq)$

$$50.00\ mL\ Ni(NO_3)_2 \times \frac{1\ L}{1000\ mL} \times \frac{0.175\ mol\ Ni(NO_3)_2}{L\ Ni(NO_3)_2} \times \frac{2\ mol\ NaOH}{1\ mol\ Ni(NO_3)_2}$$

$$\times \frac{1\ L\ NaOH}{0.100\ mol\ NaOH} = 0.175\ L\ or\ 175\ mL$$

24. $1.00\ L \times \dfrac{0.200\ mol\ Na_2S_2O_3}{L} \times \dfrac{1\ mol\ AgBr}{2\ mol\ Na_2S_2O_3} \times \dfrac{187.8\ g\ AgBr}{mol\ AgBr} = 18.8\ g\ AgBr$

26. $0.5032\ g\ BaSO_4 \times \dfrac{32.07\ g\ S}{233.4\ g\ BaSO_4} \times \dfrac{183.19\ g\ saccharine}{32.07\ g\ S} = 0.3949\ g\ saccharin$

$$\frac{Avg.\ Mass}{Tablet} = \frac{0.3949\ g}{10\ tablets} = \frac{3.949 \times 10^{-2}\ g}{tablet} = \frac{39.49\ mg}{tablet}$$

$$Avg.\ Mass\ \% = \frac{0.3949\ g\ saccharine}{0.5894\ g} \times 100 = 67.00\%\ saccharin\ by\ mass$$

28. $100.0\ mL \times \dfrac{0.0426\ mmol\ Ba^{2+}}{mL} = 4.26\ mmol\ Ba^{2+}$

$$50.0\ mL \times \frac{0.2000\ mmol\ SO_4^{2-}}{mL} = 10.0\ mmol\ SO_4^{2-}$$

The Ba^{2+} is limiting. We form 4.26 mmol $BaSO_4$.

$$4.26 \times 10^{-3}\ mol\ BaSO_4 \times \frac{233.4\ g\ BaSO_4}{mol} = 0.994\ g\ BaSO_4$$

Acid-Base Reactions

31.   We get the empirical formula from the elemental analysis. Out of 100.00 g carminic acid there are:

$$53.66 \text{ g C} \times \frac{1 \text{ mol C}}{12.011 \text{ g C}} = 4.468 \text{ mol C}; \quad 4.09 \text{ g H} \times \frac{1 \text{ mol H}}{1.008 \text{ g H}} = 4.06 \text{ mol H}$$

$$42.25 \text{ g O} \times \frac{1 \text{ mol O}}{15.999 \text{ g O}} = 2.641 \text{ mol O}$$

Taking ratios in the usual way: $\frac{4.468}{4.06} = 1.10 = \frac{11}{10}$

So let's try $\frac{4.06}{10} = 0.406$ as a common factor.

$$\frac{4.468}{0.406} = 11.0 \quad \frac{4.06}{0.406} = 10.0 \quad \frac{2.641}{0.406} = 6.50$$

$C_{22}H_{20}O_{13}$ is the empirical formula, to make all units whole numbers.

We can get the molar mass from the titration data:

$$18.02 \times 10^{-3} \text{ L soln} \times \frac{0.0406 \text{ mol NaOH}}{\text{L soln}} \times \frac{1 \text{ mol carminic acid}}{\text{mol NaOH}}$$

$$= 7.32 \times 10^{-4} \text{ mol carminic acid}$$

$$\text{Molar mass} = \frac{0.3602 \text{ g}}{7.32 \times 10^{-4} \text{ mol}} = \frac{492 \text{ g}}{\text{mol}}$$

The mass of $C_{22}H_{20}O_{13} \approx 22(12) + 20(1) + 13(16) = 492$ g. Therefore, the molecular formula of carminic acid is $C_{22}H_{20}O_{13}$.

34.   The pertinent reactions are:

$$2 \text{ NaOH(aq)} + \text{H}_2\text{SO}_4\text{(aq)} \rightarrow \text{Na}_2\text{SO}_4\text{(aq)} + 2 \text{ H}_2\text{O(l)}$$

$$\text{HCl(aq)} + \text{NaOH(aq)} \rightarrow \text{NaCl(aq)} + \text{H}_2\text{O(l)}$$

Amount of NaOH added = $0.0500 \text{ L} \times \frac{0.213 \text{ mol}}{\text{L}} = 1.07 \times 10^{-2}$ mol NaOH

Amount of NaOH neutralized by HCl:

$$0.01321 \text{ L HCl} \times \frac{0.103 \text{ mol HCl}}{\text{L HCl}} \times \frac{1 \text{ mol NaOH}}{\text{mol HCl}} = 1.36 \times 10^{-3} \text{ mol NaOH}$$

The difference, 9.3×10^{-3} mol, is the amount of NaOH neutralized by the sulfuric acid.

$$9.3 \times 10^{-3} \text{ mol NaOH} \times \frac{1 \text{ mol H}_2\text{SO}_4}{2 \text{ mol NaOH}} = 4.7 \times 10^{-3} \text{ mol H}_2\text{SO}_4$$

$$\text{Concentration of H}_2\text{SO}_4 = \frac{4.7 \times 10^{-3} \text{ mol}}{0.1000 \text{ L}} = 4.7 \times 10^{-2} \ M$$

37. $CH_3CO_2H(aq) + NaOH(aq) \rightarrow H_2O(l) + CH_3CO_2Na(aq)$

a. 16.58×10^{-3} L soln $\times \dfrac{0.5062 \text{ mol NaOH}}{\text{L soln}} \times \dfrac{1 \text{ mol acetic acid}}{\text{mol NaOH}} = 8.393 \times 10^{-3}$ mol acetic acid

$$\text{Concentration of acetic acid} = \frac{8.393 \times 10^{-3} \text{ mol}}{0.01000 \text{ L}} = 0.8393 \ M$$

b.   If we have 1.000 L of solution:

$$\text{Total mass} = 1000. \text{ mL} \times \frac{1.006 \text{ g}}{\text{mL}} = 1006 \text{ g}$$

$$\text{Mass of acetic acid} = 0.8393 \text{ mol} \times \frac{60.052 \text{ g}}{\text{mol}} = 50.40 \text{ g}$$

$$\% \text{ acetic acid} = \frac{50.40 \text{ g}}{1006 \text{ g}} \times 100 = 5.010\%$$

40. 39.47×10^{-3} L HCl $\times \dfrac{0.0984 \text{ mol HCl}}{\text{L}} \times \dfrac{1 \text{ mol NH}_3}{\text{mol HCl}} = 3.88 \times 10^{-3}$ mol NH$_3$

$$\text{Molarity of NH}_3 = \frac{3.88 \times 10^{-3} \text{ mol}}{50.00 \times 10^{-3} \text{ L}} = \frac{0.0776 \text{ mol}}{\text{L}}$$

Oxidation-Reduction Reactions

43.   a.   K, +1: O, -2; Mn, +7   b.   Ni, +4:, O, -2

c. $K_4Fe(CN)_6$; Fe, +2

K$^+$ ions and Fe(CN)$_6^{4-}$ anions; Fe(CN)$_6^{4-}$ composed of Fe^{2+} and CN$^-$ ions.

d. $(NH_4)_2HPO_4$ is made of NH$_4^+$ cations and HPO$_4^{2-}$ anions. Assign +1 as oxidation number of H and -2 as oxidation number of O. Then we get: N, -3: P, +5

e.   P, +3: O, -2

47.

	Redox?	Oxidizing Agent	Reducing Agent	Substance Oxidized	Substance Reduced
a.	Yes	O_2	CH_4	CH_4 (C)	O_2 (O)
b.	Yes	HCl	Zn	Zn	HCl (H)
c.	No	-	-	-	-
d.	Yes	O_3	NO	NO (N)	O_3 (O)

In c, no oxidation number changes from reactant to product.

48.   a.   The first step is to assign oxidation numbers to all atoms (see numbers above the atoms).

$$\overset{-3\ +1}{C_2H_6} + \overset{0}{O_2} \rightarrow \overset{+4\ -2}{CO_2} + \overset{+1\ -2}{H_2O}$$

Each carbon atom changes from -3 to +4, an increase of seven. Each oxygen atom changes from 0 to -2, a decrease of 2. We need 7/2 O-atoms for every C-atom.

$$C_2H_6 + 7/2\ O_2 \rightarrow CO_2 + H_2O$$

Balancing the remainder of the equation by inspection:

$$C_2H_6(g) + 7/2\ O_2(g) \rightarrow 2\ CO_2(g) + 3\ H_2O(g)$$

or

$$2\ C_2H_6(g) + 7\ O_2(g) \rightarrow 4\ CO_2(g) + 6\ H_2O(g)$$

b.   The oxidation state of magnesium changes from 0 to +2, an increase of 2. The oxidation state of hydrogen changes from +1 to 0, a decrease of 1. We need 2 H-atoms for every Mg-atom. The balanced equation is:

$$Mg(s) + 2\ HCl(aq) \rightarrow Mg^{2+}(aq) + 2\ Cl^-(aq) + H_2(g)$$

49.   a.   Review section 4.11 of the text for rules on balancing by the half-reaction method. The first step is to balance the two half-reactions.

$$(Cu \rightarrow Cu^{2+} + 2\ e^-) \times 3 \qquad\qquad HNO_3 \rightarrow NO + 2\ H_2O$$
$$(3\ e^- + 3\ H^+ + HNO_3 \rightarrow NO + 2\ H_2O) \times 2$$

Adding the two balanced half reactions so electrons cancel:

$$3\ Cu \rightarrow 3\ Cu^{2+} + 6\ e^-$$
$$6\ e^- + 6\ H^+ + 2\ HNO_3 \rightarrow 2\ NO + 4\ H_2O$$

$$3\ Cu(s) + 6\ H^+(aq) + 2\ HNO_3(aq) \rightarrow 3\ Cu^{2+}(aq) + 2\ NO(g) + 4\ H_2O(l)$$

or

$$3\ Cu(s) + 8\ HNO_3(aq) \rightarrow 3\ Cu(NO_3)_2(aq) + 2\ NO(g) + 4\ H_2O(l)$$

b. $(2 \text{ Cl}^- \rightarrow \text{Cl}_2 + 2 \text{ e}^-) \times 3$ $\text{Cr}_2\text{O}_7^{2-} \rightarrow 2 \text{ Cr}^{3+} + 7 \text{ H}_2\text{O}$

$6 \text{ e}^- + 14 \text{ H}^+ + \text{Cr}_2\text{O}_7^{2-} \rightarrow 2 \text{ Cr}^{3+} + 7 \text{ H}_2\text{O}$

Adding the two balanced half reactions so electrons cancel:

$$6 \text{ Cl}^- \rightarrow 3 \text{ Cl}_2 + 6 \text{ e}^-$$
$$6 \text{ e}^- + 14 \text{ H}^+ + \text{Cr}_2\text{O}_7^{2-} \rightarrow 2 \text{ Cr}^{3+} + 7 \text{ H}_2\text{O}$$

$$14 \text{ H}^+(aq) + \text{Cr}_2\text{O}_7^{2-}(aq) + 6 \text{ Cl}^-(aq) \rightarrow 3 \text{ Cl}_2(g) + 2 \text{ Cr}^{3+}(aq) + 7 \text{ H}_2\text{O}(l)$$

c. $\text{Pb} \rightarrow \text{PbSO}_4$ $\text{PbO}_2 \rightarrow \text{PbSO}_4$

$\text{Pb} + \text{H}_2\text{SO}_4 \rightarrow \text{PbSO}_4 + 2 \text{ H}^+$ $\text{PbO}_2 + \text{H}_2\text{SO}_4 \rightarrow \text{PbSO}_4 + 2 \text{ H}^+$

$\text{Pb} + \text{H}_2\text{SO}_4 \rightarrow \text{PbSO}_4 + 2 \text{ H}^+ + 2 \text{ e}^-$ $2 \text{ e}^- + 2 \text{ H}^+ + \text{PbO}_2 + \text{H}_2\text{SO}_4 \rightarrow \text{PbSO}_4 + 2 \text{ H}_2\text{O}$

Add the two half reactions:

$$2 \text{ e}^- + 2 \text{ H}^+ + \text{PbO}_2 + \text{H}_2\text{SO}_4 \rightarrow \text{PbSO}_4 + 2 \text{ H}_2\text{O}$$
$$\text{Pb} + \text{H}_2\text{SO}_4 \rightarrow \text{PbSO}_4 + 2 \text{ H}^+ + 2 \text{ e}^-$$

$$\text{Pb}(s) + 2 \text{ H}_2\text{SO}_4(aq) + \text{PbO}_2(s) \rightarrow 2 \text{ PbSO}_4(s) + 2 \text{ H}_2\text{O}(l)$$

This is the reaction that occurs in an automobile lead storage battery.

50.   a.   For basic solutions, use the same half reaction balancing procedure as with acidic solutions, with an extra step. The extra step is to convert the H^+ into H_2O by adding equal moles of OH^- to each side of reaction. This converts the reaction to a basic solution while keeping it balanced.

$\text{Al} \rightarrow \text{Al(OH)}_4^-$ $\text{MnO}_4^- \rightarrow \text{MnO}_2$

$4 \text{ OH}^- + \text{Al} \rightarrow \text{Al(OH)}_4^-$ $4 \text{ OH}^- + 4 \text{ H}^+ + \text{MnO}_4^- \rightarrow \text{MnO}_2 + 2 \text{ H}_2\text{O} + 4 \text{ OH}^-$

$4 \text{ OH}^- + \text{Al} \rightarrow \text{Al(OH)}_4^- + 3 \text{ e}^-$ $2 \text{ H}_2\text{O} + \text{MnO}_4^- \rightarrow \text{MnO}_2 + 4 \text{ OH}^-$

$3\text{e}^- + 2\text{H}_2\text{O} + \text{MnO}_4^- \rightarrow \text{MnO}_2 + 4\text{OH}^-$

$$4 \text{ OH}^- + \text{Al} \rightarrow \text{Al(OH)}_4^- + 3 \text{ e}^-$$
$$3 \text{ e}^- + 2 \text{ H}_2\text{O} + \text{MnO}_4^- \rightarrow \text{MnO}_2 + 4 \text{ OH}^-$$

$$2 \text{ H}_2\text{O}(l) + \text{Al}(s) + \text{MnO}_4^-(aq) \rightarrow \text{Al(OH)}_4^-(aq) + \text{MnO}_2(s)$$

b. $\text{Cl}_2 \rightarrow \text{Cl}^-$ $\text{Cl}_2 \rightarrow \text{ClO}^-$

$2 \text{ e}^- + \text{Cl}_2 \rightarrow 2 \text{ Cl}^-$ $2 \text{ H}_2\text{O} + \text{Cl}_2 \rightarrow 2 \text{ ClO}^- + 4 \text{ H}^+$

$4 \text{ OH}^- + 2 \text{ H}_2\text{O} + \text{Cl}_2 \rightarrow 2 \text{ ClO}^- + 4 \text{ H}^+ + 4 \text{ OH}^-$

$4 \text{ OH}^- + \text{Cl}_2 \rightarrow 2 \text{ ClO}^- + 2 \text{ H}_2\text{O} + 2 \text{ e}^-$

$$2 \text{ e}^- + \text{Cl}_2 \rightarrow 2 \text{ Cl}^-$$
$$4 \text{ OH}^- + \text{Cl}_2 \rightarrow 2 \text{ ClO}^- + 2 \text{ H}_2\text{O} + 2 \text{ e}^-$$

$$4 \text{ OH}^- + 2 \text{ Cl}_2 \rightarrow 2 \text{ Cl}^- + 2 \text{ ClO}^- + 2 \text{ H}_2\text{O}$$

Reducing: $2 \text{ OH}^-(aq) + \text{Cl}_2(g) \rightarrow \text{Cl}^-(aq) + \text{ClO}^-(aq) + \text{H}_2\text{O}(l)$

54. $Mn \rightarrow Mn^{2+} + 2\ e^-$ $HNO_3 \rightarrow NO_2$

                                                                      $HNO_3 \rightarrow NO_2 + H_2O$

                                                              $(e^- + H^+ + HNO_3 \rightarrow NO_2 + H_2O) \times 2$

                                       $Mn \rightarrow Mn^{2+} + 2\ e^-$

                              $2\ e^- + 2\ H^+ + 2\ HNO_3 \rightarrow 2\ NO_2 + 2\ H_2O$

                       $2\ H^+(aq) + Mn(s) + 2\ HNO_3(aq) \rightarrow Mn^{2+}(aq) + 2\ NO_2(g) + 2\ H_2O(l)$

          $(4\ H_2O + Mn^{2+} \rightarrow MnO_4^- + 8\ H^+ + 5\ e^-) \times 2$ $(2\ e^- + 2\ H^+ + IO_4^- \rightarrow IO_3^- + H_2O) \times 5$

                          $8\ H_2O + 2\ Mn^{2+} \rightarrow 2\ MnO_4^- + 16\ H^+ + 10\ e^-$

                       $10\ e^- + 10\ H^+ + 5\ IO_4^- \rightarrow 5\ IO_3^- + 5\ H_2O$

              $3\ H_2O(l) + 2\ Mn^{2+}(aq) + 5\ IO_4^-(aq) \rightarrow 2\ MnO_4^-(aq) + 5\ IO_3^-(aq) + 6\ H^+(aq)$

56. $(H_2C_2O_4 \rightarrow 2\ CO_2 + 2\ H^+ + 2\ e^-) \times 5$ $(5\ e^- + 8\ H^+ + MnO_4^- \rightarrow Mn^{2+} + 4\ H_2O) \times 2$

                              $5\ H_2C_2O_4 \rightarrow 10\ CO_2 + 10\ H^+ + 10\ e^-$

                    $10\ e^- + 16\ H^+ + 2\ MnO_4^- \rightarrow 2\ Mn^{2+} + 8\ H_2O$

                   $6\ H^+ + 5\ H_2C_2O_4 + 2\ MnO_4^- \rightarrow 10\ CO_2 + 2\ Mn^{2+} + 8\ H_2O$

$$0.1058 \text{ g oxalic acid} \times \frac{1 \text{ mol oxalic acid}}{90.034 \text{ g}} \times \frac{2 \text{ mol } MnO_4^-}{5 \text{ mol oxalic acid}} = 4.700 \times 10^{-4} \text{ mol}$$

$$\text{Molarity} = \frac{4.700 \times 10^{-4} \text{ mol}}{28.97 \text{ mL}} \times \frac{1000 \text{ mL}}{L} = 1.622 \times 10^{-2}\ M$$

58.   This is the same titration as in problem 4.57. The stoichiometry of the reaction depends on the reaction:

$$8\ H^+ + MnO_4^- + 5\ Fe^{2+} \rightarrow 5\ Fe^{3+} + Mn^{2+} + 4\ H_2O$$

From the titration data we can get the number of moles of Fe^{2+}. We then convert this to a mass of iron and calculate the mass percent of iron in the sample.

$$38.37 \times 10^{-3} \text{ L } MnO_4^- \times \frac{0.0198 \text{ mol } MnO_4^-}{L} \times \frac{5 \text{ mol } Fe^{2+}}{\text{mol } MnO_4^-} = 3.80 \times 10^{-3} \text{ mol } Fe^{2+}$$

$$3.80 \times 10^{-3} \text{ mol Fe} \times \frac{55.85 \text{ g Fe}}{\text{mol Fe}} = 0.212 \text{ g Fe}$$

$$\% \text{ Fe} = \frac{0.212 \text{ g}}{0.6128 \text{ g}} \times 100 = 34.6\% \text{ Fe}$$

60. $1.06 \text{ g Cu} \times \dfrac{1 \text{ mol Cu}}{63.55 \text{ g}} \times \dfrac{2 \text{ mol Ag}^+}{\text{mol Cu}} = 3.34 \times 10^{-2} \text{ mol Ag}^+$ required to dissolve all of the Cu.

We have: $250 \times 10^{-3} \text{ L} \times \dfrac{0.20 \text{ mol Ag}^+}{\text{L}} = 5.0 \times 10^{-2} \text{ mol Ag}^+$

Yes, all of the copper will dissolve.

61.   a. $16 \text{ e}^- + 18 \text{ H}^+ + 3 \text{ IO}_3^- \rightarrow \text{I}_3^- + 9 \text{ H}_2\text{O}$ $(3 \text{ I}^- \rightarrow \text{I}_3^- + 2 \text{ e}^-) \times 8$

$$24 \text{ I}^- \rightarrow 8 \text{ I}_3^- + 16 \text{ e}^-$$
$$16 \text{ e}^- + 18 \text{ H}^+ + 3 \text{ IO}_3^- \rightarrow \text{I}_3^- + 9 \text{ H}_2\text{O}$$
$$\overline{18 \text{ H}^+ + 24 \text{ I}^- + 3 \text{ IO}_3^- \rightarrow 9 \text{ I}_3^- + 9 \text{ H}_2\text{O}}$$

or $6 \text{ H}^+(aq) + 8 \text{ I}^-(aq) + \text{IO}_3^-(aq) \rightarrow 3 \text{ I}_3^-(aq) + 3 \text{ H}_2\text{O}(l)$

b. $0.6013 \text{ g KIO}_3 \times \dfrac{1 \text{ mol KIO}_3}{214.0 \text{ g KIO}_3} = 2.810 \times 10^{-3} \text{ mol KIO}_3$

$2.810 \times 10^{-3} \text{ mol KIO}_3 \times \dfrac{8 \text{ mol KI}}{\text{mol KIO}_3} \times \dfrac{166.0 \text{ g KI}}{\text{mol KI}} = 3.732 \text{ g KI}$

$2.810 \times 10^{-3} \text{ mol KIO}_3 \times \dfrac{6 \text{ mol HCl}}{\text{mol KIO}_3} \times \dfrac{1 \text{ L}}{3.00 \text{ mol HCl}} = 5.62 \times 10^{-3} \text{ L} = 5.62 \text{ mL HCl}$

c. $\text{I}_3^- + 2 \text{ e}^- \rightarrow 3 \text{ I}^-$

$2 \text{ S}_2\text{O}_3^{2-} \rightarrow \text{S}_4\text{O}_6^{2-} + 2 \text{ e}^-$

Adding the balanced half reactions gives:

$$2 \text{ S}_2\text{O}_3^{2-}(aq) + \text{I}_3^-(aq) \rightarrow 3 \text{ I}^-(aq) + \text{S}_4\text{O}_6^{2-}(aq)$$

d. $25.00 \times 10^{-3} \text{ L IO}_3^- \times \dfrac{0.0100 \text{ mol IO}_3^-}{\text{L}} \times \dfrac{3 \text{ mol I}_3^-}{\text{mol IO}_3^-} \times \dfrac{2 \text{ mol S}_2\text{O}_3^{2-}}{\text{mol I}_3^-} = 1.50 \times 10^{-3} \text{ mol S}_2\text{O}_3^{2-}$

$M_{\text{S}_2\text{O}_3^{2-}} \quad \dfrac{1.50 \times 10^{-3} \text{ mol}}{32.04 \times 10^{-3} \text{ L}} = 0.0468 \, M$

e. $0.5000 \text{ L} \times \dfrac{0.0100 \text{ mol KIO}_3}{\text{L}} \times \dfrac{214.0 \text{ g KIO}_3}{\text{mol KIO}_3} = 1.07 \text{ g KIO}_3$

Place 1.07 g KIO_3 in a 500 mL volumetric flask; add water to dissolve KIO_3; continue adding water to the mark.

Additional Exercises

62. $Zn_2P_2O_7$: $2(65.38) + 2(30.97) + 7(16.00) = \dfrac{304.69 \text{ g}}{\text{mol}}$

$0.4089 \text{ g } Zn_2P_2O_7 \times \dfrac{130.76 \text{ g Zn}}{304.69 \text{ g } Zn_2P_2O_7} = 0.1755 \text{ g Zn}$

$\% \text{ Zn} = \dfrac{0.1755 \text{ g}}{1.200 \text{ g}} \times 100 = 14.63\% \text{ Zn}$

66.   Molar masses: KCl, $39.10 + 35.45 = 74.55$ g/mol; KBr, $39.10 + 79.90 = 119.00$ g/mol

                 AgCl, $107.9 + 35.45 = 143.4$ g/mol; AgBr, $107.9 + 79.90 = 187.8$ g/mol

Let x = number of moles of KCl in mixture and y = number of moles of KBr in mixture. Since $Ag^+ + Cl^- \rightarrow AgCl$ and $Ag^+ + Br^- \rightarrow AgBr$, then x = moles AgCl and y = moles AgBr. Setting up simultaneous equations from the given information:

     $0.1024 \text{ g} = 74.55 \text{ x} + 119.0 \text{ y}$

     $0.1889 \text{ g} = 143.4 \text{ x} + 187.8 \text{ y}$

Multiply the first equation by $\dfrac{187.8}{119.0}$, and subtract from the second.

$\begin{array}{r} 0.1889 = 143.4 \text{ x} + 187.8 \text{ y} \\ \underline{-0.1616 = -117.7 \text{ x} - 187.8 \text{ y}} \\ 0.0273 = 25.7 \, x, \qquad x = 1.06 \times 10^{-3} \text{ mol KCl} \end{array}$

$1.06 \times 10^{-3} \text{ mol KCl} \times \dfrac{74.55 \text{ g KCl}}{\text{mol KCl}} = 0.0790 \text{ g KCl}$

$\% \text{ KCl} = \dfrac{0.0790 \text{ g}}{0.1024 \text{ g}} \times 100 = 77.1\%, \ \% \text{ KBr} = 100.0 - 77.1 = 22.9\%$

Alternatively, we can calculate the mass of AgX, X = Cl or Br, assuming the sample was pure KCl or KBr and set up a ratio.

If pure KCl: $0.1024 \text{ g KCl} \times \dfrac{143.4 \text{ g AgCl}}{74.55 \text{ g KCl}} = 0.1970 \text{ g AgCl}$

If pure KBr: $0.1024 \text{ g KBr} \times \dfrac{187.8 \text{ g AgBr}}{119.0 \text{ g KBr}} = 0.1616 \text{ g AgBr}$

So, 0% KCl will give 0.1616 g AgX and 100% KCl will give 0.1970 g AgX. The mass in excess of 0.1616 g will give us % KCl.

$$\frac{0.1889 - 0.1616}{0.1970 - 0.1616} \times 100 = \% \text{ KCl} = 77.1\% \text{ and } \% \text{ KBr} = 22.9\%$$

69. $50.00 \text{ mL} \times \dfrac{0.0565 \text{ mmol}}{\text{mL}} = 2.83 \text{ mmol Ag}^+ \text{ total}$

$8.32 \text{ mL} \times \dfrac{0.0510 \text{ mmol KSCN}}{\text{mL}} \times \dfrac{1 \text{ mmol Ag}^+}{\text{mmol KSCN}} = 0.424 \text{ mmol Ag}^+ \text{ unreacted}$

Thus, $2.83 - 0.424 = 2.41$ mmol Ag$^+$ reacted with I$^-$. Since this is a 1:1 reaction, the solution contained 2.41 mmol I$^-$.

$$C_{KI} = \frac{2.41 \text{ mmol}}{25.00 \text{ mL}} = 0.0964 \; M$$

72.   a. $7 \text{ H}_2\text{O} + 2 \text{ Cr}^{3+} \rightarrow \text{Cr}_2\text{O}_7^{2-} + 14 \text{ H}^+ + 6 \text{ e}^-$
                    $(2 \text{ e}^- + \text{S}_2\text{O}_8^{2-} \rightarrow 2 \text{ SO}_4^{2-}) \times 3$

$$\overline{7 \text{ H}_2\text{O(l)} + 2 \text{ Cr}^{3+}\text{(aq)} + 3 \text{ S}_2\text{O}_8^{2-}\text{(aq)} \rightarrow \text{Cr}_2\text{O}_7^{2-}\text{(aq)} + 14 \text{ H}^+\text{(aq)} + 6 \text{ SO}_4^{2-}\text{(aq)}}$$

$$(\text{Fe}^{2+} \rightarrow \text{Fe}^{3+} + \text{e}^-) \times 6$$
$$6 \text{ e}^- + 14 \text{ H}^+ + \text{Cr}_2\text{O}_7^{2-} \rightarrow 2 \text{ Cr}^{3+} + 7 \text{ H}_2\text{O}$$

$$\overline{14 \text{ H}^+\text{(aq)} + 6 \text{ Fe}^{2+}\text{(aq)} + \text{Cr}_2\text{O}_7^{2-}\text{(aq)} \rightarrow 2 \text{ Cr}^{3+}\text{(aq)} + 6 \text{ Fe}^{3+}\text{(aq)} + 7 \text{ H}_2\text{O(l)}}$$

    b. $8.58 \text{ mL} \times \dfrac{0.0520 \text{ mmol Cr}_2\text{O}_7^{2-}}{\text{mL}} \times \dfrac{6 \text{ mmol Fe}^{2+}}{\text{mmol Cr}_2\text{O}_7^{2-}} = 2.68 \text{ mmol of excess Fe}^{2+}$

$\text{Fe}^{2+} \text{ (total)} = 3.000 \text{ g Fe(NH}_4)_2 \text{ (SO}_4)_2 \cdot 6\text{H}_2\text{O} \times \dfrac{1 \text{ mol}}{392.17 \text{ g}} \times \dfrac{1000 \text{ mmol}}{1 \text{ mol}} = 7.650 \text{ mmol Fe}^{2+}$

$7.650 - 2.68 = 4.97$ mmol Fe^{2+} reacted with Cr$_2$O$_7^{2-}$ generated from the Cr plating.

The Cr plating contained:

$4.97 \text{ mmol Fe}^{2+} \times \dfrac{1 \text{ mmol Cr}_2\text{O}_7^{2-}}{6 \text{ mmol Fe}^{2+}} \times \dfrac{2 \text{ mmol Cr}^{3+}}{\text{mmol Cr}_2\text{O}_7^{2-}} = 1.66 \text{ mmol Cr}^{3+} = 1.66 \text{ mmol Cr}$

$1.66 \times 10^{-3} \text{ mol Cr} \times \dfrac{52.00 \text{ g Cr}}{\text{mol Cr}} = 8.63 \times 10^{-2} \text{ g Cr}$

$V_{Cr} = 8.63 \times 10^{-2} \text{ g} \times \dfrac{1 \text{ cm}^3}{7.19 \text{ g}} = 1.20 \times 10^{-2} \text{ cm}^3 = \text{area} \times \text{thickness}$

$\text{thickness of Cr plating} = = \dfrac{1.20 \times 10^{-2} \text{ cm}^3}{40.0 \text{ cm}^2} = 3.00 \times 10^{-4} \text{ cm} = 3.00 \; \mu\text{m}$

76.   First we will calculate the molarity while ignoring the uncertainty.

$$0.150 \text{ g} \times \frac{1 \text{ mol}}{58.44 \text{ g}} = 2.57 \times 10^{-3} \text{ moles}; \quad \text{Molarity} = \frac{2.57 \times 10^{-3} \text{ mol}}{0.1000 \text{ L}} = \frac{2.57 \times 10^{-2} \text{ mol}}{\text{L}}$$

The maximum value for the molarity is $= \dfrac{0.153 \text{ g} \times \dfrac{1 \text{ mol}}{58.44 \text{ g}}}{0.0995 \text{ L}} = \dfrac{2.63 \times 10^{-2} \text{ mol}}{\text{L}}$

The minimum value for the molarity is $= \dfrac{0.147 \text{ g} \times \dfrac{1 \text{ mol}}{58.44 \text{ g}}}{0.1005 \text{ L}} = \dfrac{2.50 \times 10^{-2} \text{ mol}}{\text{L}}$

The range of the molarity is 0.0250 M to 0.0263 M or we can express this range as 0.0257 $M \pm$ 0.0007 M.

78.   Desired uncertainty is 1% of 0.02 or ± 0.0002. So we want the solution to be 0.0200 ± 0.0002 M or the concentration should be between 0.0198 and 0.0202 M. We should use a 1-L volumetric flask to make the solution. They are good to ± 0.1%. We want to weigh out between 0.0198 mol and 0.0202 mol of KIO_3.

Molar mass of $KIO_3 = 39.10 + 126.9 + 3(16.00) = \dfrac{214.0 \text{ g}}{\text{mol}}$

$0.0198 \text{ mol} \times \dfrac{214.0 \text{ g}}{\text{mol}} = 4.2372 \text{ g}$ (For now we will carry significant figures.)

$0.0202 \text{ mol} \times \dfrac{214.0 \text{ g}}{\text{mol}} = 4.3228 \text{ g}$

We should weigh out between 4.24 and 4.32 g of KIO_3. We should weigh it to the nearest mg or 0.1 mg. Dissolve the KIO_3 in water and dilute to the mark in a one liter volumetric flask. This will produce a solution whose concentration is within the limits and is known to at least the fourth decimal place.

CHAPTER FIVE

GASES

Pressure

2. If the levels of Hg in each arm of the manometer are equal, then the pressure in the flask is equal to atmospheric pressure. When they are unequal, the difference in height in mm will be equal to the difference in pressure in mm Hg between the flask and the atmosphere. Which level is higher will tell us whether the pressure in the flask is less than or greater than atmospheric.

    a. $P_{flask} < P_{atm}$; $P_{flask} = 760. - 118 = 642$ torr

$$642 \text{ torr} \times \frac{1 \text{ atm}}{760 \text{ torr}} = 0.845 \text{ atm}$$

$$0.845 \text{ atm} \times \frac{1.013 \times 10^5 \text{ Pa}}{\text{atm}} = 8.56 \times 10^4 \text{ Pa}$$

    b. $P_{flask} > P_{atm}$; $P_{flask} = 760.$ torr $+ 215$ torr $= 975$ torr

$$975 \text{ torr} \times \frac{1 \text{ atm}}{760 \text{ torr}} = 1.28 \text{ atm}$$

$$1.28 \text{ atm} \times \frac{1.013 \times 10^5 \text{ Pa}}{\text{atm}} = 1.30 \times 10^5 \text{ Pa}$$

    c. $P_{flask} = 635 - 118 = 517$ torr; $P_{flask} = 635 + 215 = 850.$ torr

4. The pressure is proportional to the mass of the fluid. The mass is proportional to the volume of the column of fluid (or to the height of the column assuming the area of the column of fluid is constant).

$$d = \frac{\text{mass}}{\text{volume}};$$ In this case the volume of silicon oil is the same as the volume of Hg in problem 5.2.

$$V = \frac{m}{d}; \quad V_1 = V_2; \quad \frac{m_1}{d_1} = \frac{m_2}{d_2}, \quad m_2 = \frac{m_1 d_2}{d_1}$$

Since P is proportional to the mass:

$$P_{oil} = P_{Hg}\left(\frac{d_{oil}}{d_{Hg}}\right) = P_{Hg}\left(\frac{1.30}{13.6}\right) = 0.0956\ P_{Hg}$$

This conversion applies only to the column of silicon oil.

a. P_{flask} = 760. torr - (118 × 0.0956) torr = 760. - 11.3 = 749 torr

$$749\ torr \times \frac{1\ atm}{760\ torr} = 0.986\ atm;\ \ 0.986\ atm \times \frac{1.013 \times 10^5\ Pa}{atm} = 9.99 \times 10^4\ Pa$$

b. P_{flask} = 760. torr + (215 × 0.0956) torr = 760. + 20.6 = 781 torr

$$781\ torr \times \frac{1\ atm}{760\ torr} = 1.03\ atm;\ \ 1.03\ atm \times \frac{1.013 \times 10^5\ Pa}{atm} = 1.04 \times 10^5\ Pa$$

Gas Laws

7. Treat each gas separately and use the relationship $P_1V_1 = P_2V_2$, since for each gas, n and T are constant.

For H_2: $P_2 = \dfrac{P_1V_1}{V_2} = 475\ torr \times \dfrac{2.00\ L}{3.00\ L} = 317\ torr$

For N_2: $P_2 = 0.200\ atm \times \dfrac{1.00\ L}{3.00\ L} = 0.0667\ atm;\ \ 0.0667\ atm\left(\dfrac{760\ torr}{atm}\right) = 50.7\ torr$

$P_{total} = P_{H_2} + P_{N_2} = 317 + 50.7 = 368\ torr$

9. PV = nRT; Assume n is constant.

$$\frac{PV}{T} = nR = constant;\ \ \frac{P_1V_1}{T_1} = \frac{P_2V_2}{T_2}$$

$$\frac{V_2}{V_1} = \frac{T_2P_1}{T_1P_2} = \frac{(273 + 15)\ K \times 720.\ torr}{(273 + 25)\ K \times 605\ torr} = 1.15$$

V_2 = 1.15 V; The volume has increased by 15%.

11. $\dfrac{PV}{T} = nR = $ a constant; $\dfrac{P_1V_1}{T_1} = \dfrac{P_2V_2}{T_2}$

$$P_2 = \frac{P_1V_1T_2}{V_2T_1} = 710\ torr \times \frac{5.0 \times 10^2\ mL}{25\ mL} \times \frac{(273 + 820)\ K}{(273 + 30.)\ K} = 5.1 \times 10^4\ torr$$

13.   a. $PV = nRT$, n and V are constant.

$$\frac{P}{T} = \frac{nR}{V} \text{ or } \frac{P_1}{T_1} = \frac{P_2}{T_2}; \; P_2 = \frac{P_1 T_2}{T_1} = 40.0 \text{ atm} \times \frac{398 \text{ K}}{273 \text{ K}} = 58.3 \text{ atm}$$

        b. $\dfrac{P_1}{T_1} = \dfrac{P_2}{T_2}; \; T_2 = \dfrac{T_1 P_2}{P_1} = 273 \text{ K} \times \dfrac{150. \text{ atm}}{40.0 \text{ atm}} = 1.02 \times 10^3 \text{ K}$

        c. $T_2 = \dfrac{T_1 P_2}{P_1} = 273 \text{ K} \times \dfrac{25.0 \text{ atm}}{40.0 \text{ atm}} = 171 \text{ K}$

15. $PV = nRT$, V and n constant; $\dfrac{P}{T} = \dfrac{nR}{V} = \text{constant}; \; \dfrac{P_1}{T_1} = \dfrac{P_2}{T_2}$

$$P_2 = \frac{P_1 T_2}{T_1} = 13.7 \text{ MPa} \times \frac{(273 + 950) \text{ K}}{(273 + 23) \text{ K}} = 56.6 \text{ MPa}$$

17. $PV = nRT$, P constant; $\dfrac{nT}{V} = \dfrac{P}{R}; \; \dfrac{n_1 T_1}{V_1} = \dfrac{n_2 T_2}{V_2}$

$$\frac{n_2}{n_1} = \frac{T_1 V_2}{T_2 V_1} = \frac{294 \text{ K}}{335 \text{ K}} \times \frac{4.20 \times 10^3 \text{ m}^3}{4.00 \times 10^3 \text{ m}^3} = 0.921$$

19.   We can use the ideal gas law to calculate the partial pressure of each gas or to calculate the total pressure. There will be less math if we calculate the total pressure from the ideal gas law.

$$n_{O_2} = 1.80 \times 10^2 \text{ mg O}_2 \times \frac{1 \text{ g}}{1000 \text{ mg}} \times \frac{1 \text{ mol O}_2}{32.00 \text{ g O}_2} = 5.63 \times 10^{-3} \text{ mol O}_2$$

$$n_{NO} = \frac{1000 \text{ cm}^3}{L} \times \frac{9.00 \times 10^{18} \text{ molecules NO}}{cm^3} \times \frac{1 \text{ mol NO}}{6.022 \times 10^{23} \text{ molecules NO}}$$

$$= 1.49 \times 10^{-2} \text{ mol NO/L}$$

$$n_{total} = n_{N_2} + n_{O_2} + n_{NO} = 2.00 \times 10^{-2} + 5.63 \times 10^{-3} + 1.49 \times 10^{-2} = 4.05 \times 10^{-2} \text{ mol}$$

$$P_{total} = \frac{nRT}{V} = \frac{4.05 \times 10^{-2} \text{ mol} \times \dfrac{0.08206 \text{ L atm}}{\text{mol K}} \times 273 \text{ K}}{1.00 \text{ L}} = 0.907 \text{ atm}$$

$$P_{N_2} = \chi_{N_2} P_{tot} = \frac{2.00 \times 10^{-2} \text{ mol N}_2}{4.05 \times 10^{-2} \text{ mol total}} \times 0.907 \text{ atm} = 0.448 \text{ atm}$$

$$P_{O_2} = \frac{5.63 \times 10^{-3}}{4.05 \times 10^{-2}} \times 0.907 \text{ atm} = 0.126 \text{ atm}; \quad P_{NO} = \frac{1.49 \times 10^{-2}}{4.05 \times 10^{-2}} \times 0.907 \text{ atm} = 0.334 \text{ atm}$$

21. $P_{total} = 1.00 \text{ atm} = 760. \text{ torr} = P_{N_2} + P_{H_2O} = P_{N_2} + 17.5 \text{ torr}, \ P_{N_2} = 743 \text{ torr}$

$$PV = nRT; n = \frac{PV}{RT} = \frac{(743 \text{ torr}) (2.50 \times 10^2 \text{ mL})}{\left(\dfrac{0.08206 \text{ L atm}}{\text{mol K}}\right) (293 \text{ K})} \times \frac{1 \text{ atm}}{760 \text{ torr}} \times \frac{1 \text{ L}}{1000 \text{ mL}}$$

$n = 1.02 \times 10^{-2} \text{ mol N}_2; \ 1.02 \times 10^{-2} \text{ mol N}_2 \times \dfrac{28.02 \text{ g N}_2}{\text{mol N}_2} = 0.286 \text{ g N}_2$

23. $1.00 \text{ g H}_2 \times \dfrac{1 \text{ mol H}_2}{2.016 \text{ g H}_2} = 0.496 \text{ mol H}_2; \ 1.00 \text{ g He} \times \dfrac{1 \text{ mol He}}{4.003 \text{ g He}} = 0.250 \text{ mol He}$

$$P_{H_2} = \chi_{H_2} P_{tot} = \left(\frac{0.496 \text{ mol H}_2}{0.250 \text{ mol He} + 0.496 \text{ mol H}_2}\right) \times 0.480 \text{ atm} = 0.319 \text{ atm}$$

$P_{H_2} + P_{He} = 0.480 \text{ atm}, \ P_{He} = 0.480 - 0.319 = 0.161 \text{ atm}$

Gas Density, Molar Mass, and Reaction Stoichiometry

25. $PV = nRT; \ \dfrac{n}{V} = \dfrac{P}{RT};$ Let M = molar mass and d = density, then:

$$\frac{nM}{V} = \frac{PM}{RT} \text{ where } \frac{nM}{V} = d; \ d = \frac{PM}{RT}$$

For $SiCl_4$, M = 28.09 + 4(35.45) = $\dfrac{169.89 \text{ g}}{\text{mol}}$

$$d = \frac{758 \text{ torr} \times \dfrac{169.89 \text{ g}}{\text{mol}}}{\dfrac{0.08206 \text{ L atm}}{\text{mol K}} \times 358 \text{ K}} \times \frac{1 \text{ atm}}{760 \text{ torr}} = 5.77 \text{ g/L for } SiCl_4$$

For $SiHCl_3$, M = 28.09 + 1.008 + 3(35.45) = $\dfrac{135.45 \text{ g}}{\text{mol}}$

$$d = \frac{PM}{RT} = \frac{758 \text{ torr} \times \dfrac{135.45 \text{ g}}{\text{mol}}}{\dfrac{0.08206 \text{ L atm}}{\text{mol K}} \times 358 \text{ K}} \times \frac{1 \text{ atm}}{760 \text{ torr}} = 4.60 \text{ g/L for } SiHCl_3$$

27. $PV = \dfrac{gRT}{M}$ where M = molar mass

$$M = \frac{gRT}{PV} = \frac{0.800 \text{ g} \times \dfrac{0.08206 \text{ L atm}}{\text{mol K}} \times 373 \text{ K}}{750. \text{ torr} \times 0.256 \text{ L}} \times \frac{760 \text{ torr}}{\text{atm}} = 96.9 \text{ g/mol}$$

Molar mass of $CHCl = 12.0 + 1.0 + 35.5 = 48.5$, so molecular formula is $C_2H_2Cl_2$.

29.   We assume that 28.01 g/mol is the true value for the molar mass of N_2. The value of 28.15 g/mol is the average of the amount of N_2 and Ar in air. Let x = % of the number of moles that are N_2 molecules. Then $100 - x$ = % of the number of moles that are Ar atoms. Solving:

$$28.15 = \frac{x(28.01) + (100 - x)(39.95)}{100}$$

$$2815 = 28.01\,x + 3995 - 39.95\,x; \quad 11.94\,x = 1180.$$

$$x = 98.83\%\ N_2; \quad \%\ Ar = 100.00 - x = 1.17\%\ Ar$$

Ratio of moles of Ar to moles of $N_2 = \dfrac{1.17}{98.83} = 1.18 \times 10^{-2}$.

31. $1.00 \times 10^3\ kg\ Mo \times \dfrac{1000\ g}{kg} \times \dfrac{1\ mol\ Mo}{95.94\ g\ Mo} = 1.04 \times 10^4\ mol\ Mo$

$1.04 \times 10^4\ mol\ Mo \times \dfrac{1\ mol\ MoO_3}{mol\ Mo} \times \dfrac{7/2\ mol\ O_2}{mol\ MoO_3} = 3.64 \times 10^4\ mol\ O_2$

$$V_{O_2} = \frac{nRT}{P} = \frac{(3.64 \times 10^4\ mol)\left(\dfrac{0.08206\ L\ atm}{mol\ K}\right)(290.\ K)}{1.00\ atm} = 8.66 \times 10^5\ L\ of\ O_2$$

$8.66 \times 10^5\ L\ O_2 \times \dfrac{100\ L\ air}{21\ L\ O_2} = 4.1 \times 10^6\ L\ air$

$1.04 \times 10^4\ mol\ Mo \times \dfrac{3\ mol\ H_2}{mol\ Mo} = 3.12 \times 10^4\ mol\ H_2$

$$V_{H_2} = \frac{(3.12 \times 10^4\ mol)\left(\dfrac{0.08206\ L\ atm}{mol\ K}\right)(290.\ K)}{1.00\ atm} = 7.42 \times 10^5\ L\ of\ H_2$$

33.   For ammonia (in one minute):

$$n_{NH_3} = \frac{PV}{RT} = \frac{(90.\ atm)(500.\ L)}{\left(\dfrac{0.08206\ L\ atm}{mol\ K}\right)(496\ K)} = 1.1 \times 10^3\ mol$$

NH_3 flows into the reactor at a rate of 1.1×10^3 mol/min.

For CO_2 (in one minute):

$$n_{CO_2} = \frac{PV}{RT} = \frac{(45\ atm)(600.\ L)}{\left(\dfrac{0.08206\ L\ atm}{mol\ K}\right)(496\ K)} = 6.6 \times 10^2\ mol$$

CO_2 flows into the reactor at 6.6×10^2 mol/min.

To react completely with 1.1×10^3 mol NH_3/min, need:

$$\frac{1.1 \times 10^3 \text{ mol } NH_3}{\text{min}} \times \frac{1 \text{ mol } CO_2}{2 \text{ mol } NH_3} = 5.5 \times 10^2 \text{ mol } CO_2/\text{min}$$

Since 660 mol CO_2/min are present, ammonia is the limiting reagent.

$$\frac{1.1 \times 10^3 \text{ mol } NH_3}{\text{min}} \times \frac{1 \text{ mol urea}}{2 \text{ mol } NH_3} \times \frac{60.06 \text{ g urea}}{\text{mol urea}} = 3.3 \times 10^4 \text{ g urea/min}$$

35. $4.10 \text{ g HgO} \times \dfrac{1 \text{ mol HgO}}{216.6 \text{ g HgO}} \times \dfrac{1 \text{ mol } O_2}{2 \text{ mol HgO}} = 9.46 \times 10^{-3} \text{ mol } O_2$

$$V = \frac{nRT}{P} = \frac{9.46 \times 10^{-3} \text{ mol} \times \dfrac{0.08206 \text{ L atm}}{\text{mol K}} \times 303 \text{ K}}{725 \text{ torr}} \times \frac{760 \text{ torr}}{\text{atm}} = 0.247 \text{ L}$$

36.   10.10 atm - 7.62 atm = 2.48 atm is the pressure of the amount of F_2 reacted.

$$PV = nRT, \text{ V and T are constant}; \quad \frac{P}{n} = \text{constant}, \quad \frac{P_1}{n_1} = \frac{P_2}{n_2} \quad \text{or} \quad \frac{P_1}{P_2} = \frac{n_1}{n_2}$$

$$\frac{\text{moles } F_2 \text{ reacted}}{\text{moles Xe reacted}} = \frac{2.48 \text{ atm}}{1.24 \text{ atm}} = 2; \quad \text{So Xe} + 2 F_2 \rightarrow XeF_4$$

38. $0.2766 \text{ g } CO_2 \times \dfrac{12.011 \text{ g C}}{44.009 \text{ g } CO_2} = 7.549 \times 10^{-2} \text{ g C}$

$$\% \text{ C} = \frac{7.549 \times 10^{-2} \text{ g}}{0.1023 \text{ g}} \times 100 = 73.79\% \text{ C}$$

$$0.0991 \text{ g } H_2O \times \frac{2.016 \text{ g H}}{18.02 \text{ g } H_2O} = 1.11 \times 10^{-2} \text{ g H}$$

$$\% \text{ H} = \frac{1.11 \times 10^{-2} \text{ g}}{0.1023 \text{ g}} \times 100 = 10.9\% \text{ H}$$

$$PV = nRT; \quad n = \frac{PV}{RT} = \frac{1.00 \text{ atm} \times 27.6 \times 10^{-3} \text{ L}}{\dfrac{0.08206 \text{ L atm}}{\text{mol K}} \times 273 \text{ K}} = 1.23 \times 10^{-3} \text{ mol } N_2$$

$$1.23 \times 10^{-3} \text{ mol } N_2 \times \frac{28.02 \text{ g } N_2}{\text{mol } N_2} = 3.45 \times 10^{-2} \text{ g nitrogen}$$

$$\% \text{ N} = \frac{3.45 \times 10^{-2} \text{ g}}{0.4831 \text{ g}} \times 100 = 7.14\% \text{ N}$$

% O = 100.00 - (73.79 + 10.9 + 7.14) = 8.2% O

Out of 100.00 g of compound, there are:

$$73.79 \text{ g C} \times \frac{1 \text{ mol}}{12.011 \text{ g}} = 6.144 \text{ mol C}; \quad 7.14 \text{ g N} \times \frac{1 \text{ mol}}{14.01 \text{ g}} = 0.510 \text{ mol N}$$

$$10.9 \text{ g H} \times \frac{1 \text{ mol}}{1.008 \text{ g}} = 10.8 \text{ mol H}; \quad 8.2 \text{ g O} \times \frac{1 \text{ mol}}{16.00 \text{ g}} = 0.51 \text{ mol O}$$

Divide all values by 0.51. We get the empirical formula $C_{12}H_{21}NO$.

$$M = \frac{dRT}{P} = \frac{\dfrac{4.02 \text{ g}}{L} \times \dfrac{0.08206 \text{ L atm}}{\text{mol K}} \times 400. \text{ K}}{256 \text{ torr}} \times \frac{760 \text{ torr}}{\text{atm}} = 392 \text{ g/mol}$$

Molar mass of $C_{12}H_{21}NO \approx 195$ g/mol and $\dfrac{392}{195} \approx 2$.

Thus, the molecular formula is $C_{24}H_{42}N_2O_2$

Kinetic Molecular Theory and Real Gases

41. $(KE)_{avg} = 3/2$ RT; KE depends only on temperature. At each temperature CH_4 and N_2 will have
        the same average KE. For energy units of joules (J), use R = 8.3145 J mol^{-1} K^{-1}.

at 273 K: $(KE)_{avg} = \dfrac{3}{2} \times \dfrac{8.3145 \text{ J}}{\text{mol K}} \times 273 \text{ K} = 3.40 \times 10^3$ J/mol

at 546 K: $(KE)_{avg} = \dfrac{3}{2} \times \dfrac{8.3145 \text{ J}}{\text{mol K}} \times 546 \text{ K} = 6.81 \times 10^3$ J/mol

44.   a.   They will all have the same average kinetic energy since they are all at the same
             temperature.

        b.   Flask C: Lightest molecules have the greatest root mean square velocity (at constant T).

        c.   Flask A: Collision frequency is proportional to avg. velocity × n/V. Moles are proportional
             to pressure at constant T and V, and average velocity is proportional to $(1/M)^{1/2}$.

	n (relative)	$u_{avg.}$ (relative)	Coll. Freq. (relative)
A	1.0	1.0	1.0
B	0.33	1.0	0.33
C	0.13	3.7	0.49

47. $\dfrac{R_1}{R_2} = \left(\dfrac{M_2}{M_1}\right)^{1/2}$ where R = rate of diffusion and M = molar mass of unknown

$\dfrac{R_1}{R_2} = \left(\dfrac{M_2}{M_1}\right)^{1/2}$; $\dfrac{31.50}{30.50} = \left(\dfrac{31.998}{M}\right)^{1/2} = 1.033$

$\dfrac{31.998}{M} = 1.067$, M = 29.99; Of the choices, the gas would be NO, nitric oxide.

49. $\dfrac{\text{Rate (1)}}{\text{Rate (2)}} = \left(\dfrac{M_2}{M_1}\right)^{1/2}$; Let Gas (1) = He, Gas (2) = NF_3

$\dfrac{\dfrac{1.0\ L}{4.5\ min}}{\dfrac{1.0\ L}{t}} = \left(\dfrac{71.0}{4.00}\right)^{1/2}$, $\dfrac{t}{4.5\ min} = 4.21$, t = 19 min

50.   a.   PV = nRT

$P = \dfrac{nRT}{V} = \dfrac{0.5000\ mol\left(\dfrac{0.08206\ L\ atm}{mol\ K}\right)(25.0 + 273.2)\ K}{1.0000\ L} = 12.24\ atm$

b. $\left[P + a\left(\dfrac{n}{V}\right)^2\right](V - nb) = nRT$; For N_2: a = 1.39 atm L^2/mol^2 and b = 0.0391 L/mol

$\left[P + 1.39\left(\dfrac{0.5000}{1.0000}\right)^2 atm\right](1.0000\ L - 0.5000 \times 0.0391\ L) = 12.24\ L\ atm$

(P + 0.348 atm)(0.9805 L) = 12.24 L atm

$P = \dfrac{12.24\ L\ atm}{0.9805\ L} - 0.348\ atm = 12.48 - 0.348 = 12.13\ atm$

c.   The ideal gas law is high by 0.11 atm or (0.11/12.13) × 100 = 0.91%.

52.   Van der Waals' equation: $P = \dfrac{nRT}{V - nb} - a\left(\dfrac{n}{V}\right)^2$

P is the measured pressure and V is the volume of the container. For NH_3, a = 4.17 L^2 atm/mol^2 and b = 0.0371 L/mol.

For the first experiment (assuming four significant figures in all values):

$$P = \frac{nRT}{V - nb} - a\left(\frac{n}{V}\right)^2 = \frac{1.000 \times 0.08206 \times 273.2}{172.1 - 0.0371} - 4.17\left(\frac{1.000}{172.1}\right)^2$$

P = 0.1303 - 0.0001 = 0.1302 atm. In Example 5.1, P_{obs} = 0.1300 atm. The difference is less than 0.1%. The ideal gas law also gives 0.1302 atm. At low pressures, the van der Waals equation agrees with the ideal gas law.

For experiment 6, the measured pressure is 1.000 atm. The ideal gas law gives P = 1.015 atm and the van der Waals equation gives P = 1.017 - 0.086 = 1.008 atm. The van der Waals equation accounts for approximately one-half of the deviation from ideal behavior. Note: As pressure increases, deviation from the ideal gas law increases.

Atmospheric Chemistry

54. χ_{NO} = 5 × 10^{-7} from Table 5.4; $P_{NO} = \chi_{NO}P_{total}$ = 5 × 10^{-7} × 1.0 atm = 5 × 10^{-7} atm

$$PV = nRT;\; \frac{n}{V} = \frac{P}{RT} = \frac{5 \times 10^{-7}\text{ atm}}{\left(\dfrac{0.08206\text{ L atm}}{\text{mol K}}\right)(273\text{ K})} = \frac{2 \times 10^{-8}\text{ mol}}{L}$$

$$\frac{2 \times 10^{-8}\text{ mol}}{L} \times \frac{1\text{ L}}{1000\text{ cm}^3} \times \frac{6.02 \times 10^{23}\text{ molecules}}{\text{mol}} = \frac{1 \times 10^{13}\text{ molecules NO}}{\text{cm}^3}$$

55.   a.   If we have 10^6 L of air, there are 3.0 × 10^2 L of CO. Since n ∝ V:

$$P_{CO} = \chi_{CO}P_{tot} = \frac{3.0 \times 10^2}{1.0 \times 10^6} \times 628\text{ torr} = 0.19\text{ torr}$$

b. $n_{CO} = \dfrac{P_{CO}V}{RT};$ Assume 1.0 m^3 air, 1 m^3 = 1000 L.

$$n_{CO} = \frac{\dfrac{0.19}{760}\text{ atm} \times (1.0 \times 10^3\text{ L})}{\dfrac{0.08206\text{ L atm}}{\text{mol K}} \times 273\text{ K}} = 1.1 \times 10^{-2}\text{ mol}$$

$$1.1 \times 10^{-2}\text{ mol} \times \frac{6.022 \times 10^{23}\text{ molecules}}{\text{mol}} = 6.6 \times 10^{21}\text{ CO molecules in 1.0 m}^3\text{ of air}$$

c. $$\frac{6.6 \times 10^{21}\text{ molecules}}{\text{m}^3} \times \left(\frac{1\text{ m}}{100\text{ cm}}\right)^3 = \frac{6.6 \times 10^{15}\text{ molecules CO}}{\text{cm}^3}$$

59.   For benzene:

$$89.6 \times 10^{-9} \text{ g} \times \frac{1 \text{ mol}}{78.11 \text{ g}} = 1.15 \times 10^{-9} \text{ mol}$$

$$V_{ben} = \frac{nRT}{P} = \frac{1.15 \times 10^{-9} \text{ mol} \times \frac{0.08206 \text{ L atm}}{\text{mol K}} \times 296 \text{ K}}{748 \text{ torr}} \times \frac{760 \text{ torr}}{\text{atm}} = 2.84 \times 10^{-8} \text{ L}$$

$$\text{Mixing ratio} = \frac{2.84 \times 10^{-8} \text{ L}}{3.00 \text{ L}} \times 10^6 = 9.47 \times 10^{-3} \text{ ppmv}$$

$$\text{or ppbv} = \frac{\text{vol. of X} \times 10^9}{\text{total vol.}} = \frac{2.84 \times 10^{-8} \text{ L}}{3.00 \text{ L}} \times 10^9 = 9.47 \text{ ppbv}$$

$$\frac{1.15 \times 10^{-9} \text{ mol benzene}}{3.00 \text{ L}} \times \frac{1 \text{ L}}{1000 \text{ cm}^3} \times \frac{6.022 \times 10^{23} \text{ molecules}}{\text{mol}}$$

$$= 2.31 \times 10^{11} \text{ molecules benzene/cm}^3$$

For toluene:

$$153 \times 10^{-9} \text{ g C}_7\text{H}_8 \times \frac{1 \text{ mol}}{92.13 \text{ g}} = 1.66 \times 10^{-9} \text{ mol toluene}$$

$$V_{tol} = \frac{nRT}{P} = \frac{1.66 \times 10^{-9} \text{ mol} \times \frac{0.08206 \text{ L atm}}{\text{mol K}} \times 296 \text{ K}}{748 \text{ torr}} \times \frac{760 \text{ torr}}{\text{atm}} = 4.10 \times 10^{-8} \text{ L}$$

$$\text{Mixing ratio} = \frac{4.10 \times 10^{-8} \text{ L}}{3.00 \text{ L}} \times 10^6 = 1.37 \times 10^{-2} \text{ ppmv (or 13.7 ppbv)}$$

$$\frac{1.66 \times 10^{-9} \text{ mol toluene}}{3.00 \text{ L}} \times \frac{1 \text{ L}}{1000 \text{ cm}^3} \times \frac{6.022 \times 10^{23} \text{ molecules}}{\text{mol}}$$

$$= 3.33 \times 10^{11} \text{ molecules toluene/cm}^3$$

Additional Exercises

61. $$750 \text{ mL juice} \times \frac{12 \text{ mL alcohol}}{100 \text{ mL juice}} = 90. \text{ mL alcohol present}$$

$$90. \text{ mL alcohol} \times \frac{0.79 \text{ g}}{\text{mL}} = 71 \text{ g C}_2\text{H}_5\text{OH}$$

$$71 \text{ g C}_2\text{H}_5\text{OH} \times \frac{1 \text{ mol C}_2\text{H}_5\text{OH}}{46.1 \text{ g C}_2\text{H}_5\text{OH}} \times \frac{2 \text{ mol CO}_2}{2 \text{ mol C}_2\text{H}_5\text{OH}} = 1.5 \text{ mol CO}_2$$

The CO_2 will occupy $(825 - 750. =)$ 75 mL not occupied by the liquid (headspace).

$$P = \frac{nRT}{V} = \frac{1.5 \text{ mol} \times \dfrac{0.08206 \text{ L atm}}{\text{mol K}} \times 298 \text{ K}}{75 \times 10^{-3} \text{ L}} = 490 \text{ atm}$$

Actually, enough CO_2 will dissolve in the wine to lower the pressure of CO_2 to a much more reasonable value.

63.   a.   Volume of hot air: $V = \dfrac{4}{3} \pi r^3 = \dfrac{4}{3} \pi (2.50)^3 = 65.4 \text{ m}^3$

(Note: radius = diameter/2 = 5.00/2 = 2.50 m)

$$65.4 \text{ m}^3 \times \left(\frac{10 \text{ dm}}{\text{m}} \right)^3 \times \frac{1 \text{ L}}{\text{dm}^3} = 6.54 \times 10^4 \text{ L}$$

$$n = \frac{PV}{RT} = \frac{\left(745 \text{ torr} \times \dfrac{1 \text{ atm}}{760 \text{ torr}} \right) \times 6.54 \times 10^4 \text{ L}}{\dfrac{0.08206 \text{ L atm}}{\text{mol K}} \times (273 + 65) \text{ K}} = 2.31 \times 10^3 \text{ mol}$$

$$\text{Mass} = 2.31 \times 10^3 \text{ mol} \times \frac{29.0 \text{ g}}{\text{mol}} = 6.70 \times 10^4 \text{ g}$$

Mass of air displaced:

$$n = \frac{PV}{RT} = \frac{\dfrac{745}{760} \text{ atm} \times 6.54 \times 10^4 \text{ L}}{\dfrac{0.08206 \text{ L atm}}{\text{mol K}} \times (273 + 21) \text{ K}} = 2.66 \times 10^3 \text{ mol}$$

$$\text{Mass} = 2.66 \times 10^3 \text{ mol} \times \frac{29.0 \text{ g}}{\text{mol}} = 7.71 \times 10^4 \text{ g}$$

Lift $= 7.71 \times 10^4 \text{ g} - 6.70 \times 10^4 \text{ g} = 1.01 \times 10^4 \text{ g}$

b.   Mass displaced is the same, 7.71×10^4 g. Moles of He in balloon will be the same as moles of air displaced, 2.66×10^3 mol, since P, V and T are the same.

$$\text{Mass of He} = 2.66 \times 10^3 \text{ mol} \times \frac{4.003 \text{ g}}{\text{mol}} = 1.06 \times 10^4 \text{ g}$$

Lift $= 7.71 \times 10^4 \text{ g} - 1.06 \times 10^4 \text{ g} = 6.65 \times 10^4 \text{ g}$

c. Mass of hot air:

$$n = \frac{PV}{RT} = \frac{\dfrac{630.}{760}\ \text{atm} \times 6.54 \times 10^4\ \text{L}}{\dfrac{0.08206\ \text{L atm}}{\text{mol K}} \times 338\ \text{K}} = 1.95 \times 10^3\ \text{mol}$$

$$1.95 \times 10^3\ \text{mol} \times \frac{29.0\ \text{g}}{\text{mol}} = 5.66 \times 10^4\ \text{g of hot air}$$

Mass of air displaced:

$$n = \frac{PV}{RT} = \frac{\dfrac{630.}{760}\ \text{atm} \times 6.54 \times 10^4\ \text{L}}{\dfrac{0.08206\ \text{L atm}}{\text{mol K}} \times 294\ \text{K}} = 2.25 \times 10^3\ \text{mol}$$

$$2.25 \times 10^3\ \text{mol} \times \frac{29.0\ \text{g}}{\text{mol}} = 6.53 \times 10^4\ \text{g}$$

Lift = 6.53×10^4 g - 5.66×10^4 g = 8.7×10^3 g

d. mass of hot air = 6.70×10^4 g (from part a)

Mass of air displaced:

$$n = \frac{PV}{RT} = \frac{\dfrac{745}{760}\ \text{atm} \times 6.54 \times 10^4\ \text{L}}{\dfrac{0.08206\ \text{L atm}}{\text{mol K}} \times 265\ \text{K}} = 2.95 \times 10^3\ \text{mol}$$

$$2.95 \times 10^3\ \text{mol} \times \frac{29.0\ \text{g}}{\text{mol}} = 8.56 \times 10^4\ \text{g}$$

Lift = 8.56×10^4 g - 6.70×10^4 g = 1.86×10^4 g

65.   The partial pressure of CO_2 that reacted is 740. - 390. = 350. torr. Thus, the number of moles of CO_2 that reacts is given by:

$$n = \frac{PV}{RT} = \frac{\dfrac{350.}{760}\ \text{atm} \times 3.00\ \text{L}}{\dfrac{0.08206\ \text{L atm}}{\text{mol K}} \times 293\ \text{K}} = 5.75 \times 10^{-2}\ \text{mol } CO_2$$

$$5.75 \times 10^{-2}\ \text{mol } CO_2 \times \frac{1\ \text{mol MgO}}{1\ \text{mol } CO_2} \times \frac{40.31\ \text{g MgO}}{\text{mol HgO}} = 2.32\ \text{g MgO}$$

$$\% \text{ MgO} = \frac{2.32\ \text{g}}{2.85\ \text{g}} \times 100 = 81.4\%\ \text{MgO}$$

67.   A concentration of 1.0 ppbv means there is 1.0 L of CH_2O for every 1.0×10^9 L of air measured
       at the same temperature and pressure. The molar volume of an ideal gas is 22.42 at STP.

$$\frac{1.0 \text{ L } CH_2O}{1.0 \times 10^9 \text{ L}} \times \frac{1 \text{ mol } CH_2O}{22.42 \text{ L}} \times \frac{6.022 \times 10^{23} \text{ molecules}}{\text{mol}} \times \frac{1 \text{ L}}{1000 \text{ cm}^3} = \frac{2.7 \times 10^{10} \text{ molecules}}{\text{cm}^3}$$

$$V = \left(18.0 \text{ ft} \times \frac{12 \text{ in}}{\text{ft}} \times \frac{2.54 \text{ cm}}{\text{in}} \right) \left(24.0 \text{ ft} \times \frac{12 \text{ in}}{\text{ft}} \times \frac{2.54 \text{ cm}}{\text{in}} \right)$$

$$\times \left(8.0 \text{ ft} \times \frac{12 \text{ in}}{\text{ft}} \times \frac{2.54 \text{ cm}}{\text{in}} \right) = 9.8 \times 10^7 \text{ cm}^3$$

$$9.8 \times 10^7 \text{ cm}^3 \times \frac{2.7 \times 10^{10} \text{ molecules}}{\text{cm}^3} \times \frac{1 \text{ mol}}{6.022 \times 10^{23} \text{ molecules}} \times \frac{30.03 \text{ g}}{\text{mol}} = 1.3 \times 10^{-4} \text{ g } CH_2O$$

69. $P_1V_1 = P_2V_2$; The total volume is 1.00 L + 1.00 L + 2.00 L = 4.00 L.

For He: $P_2 = \dfrac{P_1V_1}{V_2} = 200.$ torr $\times \dfrac{1.00 \text{ L}}{4.00 \text{ L}} = 50.0$ torr He

For Ne: $P_2 = 0.400$ atm $\times \dfrac{1.00 \text{ L}}{4.00 \text{ L}} = 0.100$ atm

0.100 atm $\times \dfrac{760 \text{ torr}}{\text{atm}} = 76.0$ torr Ne

For Ar: $P_2 = 24.0$ kPa $\times \dfrac{2.00 \text{ L}}{4.00 \text{ L}} = 12.0$ kPa

12.0 kPa $\times \dfrac{1 \text{ atm}}{101.3 \text{ kPa}} \times \dfrac{760 \text{ torr}}{\text{atm}} = 90.0$ torr Ar

$P_{total} = 50.0 + 76.0 + 90.0 = 216.0$ torr

71.   Out of 100.00 g compounds, there are:

58.51 g C $\times \dfrac{1 \text{ mol C}}{12.011 \text{ g C}} = 4.871$ mol C; $\dfrac{4.871}{2.436} = 2$

7.37 g H $\times \dfrac{1 \text{ mol H}}{1.008 \text{ g H}} = 7.31$ mol H; $\dfrac{7.31}{2.436} = 3$

34.12 g N $\times \dfrac{1 \text{ mol N}}{14.007 \text{ g N}} = 2.436$ mol N

Empirical formula: C_2H_3N

$$\frac{\text{Rate (1)}}{\text{Rate (2)}} = \left(\frac{M_2}{M_1}\right)^{1/2}; \text{ Let Gas (1)} = \text{He}; \ 3.20 = \left(\frac{M_2}{4.003}\right)^{1/2}, \ M_2 = 41.0$$

Mass of C_2H_3N: $2(12.0) + 3(1.0) + 1(14.0) = 41.0$

So molecular formula is also C_2H_3N.

73. $PV = nRT = \text{Const.}; \ P_1V_1 = P_2V_2$

Let condition (1) correspond to He from tank that can be used to fill balloons. We must leave 1.0 atm of He in the tank, so $P_1 = 200.$ atm - $1.00 = 199$ atm and $V_1 = 15.0$ L. Condition (2) will correspond to the filled balloons with $P_2 = 1.00$ atm and $V_2 = N(2.00 \text{ L})$ where N is the number of filled balloons.

$(199)(15.0) = (1.00)(2.00)\text{N}; \ \text{N} = 1492.5$; We can't fill 0.5 of a balloon. So N = 1492 balloons or to 3 significant figures, 1490 balloons.

77. $M = \dfrac{dRT}{P}$, P & M constant; $dT = \dfrac{PM}{R} = \text{const}$

$d = \text{const } (1/T)$ or $d_1T_1 = d_2T_2$, where T in kelvin (K).

$T = x + {}^\circ C; \ 1.2930(x + 0.0) = 0.9460(x + 100.0)$

$1.2930\,x = 0.9460\,x + 94.60, \ 0.3470\,x = 94.60, \ x = 272.6$

From these data absolute zero would be $-272.6^\circ C$. Actual value is $-273.15^\circ C$.

79.   If we had 100.0 g of the gas, we would have 50.0 g He and 50.0 g Xe.

$$\chi_{\text{He}} = \frac{n_{\text{He}}}{n_{\text{He}} + n_{\text{Xe}}} = \frac{\dfrac{50.0}{4.003}}{\dfrac{50.0}{4.003} + \dfrac{50.0}{131.3}} = \frac{12.5}{12.5 + 0.381} = 0.970; \ \chi_{\text{Xe}} = 0.030$$

$P_{\text{He}} = 0.970 \times 600. \text{ torr} = 582 \text{ torr}; \ P_{\text{Xe}} = 600. - 582 = 18 \text{ torr}$

82.   The force per impact, which is proportional to Δmu, is greater for He because it depends on $\sqrt{M}$.

$$\frac{\text{Impact Force (H}_2)}{\text{Impact Force (He)}} = \sqrt{\frac{2.016}{4.003}} = 0.7097$$

85. $\dfrac{PV}{nRT} = 1 + \beta P; \ \dfrac{n}{V}(M) = d$ Where M = molar mass;

$$\frac{M}{RT} \times \frac{P}{d} = 1 + \beta P, \ \frac{P}{d} = \frac{RT}{M} + \frac{\beta RTP}{M};$$

This is in the equation for a straight line: $y = b + mx$. If we plot P/d vs P and extrapolate to P = 0, we get a y-intercept = b = 1.3980 = RT/M.

at 0.00°C, $M = \dfrac{0.08206 \times 273.15}{1.3980} = 16.03$

89. $\Delta(mu) = 2mu$ = change in momentum per impact

$$\Delta(mu)_{O_2} = 2M_{O_2}\left(\frac{3RT}{M_{O_2}}\right)^{1/2} \qquad\qquad \Delta(mu)_{He} = 2M_{He}\left(\frac{3RT}{M_{He}}\right)^{1/2}$$

$$\frac{\Delta(mu)_{O_2}}{\Delta(mu)_{He}} = \frac{2M_{O_2}\left(\dfrac{3RT}{M_{O_2}}\right)^{1/2}}{2M_{He}\left(\dfrac{3\,RT}{M_{He}}\right)^{1/2}} = \frac{M_{O_2}}{M_{He}}\left(\frac{M_{He}}{M_{O_2}}\right)^{1/2} = \frac{31.998}{4.003}\left(\frac{4.003}{31.998}\right)^{1/2} = 2.827$$

The change in momentum per impact is 2.827 times larger for O_2 molecules than for He atoms.

$$Z = A\frac{N}{V}\left(\frac{RT}{2\pi M}\right)^{1/2} = \text{collision rate}$$

$$\frac{Z_{O_2}}{Z_{He}} = \frac{A\left(\dfrac{N}{V}\right)\left(\dfrac{RT}{2\pi M_{O_2}}\right)^{1/2}}{A\left(\dfrac{N}{V}\right)\left(\dfrac{RT}{2\pi M_{He}}\right)^{1/2}} = \frac{\left(\dfrac{1}{M_{O_2}}\right)^{1/2}}{\left(\dfrac{1}{M_{He}}\right)^{1/2}} = \left(\frac{M_{He}}{M_{O_2}}\right)^{1/2} = 0.3537;\quad \frac{Z_{He}}{Z_{O_2}} = 2.827$$

There are 2.827 times as many impacts per second for He as compared to O_2.

92. $n_{Ar} = \dfrac{228\text{ g}}{39.95\text{ g/mol}} = 5.71\text{ mol Ar}$

$\chi_{CH_4} = \dfrac{n_{CH_4}}{n_{CH_4} + n_{Ar}} = 0.650 = \dfrac{n_{CH_4}}{n_{CH_4} + (5.71)}$

$0.650\,(n_{CH_4} + 5.71) = n_{CH_4}$, $3.71 = 0.350\,n_{CH_4}$, $n_{CH_4} = 10.6\text{ mol }CH_4$

$KE_{avg} = \dfrac{3}{2}RT$ for 1 mol

So $KE_{tot} = (10.6 + 5.71\text{ mol}) \times 3/2 \times 8.3145\text{ J mol}^{-1}\text{ K}^{-1} \times 298\text{ K} = 6.06 \times 10^4\text{ J} = 60.6\text{ kJ}$

96.   Balanced equations:

$$4 NH_3 + 5 O_2 \rightarrow 4 NO + 6 H_2O \text{ and } 4 NH_3 + 7 O_2 \rightarrow 4 NO_2 + 6 H_2O$$

Let $4x$ = number of mol of NO formed and let $4y$ = number of mol of NO_2 formed. Then:

$$4x\ NH_3 + 5x\ O_2 \rightarrow 4x\ NO + 6x\ H_2O \text{ and } 4y\ NH_3 + 7y\ O_2 \rightarrow 4y\ NO_2 + 6y\ H_2O$$

All NH_3 reacted, so $4x + 4y = 2.00$. $10.00 - 6.75 = 3.25$ mol O_2 reacted, so $5x + 7y = 3.25$.

Solving:

$$
\begin{array}{l}
20\ x + 28\ y = \ 13.0 \\
\underline{-20\ x - 20\ y = -10.0} \\
\qquad 8\ y = \quad 3.0, \ \ y = 0.38; \ \ 4x + 4 \times 0.38 = 2.00, \ \ x = 0.12
\end{array}
$$

mol NO $= 4x = 4 \times 0.12 = 0.48$ mol NO formed

99.   The reaction is 1:1 between ethene and hydrogen. A greater volume of H_2 and thus, more moles of H_2 are flowing into the reactor. Ethene is the limiting reagent.

In one minute:

$$n_{C_2H_4} = \frac{PV}{RT} = \frac{(25.0 \text{ atm}) (1000. \text{ L})}{\left(\dfrac{0.08206 \text{ L atm}}{\text{mol K}} \right) (573 \text{ K})} = 532 \text{ mol } C_2H_4 \text{ reacted}$$

Theoretical yield:

$$\frac{532 \text{ mol } C_2H_4}{\text{min}} \times \frac{1 \text{ mol } C_2H_6}{\text{mol } C_2H_4} \times \frac{30.07 \text{ g } C_2H_6}{\text{mol } C_2H_6} \times \frac{1 \text{ kg}}{1000 \text{ g}} = 16.0 \text{ kg } C_2H_6/\text{min}$$

$$\% \text{ yield} = \frac{15.0 \text{ kg/min}}{16.0 \text{ kg/min}} \times 100 = 93.8\%$$

102. n_{tot} = total # of mol of gas that have effused into the container.

$$n_{tot} = \frac{PV}{RT} = \frac{1.20 \times 10^{-6} \text{ atm} \times 1.00 \text{ L}}{\dfrac{0.08206 \text{ L atm}}{\text{mol K}} \times 300. \text{ K}} = 4.87 \times 10^{-8} \text{ mol}$$

This amount has entered over a time span of 24 hours:

$$24 \text{ hr} \times \frac{60 \text{ min}}{1 \text{ hr}} \times \frac{60 \text{ s}}{1 \text{ min}} = 8.64 \times 10^4 \text{ s}$$

So: $\dfrac{4.87 \times 10^{-8} \text{ mol}}{8.64 \times 10^4 \text{ s}} = 5.64 \times 10^{-13}$ mol/s have entered the container.

$$\frac{5.64 \times 10^{-13} \text{ mol}}{s} \times \frac{6.022 \times 10^{23}}{1 \text{ mol}} = 3.40 \times 10^{11} \text{ molecules/s}$$

The frequency of collisions of the gas with a given area is:

$$Z = A\left(\frac{N}{V}\right)\left(\frac{RT}{2\pi M}\right)^{1/2}; \quad Z_{tot} = \frac{3.40 \times 10^{11} \text{ molecules}}{s} = Z_{N_2} + Z_{O_2}$$

$$\frac{n}{V} = \frac{P}{RT} = \frac{1.00 \text{ atm}}{\dfrac{0.08206 \text{ L atm}}{\text{mol K}} \times 300. \text{ K}} = 4.06 \times 10^{-2} \text{ mol/L}$$

$$\frac{N}{V} = \frac{4.06 \times 10^{-2} \text{ mol}}{L} \times \frac{6.022 \times 10^{23} \text{ molecules}}{\text{mol}} \times \frac{1000 \text{ L}}{m^3} = 2.44 \times 10^{25} \text{ molecules/m}^3$$

For N_2: $\left(\dfrac{N}{V}\right) = (0.78)(2.44 \times 10^{25}) = 1.9 \times 10^{25}$ molecules/m^3

For O_2: $\left(\dfrac{N}{V}\right) = (0.22)(2.44 \times 10^{25}) = 5.4 \times 10^{24}$ molecules/m^3

$Z_{tot} = 3.40 \times 10^{11}$ molecules/s $= Z_{N_2} + Z_{O_2}$

$$3.40 \times 10^{-11} = A\left[1.9 \times 10^{25}\left(\frac{8.3145 \times 300.}{2\pi(28.0 \times 10^{-3})}\right)^{1/2} + 5.4 \times 10^{24}\left(\frac{8.3145 \times 300.}{2\pi(32.0 \times 10^{-3})}\right)^{1/2}\right]$$

$$\frac{3.40 \times 10^{11} \text{ molecules}}{s} = A\left[\frac{2.3 \times 10^{27} \text{ molecules}}{m^2 s} + \frac{6.0 \times 10^{26} \text{ molecules}}{m^2 s}\right]$$

$$A = \frac{3.40 \times 10^{11}}{2.9 \times 10^{27}} \text{ m}^2 = 1.2 \times 10^{-16} \text{ m}^2 = \pi r^2$$

$$r = \left(\frac{1.2 \times 10^{-16} \text{ m}^2}{\pi}\right)^{1/2} = 6.2 \times 10^{-9} \text{ m} = 6.2 \text{ nm}$$

diameter $= 2r = 2(6.2 \times 10^{-9} \text{ m}) = 1.2 \times 10^{-8} \text{ m} = 12 \text{ nm}$

105.   After the hole develops, assume each He that collides with the hole goes into the Rn side and that each Rn that collides with the hole goes into the He side. Assume no molecules return to the side in which they began. Initial moles of each gas:

$$n = \frac{PV}{RT} = \frac{(2.00 \times 10^{-6} \text{ atm})(1.00 \text{ L})}{\dfrac{0.08206 \text{ L atm}}{\text{mol K}} \times 300. \text{ K}} = 8.12 \times 10^{-8} \text{ mol}$$

$$Z_{He} = A \times \frac{N}{V} \times \left(\frac{RT}{2\pi M}\right)^{1/2}, \quad \frac{N}{V} = \frac{P}{RT} \times N_A \times 1000 \text{ L/m}^3 \text{ and } A = \pi r^2$$

$$Z_{He} = \pi (1.00 \times 10^{-6} \text{ m})^2 \times \frac{2.00 \times 10^{-6}}{0.08206 \times 300.} \times (6.022 \times 10^{23}) \times 1000$$

$$\times \left(\frac{8.3145 \times 300.}{2\pi (4.003 \times 10^{-3})}\right)^{1/2} = 4.84 \times 10^{10} \text{ collisons/s}$$

Therefore, 4.84×10^{10} atoms/s leave He side.

$$10.0 \text{ hr} \times \frac{60 \text{ min}}{1 \text{ hr}} \times \frac{60 \text{ s}}{1 \text{ min}} \times \frac{4.84 \times 10^{10} \text{ atoms}}{\text{s}} = 1.74 \times 10^{15} \text{ atoms}$$

or $\quad \dfrac{1.74 \times 10^{15} \text{ atoms}}{6.022 \times 10^{23} \text{ atoms/mol}} = 2.89 \times 10^{-9}$ mol He leave in 10.0 hr

$$Z_{Rn} = \pi (1.00 \times 10^{-6} \text{ m})^2 \times \frac{2.00 \times 10^{-6}}{0.08206 \times 300.} \times (6.022 \times 10^{23}) \times 1000$$

$$\times \left(\frac{8.3145 \times 300.}{2\pi (222 \times 10^{-3})}\right)^{1/2} = 6.50 \times 10^{9} \text{ collisions/s}$$

6.50×10^{9} atoms/s leave Rn side.

$$3.60 \times 10^4 \text{ s} \times \frac{6.50 \times 10^9 \text{ atoms}}{\text{s}} \times \frac{1 \text{ mol}}{6.022 \times 10^{23} \text{ atoms}} = 3.89 \times 10^{-10} \text{ mol Rn leave in 10.0 hr.}$$

Side that began with He now contains:

$8.12 \times 10^{-8} - 2.89 \times 10^{-9} = 7.83 \times 10^{-8}$ mol He $+ 3.89 \times 10^{-10}$ mol Rn $= 7.87 \times 10^{-8}$ mol total

The pressure in the He side is:

$$P = \frac{nRT}{V} = \frac{(7.87 \times 10^{-8} \text{ mol}) \times 0.08206 \times 300. \text{ K}}{1.00 \text{ L}} = 1.94 \times 10^{-6} \text{ atm}$$

We can get the pressure in the Rn chamber two ways. No gas has escaped. Since the initial P's were equal and the P in one of the sides decreased by 0.06×10^{-6} atm, then the P in the second side must increase by 0.06×10^{-6} atm. So the pressure on the side that originally contained Rn is 2.06×10^{-6} atm. Or we can calculate the P the same way as with He. The Rn side contains:

$8.12 \times 10^{-8} - 3.89 \times 10^{-10} = 8.08 \times 10^{-8}$ mol Rn $+ 2.89 \times 10^{-9}$ mol He $= 8.37 \times 10^{-8}$ mol total

$$P = \frac{nRT}{V} = \frac{(8.37 \times 10^{-8} \text{ mol}) \times 0.08206 \times 300. \text{ K}}{1.00 \text{ L}} = 2.06 \times 10^{-6} \text{ atm}$$

108.   a.   Out of 100.00 g of Z, we have:

$$34.38 \text{ g Ni} \times \frac{1 \text{ mol}}{58.69 \text{ g}} = 0.5858 \text{ mol Ni}$$

$$28.13 \text{ g C} \times \frac{1 \text{ mol}}{12.011 \text{ g}} = 2.342 \text{ mol C}; \quad \frac{2.342}{0.5858} = 4$$

$$37.48 \text{ g O} \times \frac{1 \text{ mol}}{15.999 \text{ g}} = 2.343 \text{ mol O}; \quad \frac{2.343}{0.5858} = 4$$

The empirical formula is NiC_4O_4.

b. $$\frac{\text{rate Z}}{\text{rate Ar}} = \left(\frac{M_{Ar}}{M_Z} \right)^{1/2} = \left(\frac{39.95}{M_Z} \right)^{1/2}$$

Since initial mol Ar = mol Z, then:

$$0.4837 = \left(\frac{39.95}{M_Z} \right)^{1/2}, \quad M_Z = 170.8 \text{ g/mol}$$

c. NiC_4O_4: M = 58.69 + 4(12.01) + 4(16.00) = 170.73 g/mol

Molecular formula is NiC_4O_4.

d.   Each effusion step changes the concentration of Z in the gas by a factor of 0.4837. The original concentration of Z molecules to Ar atoms is a 1:1 ratio. After 5 stages:

$$n_Z/n_{Ar} = (0.4837)^5 = 2.648 \times 10^{-2}$$

111.   a. $2 \text{ CH}_4(g) + 2 \text{ NH}_3(g) + 3 \text{ O}_2(g) \rightarrow 2 \text{ HCN}(g) + 6 \text{ H}_2\text{O}(g)$

b.   Volumes of gases are proportional to moles. So methane and ammonia are in stoichiometric amounts and oxygen is in excess. For 1 second:

$$n_{CH_4} = \frac{PV}{RT} = \frac{(1.00 \text{ atm}) (20.0 \text{ L})}{(0.08206) (423 \text{ K})} = 0.576 \text{ mol CH}_4$$

$$\frac{0.576 \text{ mol CH}_4}{s} \times \frac{2 \text{ mol HCN}}{2 \text{ mol CH}_4} \times \frac{27.03 \text{ g HCN}}{\text{mol HCN}} = 15.6 \text{ g HCN/s}$$

CHAPTER SIX

CHEMICAL EQUILIBRIUM

Characteristics of Chemical Equilibrium

2.   False. For example consider two cases:

   i. $k_f = 10^6 \text{ s}^{-1}$ $k_r = 10^8 \text{ s}^{-1}$ fast reaction

      $K = k_f/k_r = 10^{-2}$ small K

   ii. $k_f = 10^{-5} \text{ s}^{-1}$ $k_r = 10^{-9} \text{ s}^{-1}$ slow reaction

      $K = k_f/k_r = 10^4$ large K

   The equilibrium constant is the ratio of the two rate constants. This ratio does not necessarily get larger as the reactions get faster. The two examples illustrate this. If one starts with a mixture not at equilibrium, equilibrium will be reached faster if the rates of the forward and reverse reactions are fast.

4.   No, it doesn't matter which direction the equilibrium position is reached. Both mixtures will give the same equilibrium position.

The Equilibrium Constant

7.   The units for both reactions are:

$$\frac{(\text{molecules/cm}^3)}{(\text{molecules/cm}^3)(\text{molecules/cm}^3)} = \frac{\text{cm}^3}{\text{molecules}}$$

   a. $K = \dfrac{1.26 \times 10^{-11}\ \text{cm}^3}{\text{molecules}} \times \dfrac{1\ \text{L}}{1000\ \text{cm}^3} \times \dfrac{6.022 \times 10^{23}\ \text{molecules}}{\text{mol}} = 7.59 \times 10^9\ \text{L/mol}$

   $K_p = K(RT)^{\Delta n}$, where Δn = moles gaseous products - moles gaseous reactants
   $$\Delta n = 1 - 2 = -1$$

$$K_p = \frac{7.59 \times 10^9 \text{ L/mol}}{\left(\dfrac{0.08206 \text{ L atm}}{\text{mol K}}\right) \times 300. \text{ K}} = 3.08 \times 10^8 \text{ atm}^{-1}$$

b. $K = \dfrac{2.09 \times 10^{-12} \text{ cm}^3}{\text{molecules}} \times \dfrac{1 \text{ L}}{1000 \text{ cm}^3} \times \dfrac{6.022 \times 10^{23} \text{ molecules}}{\text{mol}} = 1.26 \times 10^9 \text{ L/mol}$

$$K_p = K(RT)^{\Delta n}, \quad \Delta n = -1$$

$$K_p = \frac{1.26 \times 10^9 \text{ L/mol}}{\left(\dfrac{0.08206 \text{ L atm}}{\text{mol K}}\right) \times 300. \text{ K}} = 5.12 \times 10^7 \text{ atm}^{-1}$$

c. $K^* = \dfrac{[HO_2NO_2]}{[HO_2][NO_2]} = 1.26 \times 10^{-11} \text{ cm}^3/\text{molecules}$

$[HO_2NO_2] = (1.26 \times 10^{-11})(1.65 \times 10^{10})(6.00 \times 10^{12}) = 1.25 \times 10^{12} \text{ molecules/cm}^3$

9. $K = 278 = \dfrac{[SO_3]^2}{[SO_2]^2[O_2]}$ for $2 SO_2(g) + O_2(g) \rightleftharpoons 2 SO_3(g)$

a. $SO_2(g) + 1/2 O_2(g) \rightleftharpoons SO_3(g)$; $K_{eq} = \dfrac{[SO_3]}{[SO_2][O_2]^{1/2}} = K^{1/2} = 16.7$

b. $2 SO_3(g) \rightleftharpoons 2 SO_2(g) + O_2(g)$; $K_{eq} = \dfrac{[SO_2]^2[O_2]}{[SO_3]^2} = \dfrac{1}{K} = 3.60 \times 10^{-3}$

c. $SO_3(g) \rightleftharpoons SO_2(g) + 1/2 O_2(g)$; $K_{eq} = \dfrac{[SO_2][O_2]^{1/2}}{[SO_3]} = \left(\dfrac{1}{K}\right)^{1/2} = 6.00 \times 10^{-2}$

d. $4 SO_2(g) + 2 O_2(g) \rightleftharpoons 4 SO_3(g)$; $K_{eq} = \dfrac{[SO_3]^4}{[SO_2]^4[O_2]^2} = K^2 = 7.73 \times 10^4$

11. $H_2(g) + I_2(g) \rightleftharpoons 2 HI(g)$

$$K = \frac{[HI]^2}{[H_2][I_2]} = \frac{\left(\dfrac{3.50 \text{ mol}}{3.00 \text{ L}}\right)^2}{\left(\dfrac{4.10 \text{ mol}}{3.00 \text{ L}}\right)\left(\dfrac{0.30 \text{ mol}}{3.00 \text{ L}}\right)} = 10.$$

13. $NH_4Cl(s) \rightleftharpoons NH_3(g) + HCl(g)$

$K_P = P_{NH_3} \times P_{HCl}$; At equilibrium, $P_{total} = P_{NH_3} + P_{HCl}$ and $P_{NH_3} = P_{HCl}$.

$P_{total} = 4.4$ atm $= 2P_{NH_3}$; Thus, $P_{NH_3} = P_{HCl} = 2.2$ atm.

$K_p = (2.2$ atm$)(2.2$ atm$) = 4.8$ atm^2

15. $SO_2(g)$ + $NO_2(g)$ $\rightleftharpoons$ $SO_3(g)$ + $NO(g)$

Initial	$\dfrac{2.00 \text{ mol}}{V}$	$\dfrac{2.00 \text{ mol}}{V}$	0	0
Change	$\dfrac{-1.30 \text{ mol}}{V}$	$\dfrac{-1.30 \text{ mol}}{V}$ $\rightarrow$	$\dfrac{+1.30 \text{ mol}}{V}$	$\dfrac{+1.30 \text{ mol}}{V}$
Equil.	$\dfrac{0.70 \text{ mol}}{V}$	$\dfrac{0.70 \text{ mol}}{V}$	$\dfrac{1.30 \text{ mol}}{V}$	$\dfrac{1.30 \text{ mol}}{V}$

$K = \dfrac{[SO_3][NO]}{[SO_2][NO_2]} = \dfrac{(1.30)(1.30)}{(0.70)(0.70)} = 3.4$ (Volume cancels.)

Equilibrium Calculations

18. $K = 2.2 = \dfrac{[CH_3CO_2C_2H_5][H_2O]}{[CH_3CO_2H][C_2H_5OH]}$

$2.2 = \dfrac{(2.0)[H_2O]}{(0.10)(5.0)}$, $[H_2O] = 0.55 \, M$

We can neglect the solvent in writing equilibrium constant expressions because the solvent concentration is large and essentially constant. This is why we do not include water in the expression for K in reactions that occur in AQUEOUS solution. This is not the case for this reaction; water is not the solvent. Water is a product of the reaction in some other solvent and [H$_2$O] must appear in the expression for K.

20. $H_2O(g) + Cl_2O(g) \rightleftharpoons 2 HOCl(g)$ $K = 0.090 = \dfrac{[HOCl]^2}{[H_2O][Cl_2O]}$

   a.   The initial concentrations of H$_2$O and Cl$_2$O are:

$\dfrac{1.0 \text{ g H}_2\text{O}}{1.0 \text{ L}} \times \dfrac{1 \text{ mol}}{18.0 \text{ g}} = 5.6 \times 10^{-2}$ mol/L

$\dfrac{2.0 \text{ g Cl}_2\text{O}}{1.0 \text{ L}} \times \dfrac{1 \text{ mol}}{86.9 \text{ g}} = 2.3 \times 10^{-2}$ mol/L

$$H_2O(g) \quad + \quad Cl_2O(g) \quad \rightleftharpoons \quad 2\ HOCl(g)$$

Initial	$5.6 \times 10^{-2}\ M$	$2.3 \times 10^{-2}\ M$	0

x mol/L H_2O reacts to reach equilibrium

Change	$-x$	$-x$	$\rightarrow$	$+2x$
Equil.	$5.6 \times 10^{-2} - x$	$2.3 \times 10^{-2} - x$		$2x$

$$K = 0.090 = \frac{(2x)^2}{(5.6 \times 10^{-2} - x)(2.3 \times 10^{-2} - x)}$$

$$1.16 \times 10^{-4} - 7.11 \times 10^{-3}\,x + 0.090\,x^2 = 4\,x^2$$

$$3.91\,x^2 + 7.11 \times 10^{-3}\,x - 1.16 \times 10^{-4} = 0$$

For a quadratic equation of the form $ax^2 + bx + c = 0$, the solutions are:

$$x = \frac{-b \pm (b^2 - 4ac)^{1/2}}{2a} \qquad \text{See Appendix A1.4 of the text.}$$

Note: Rounding off intermediate answers in solving the quadratic formula and in the approximations method described below, leads to excessive round off error. In these problems we will discontinue the usual practice in this Solutions Guide and carry extra significant figures and round at the end.

For this equation:

$$x = \frac{-7.11 \times 10^{-3} \pm (5.06 \times 10^{-5} + 1.81 \times 10^{-3})^{1/2}}{7.82}$$

$$x = \frac{-7.11 \times 10^{-3} \pm (1.86 \times 10^{-3})^{1/2}}{7.82} = \frac{-7.11 \times 10^{-3} \pm 4.31 \times 10^{-2}}{7.82}$$

$$x = 4.6 \times 10^{-3} \text{ or } -6.4 \times 10^{-3}$$

A negative answer makes no physical sense; we can't have less than nothing.
So $x = 4.6 \times 10^{-3}\ M$.

$$[HOCl] = 2x = 9.2 \times 10^{-3}\ M$$

$$[H_2O] = 5.6 \times 10^{-2} - x = 5.6 \times 10^{-2} - 0.46 \times 10^{-2} = 5.1 \times 10^{-2}\ M$$

$$[Cl_2O] = 2.3 \times 10^{-2} - x = 0.023 - 0.0046 = 1.8 \times 10^{-2}\ M$$

There is an easier way to solve this problem in terms of algebra. There are a lot of manipulations necessary to get a solution using the quadratic formula. If we make an early mistake, it takes a lot of work to get the final answer and find out it is wrong. As a case in point it took me (KCB) about 20 minutes to find the mistake I made when initially solving this problem. In an early step I copied an exponent wrong. We can use our chemical sense to simplify the algebra. For this problem we are trying to solve the equation:

$$\frac{4x^2}{(5.6 \times 10^{-2} - x)(2.3 \times 10^{-2} - x)} = 0.090$$

However, the value of the equilibrium constant, 0.090, is not very large; not much H_2O and Cl_2O will react to reach equilibrium. In this case, if we assume:

0.056 - x ≈ 0.056 and 0.023 - x ≈ 0.023, then the equation becomes:

$$\frac{4x^2}{(0.056)(0.023)} = 0.090$$

We can get a value for x with much less effort. Solving: $x = 5.4 \times 10^{-3}$

If we check how good our assumptions were, we get:

0.056 - x = 0.056 - 0.0054 = 0.0506

0.023 - x = 0.023 - 0.0054 = 0.0176

These aren't very good assumptions. All is not lost! We can use 0.0506 and 0.0176 as refined approximations and solve:

$$\frac{4x^2}{(0.0506)(0.0176)} = 0.090, \quad x = 4.5 \times 10^{-3}$$

We use this value of x to get yet another approximation for $[H_2O]$ and $[Cl_2O]$.

0.056 - 0.0045 = 0.0515 and 0.023 - 0.0045 = 0.0185

$$\frac{4x^2}{(0.0515)(0.0185)} = 0.090, \quad x = 4.6 \times 10^{-3}$$

Doing one more iteration:

0.056 - 0.0046 = 0.0514 and 0.023 - 0.0046 = 0.0184

$$\frac{4x^2}{(0.0514)(0.0184)} = 0.090, \quad x = 4.6 \times 10^{-3}$$

We just got the same answer in consecutive iterations; we have converged on the true answer. It is the same answer to two significant figures that we determined exactly by solving using the quadratic formula. This method, called the method of successive approximations (see Appendix 1.4 in the text), at first appears to be more laborious. However, any one iteration is less time consuming than using the quadratic formula; it is easier to make an arithmetic mistake using the quadratic formula; and we can discover mistakes in a shorter period of time using successive approximations. Even more compelling, we're using our chemical sense to make approximations and, after all, this is a chemistry text. Try the method; once you get the hang of it you'll prefer successive approximation to the quadratic formula.

b. $H_2O(g)$ + $Cl_2O(g)$ $\rightleftharpoons$ 2 $HOCl(g)$

Initial   0   0   1.0 mol/2.0 L = 0.50 M
                     2x mol/L HOCl reacts to reach equilibrium
Change   +x +x $\leftarrow$ -2x
Equil. x x 0.50 - 2x

$$K = 0.090 = \frac{[HOCl]^2}{[H_2O][Cl_2O]} = \frac{(0.50 - 2x)^2}{x^2}$$

We can solve this exactly very quickly. The expression is a perfect square, so we can take the square root of each side:

$$0.30 = \frac{0.50 - 2x}{x}, \quad 0.30\,x = 0.50 - 2x, \quad 2.30\,x = 0.50$$

$x = 0.217$ (carry extra significant figures)

$x = [H_2O] = [Cl_2O] = 0.217 = 0.22\ M;\ [HOCl] = 0.50 - 2x = 0.50 - 0.434 = 0.07\ M$

23. $N_2(g)$ + $O_2(g)$ $\rightleftharpoons$ 2 $NO(g)$ $K = K_p = 0.050$

Initial   0.80 atm   0.20 atm   0
                x atm of N_2 reacts to reach equilibrium
Change   - x - x $\rightarrow$ +2x
Equil.   0.80 - x 0.20 - x 2x

$$K = 0.050 = \frac{P_{NO}^2}{P_{N_2}P_{O_2}} = \frac{(2x)^2}{(0.80 - x)(0.20 - x)}$$

If 0.80 - x ≈ 0.80 and 0.20 - x ≈ 0.20, then:

$$0.050 = \frac{4x^2}{(0.80)(0.20)}, \quad x = 0.045;\ x \text{ is } 22.5\% \text{ of } 0.20.$$

Assumptions are not valid by the 5% rule. Using successive approximations:

0.80 - x = 0.80 - 0.045 = 0.755, 0.20 - x = 0.20 - 0.045 = 0.155

$$\frac{4x^2}{(0.755)(0.155)} = 0.050, \ x = 0.038; \qquad \frac{4x^2}{(0.762)(0.162)} = 0.050, \ x = 0.039$$

$$\frac{4x^2}{(0.761)(0.161)} = 0.050, \ x = 0.039 \quad \text{consistent answer}$$

$$P_{NO} = 2x = 2(0.039) = 7.8 \times 10^{-2} \text{ atm}$$

25. $2 \ SO_2(g) \quad + \quad O_2(g) \quad \rightleftharpoons \quad 2 \ SO_3(g) \qquad K_p = 0.25$

Initial	0.50 atm	0.50 atm	0
	$2x$ atm SO_2 reacts to reach equilibrium		
Change	$-2x$	$-x$ $\rightarrow$	$+2x$
Equil.	$0.50 - 2x$	$0.50 - x$	$2x$

$$\frac{P_{SO_3}^2}{P_{SO_2}^2 P_{O_2}} = \frac{(2x)^2}{(0.50 - 2x)^2(0.50 - x)} \approx \frac{4x^2}{(0.50)^3} = 0.25 \qquad \text{(Assuming } x \text{ is small.)}$$

$x = 0.088$; Assumptions not good (x is 18% of 0.50). Using the method of successive approximations (Appendix 1.4):

$$\frac{4x^2}{[0.50 - 2(0.088)]^2 \ [0.50 - (0.088)]} = \frac{4x^2}{(0.324)^2(0.412)} = 0.25, \ x = 0.052$$

$$\frac{4x^2}{[0.50 - 2(0.052)]^2 \ [0.50 - (0.052)]} = \frac{4x^2}{(0.396)^2(0.448)} = 0.25, \ x = 0.066$$

$$\frac{4x^2}{(0.368)^2(0.434)} = 0.25, \ x = 0.061; \quad \frac{4x^2}{(0.378)^2(0.439)} = 0.25, \ x = 0.063$$

The next trials converge at 0.062.

$$P_{SO_2} = 0.50 - 2x = 0.376 = 0.38 \text{ atm}; \ P_{SO_3} = 2x = 0.124 = 0.12 \text{ atm}$$

$$P_{O_2} = 0.50 - x = 0.438 = 0.44 \text{ atm}$$

27.   a. $K_p = K(RT)^{\Delta n} = \dfrac{4.5 \times 10^9 \text{ L}}{\text{mol}} \left(\dfrac{0.08206 \text{ L atm}}{\text{mol K}} \times 373 \text{ K} \right)^{-1} \qquad \Delta n = 1 - 2 = -1$

$K_p = 1.5 \times 10^8 \text{ atm}^{-1}$

b. $CO(g) + Cl_2(g) \quad \rightleftharpoons \quad COCl_2(g) \qquad K_p = 1.5 \times 10^8$

K_p is so large that at equilibrium we will have almost all $COCl_2$. Assume $P_{tot} \approx P_{COCl_2} \approx 5.0$.

Initial	0	0	5.0 atm
	x atm $COCl_2$ reacts to reach equilibrium		
Change	$+x$	$+x$ $\leftarrow$	$-x$
Equil.	x	x	$5.0 - x$

$$1.5 \times 10^8 = \frac{5.0 - x}{x^2} \approx \frac{5.0}{x^2} \quad \text{(Assuming } 5.0 - x \approx 5.0\text{)}$$

Solving: $x = 1.8 \times 10^{-4}$ atm. Check assumptions: $5.0 - x = 5.0 - 1.8 \times 10^{-4} = 5.0$ atm.
Assumptions are good (well within the 5% rule).

$P_{CO} = P_{Cl_2} = 1.8 \times 10^{-4}$ atm and $P_{COCl_2} = 5.0$ atm

Le Chatelier's Principle

29.   We can do two things in the choice of solvent. First we must avoid water. Any extra water we
add from the solvent tends to push the equilibrium to the left. This eliminates water and 95%
ethanol as solvent choices. Of the remaining two solvents, acetonitrile will not take part in the
reaction, whereas ethanol is a reactant. If we use ethanol as the solvent it will drive the
equilibrium to the right, thereby reducing the concentrations of the objectionable butyric acid to
a minimum. Thus, the best solvent is 100% ethanol.

31.   A change in volume will change the partial pressure of all reactants and products by the same
factor. The shift in equilibrium depends on the number of gaseous particles on each side. An
increase in volume will shift the equilibrium to the side with the greater number of particles in
the gas phase. A decrease in volume will favor the side with the fewer number of gas phase
particles. If there are the same number of gas phase particles on each side of the reaction, then a
change in volume will not shift the equilibrium.

34. $CoCl_2(s) + 6\ H_2O(g) \rightleftharpoons CoCl_2 \cdot 6\ H_2O(s)$

If rain is imminent, there would be a lot of water vapor in the air. Reaction would shift to the
right and the indicator would turn <u>pink</u> (due to $CoCl_2 \cdot 6H_2O$ formation).

36.   a.   right   b.   left   c.   right   d.   no effect   e.   no effect ($\Delta n = 0$)

    f.   An increase in temperature will shift the equilibrium to the right.

Additional Exercises

38.   a.
$$Na_2O(s) \rightleftharpoons 2\ Na(l) + 1/2\ O_2(g) \qquad K_1$$
$$2\ Na(l) + O_2(g) \rightleftharpoons Na_2O_2(s) \qquad 1/K_3$$

$$Na_2O(s) + 1/2\ O_2(g) \rightleftharpoons Na_2O_2(s) \qquad K_{eq} = (K_1)(1/K_3)$$

$$K_{eq} = \frac{2 \times 10^{-25}}{5 \times 10^{-29}} = 4 \times 10^3$$

b.
$$NaO(g) \rightleftharpoons Na(l) + 1/2\ O_2(g) \qquad K_2$$
$$Na_2O(s) \rightleftharpoons 2\ Na(l) + 1/2\ O_2(g) \qquad K_1$$
$$2\ Na(l) + O_2(g) \rightleftharpoons Na_2O_2(s) \qquad 1/K_3$$

$$NaO(g) + Na_2O(s) \rightleftharpoons Na_2O_2(s) + Na(l)$$

$$K_{eq} = \frac{K_1 K_2}{K_3} = 8 \times 10^{-2}$$

c.
$$2\ NaO(g) \rightleftharpoons 2\ Na(l) + O_2(g) \qquad K_2^2$$
$$2\ Na(l) + O_2(g) \rightleftharpoons Na_2O_2(s) \qquad 1/K_3$$

$$2\ NaO(g) \rightleftharpoons Na_2O_2(s)$$

$$K_{eq} = \frac{K_2^2}{K_3} = 8 \times 10^{18}$$

40.
$$H_2(g) \quad + \quad S(s) \quad \rightleftharpoons \quad H_2S(g)$$

	$H_2(g)$	$S(s)$		$H_2S(g)$
Initial	0.15 M	-		0
Change	-x	-	$\rightarrow$	+x
Equil.	0.15 - x	-		x

$$K = 6.8 \times 10^{-2} = \frac{[H_2S]}{[H_2]} = \frac{x}{0.15 - x}, \quad 0.0102 - 0.068\ x = x \qquad \text{(Carrying extra sig. figs.)}$$

$$x = \frac{0.0102}{1.068} = 9.6 \times 10^{-3} \text{ mol/L}$$

$$P_{H_2S} = \frac{nRT}{V} = \frac{9.6 \times 10^{-3} \text{ mol} \left(\dfrac{0.08206 \text{ L atm}}{\text{mol K}} \right) \times 363 \text{ K}}{1.0 \text{ L}} = 0.29 \text{ atm}$$

41.   When SO_2 is added, the equilibrium will shift to the left, producing more SO_2Cl_2 and some
       energy. The energy increases the temperature of the reaction mixture.

44.   a.   shift left

       b.   Since the reaction is endothermic, an increase in temperature will shift the equilibrium to the
             right.

       c.   no effect   d.   shift right

46. $PV = nRT$; $\dfrac{n}{V} = \dfrac{P}{RT}$; $\dfrac{nM}{V} = d = \dfrac{PM}{RT}$

$$0.168 \text{ g/L} = \frac{P_{O_2}\,(32.00) + P_{O_3}\,(48.00)}{\dfrac{0.08206 \text{ L atm}}{\text{mol K}} \times 448 \text{ K}}, \quad 32.00\ P_{O_2} + 48.00\ P_{O_3} = 6.18 \ \ (\text{P in atm})$$

$$P_{\text{total}} = P_{O_2} + P_{O_3} = 128 \text{ torr} \times \frac{1 \text{ atm}}{760 \text{ torr}} = 0.168 \text{ atm}$$

Solving using simultaneous equations:

$$
\begin{aligned}
32.00\ P_{O_2} + 48.00\ P_{O_3} &= 6.18 \\
-32.00\ P_{O_2} - 32.00\ P_{O_3} &= -5.38 \\
\hline
16.00\ P_{O_3} &= 0.80
\end{aligned}
$$

$$P_{O_3} = \frac{0.80}{16.00} = 0.050 \text{ atm} \quad \text{and} \quad P_{O_2} = 0.118 \text{ atm}$$

$$K_p = \frac{P_{O_3}^2}{P_{O_2}^3} = \frac{(0.050)^2}{(0.118)^3} = 1.5 \text{ atm}^{-1}$$

48. $$N_2(g) \ + \ 3\ H_2(g) \ \rightleftharpoons \ 2\ NH_3(g)$$

Initial	0	0	P_0	P_0 = initial pressure of NH_3
Change	$+x$	$+3x$	$\leftarrow$ $-2x$	
Equil.	x	$3x$	$P_0 - 2x$	

From problem, $P_0 - 2x = \dfrac{P_0}{2.00}$, so $P_0 = 4.00\,x$

$$K_p = \frac{(4x - 2x)^2}{(x)(3x)^3} = \frac{(2x)^2}{(x)(3x)^3} = \frac{4x^2}{27x^4} = \frac{4}{27x^2} = 5.3 \times 10^5 \text{ atm}^{-2}, \ \ x = 5.3 \times 10^{-4} \text{ atm}$$

$$P_0 = 4.00\,x = 2.1 \times 10^{-3} \text{ atm}$$

50. $P_0(O_2) = 4.49$ atm   (Calculated from the ideal gas equation.)

	$CH_4(g)$ +	$2\ O_2(g) \rightarrow$	$CO_2(g)$ +	$2\ H_2O(g)$
Change	$-x$	$-2x \rightarrow$	$+x$	$+2x$

	$CH_4(g)$ +	$3/2\ O_2(g) \rightarrow$	$CO(g)$ +	$2\ H_2O(g)$
Change	$-y$	$-3/2\,y \rightarrow$	$+y$	$+2y$

Amount of O_2 reacted = 4.49 atm - 0.326 atm = 4.16 atm O_2

$2\,x + 3/2\,y = 4.16$ atm O_2 and $2\,x + 2\,y = 4.45$ atm H_2O

Solving using simultaneous equations:

$$2x + 2y = 4.45$$
$$\underline{-2x - 3/2\,y = -4.16}$$
$$0.50\,y = 0.29, \quad y = 0.58 \text{ atm} = P_{CO}$$

$$2x + 2(0.58) = 4.45, \quad x = \frac{4.45 - 1.16}{2} = 1.65 \text{ atm} = P_{CO_2}$$

52. $$SO_2Cl_2(g) \quad \rightleftharpoons \quad Cl_2(g) \quad + \quad SO_2(g)$$

Initial	P_0	0	0
Change	$-x$	$+x$	$+x$
Equil.	$P_0 - x$	x	x

P_0 = initial pressure of SO_2Cl_2

$$P_{total} = 0.900 \text{ atm} = P_0 - x + x + x = P_0 + x$$

$$\frac{x}{P_0} \times 100 = 12.5, \quad P_0 = 8.00\,x$$

Solving: $0.900 = P_0 + x = 9.00\,x, \quad x = 0.100$

$x = 0.100 \text{ atm} = P_{Cl_2} = P_{SO_2}; \quad P_0 - x = 0.800 - 0.100 = 0.700 \text{ atm} = P_{SO_2Cl_2}$

$$K_p = \frac{P_{Cl_2} \times P_{SO_2}}{P_{SO_2Cl_2}} = \frac{(0.100)^2}{0.700} = 1.43 \times 10^{-2} \text{ atm}$$

54. $$N_2O_4(g) \rightleftharpoons 2\,NO_2(g) \qquad K_p = \frac{P_{NO_2}^2}{P_{N_2O_4}} = \frac{(1.2)^2}{0.33} = 4.4$$

Doubling the volume decreases each partial pressure by a factor of 2 (P= nRT/V).

$P_{NO_2} = 0.60$ atm and $P_{N_2O_4} = 0.17$ atm are the new partial pressures.

$$Q = \frac{(0.60)^2}{0.17} = 2.1, \quad Q < K \qquad \text{Equilibrium will shift to the right.}$$

$$N_2O_4(g) \quad \rightleftharpoons \quad 2\,NO_2(g)$$

Initial	0.17 atm	0.60 atm
Equil.	0.17 - x	0.60 + 2x

$$K_p = 4.4 = \frac{(0.60 + 2x)^2}{(0.17 - x)}, \quad 4x^2 + 6.8\,x - 0.39 = 0$$

Solving using the quadratic formula: $x = 0.056$

$$P_{NO_2} = 0.60 + 2(0.056) = 0.71 \text{ atm}; \quad P_{N_2O_4} = 0.17 - 0.056 = 0.11 \text{ atm}$$

56. $CCl_4(g)$ $\rightleftharpoons$ $C(s)$ + $2\,Cl_2(g)$

Initial	P_0	-	0	P_0 = initial pressure of CCl_4
Change	$-x$	$\rightarrow$ -	$+2x$	
Equil.	$P_0 - x$	-	$2x$	

$P_{total} = P_0 - x + 2x = P_0 + x = 1.20$ atm

$$\frac{(2x)^2}{P_0 - x} = 0.76, \quad 4x^2 = 0.76\,P_0 - 0.76\,x, \quad P_0 = \frac{4x^2 + 0.76x}{0.76}; \text{ Substituting into } P_0 + x = 1.20:$$

$$\frac{4x^2}{0.76} + x + x = 1.20 \text{ atm}, \quad 5.3\,x^2 + 2x - 1.20 = 0; \text{ Solving using quadratic formula:}$$

$$x = \frac{-2 \pm (4 + 25.4)^{1/2}}{2(5.3)} = 0.32 \text{ atm}; \quad P_0 + 0.32 = 1.20, \quad P_0 = 0.88 \text{ atm}$$

58. $SO_3(g)$ $\rightleftharpoons$ $SO_2(g)$ + $1/2\,O_2(g)$

Initial	P_0	0	0	P_0 = initial pressure of SO_3
Change	$-x$	$+x$	$+x/2$	
Equil.	$P_0 - x$	x	$x/2$	

Average molar mass of the mixture is:

$$M = \frac{dRT}{P} = \frac{(1.60 \text{ g/L})\,(0.08206 \text{ L atm mol}^{-1}\,K^{-1})\,(873 \text{ K})}{1.80 \text{ atm}} = 63.7 \text{ g/mol}$$

The average molar mass is determined by:

$$\frac{n_{SO_3}\,(80.07 \text{ g/mol}) + n_{SO_2}\,(64.07 \text{ g/mol}) + n_{O_2}\,(32.00 \text{ g/mol})}{n_{total}}$$

The partial pressure of each gas is proportional to the number of moles of each gas, so:

$$63.7 \text{ g/mol} = \frac{P_{SO_3}\,(80.07) + P_{SO_2}\,(64.07) + P_{O_2}\,(32.00)}{P_{tot}}$$

$P_{total} = P_0 - x + x + x/2 = P_0 + x/2 = 1.80$ atm, $P_0 = 1.80 - x/2$

$$63.7 = \frac{(P_0 - x)\,(80.07) + x(64.07) + \frac{x}{2}(32.00)}{1.80}$$

$$63.7 = \frac{(1.80 - 3/2x)\,(80.07) + x(64.07) + \frac{x}{2}(32.00)}{1.80}$$

$$115 = 144 - 120.1\,x + 64.07\,x + 16.00\,x, \ \ 40.0\,x = 29, \ \ x = 0.73$$

$$P_{SO_3} = P_0 - x = 1.80 - 3/2\,x = 0.71 \text{ atm}; \ \ P_{SO_2} = 0.73 \text{ atm}; \ \ P_{O_2} = x/2 = 0.37 \text{ atm}$$

$$K_p = \frac{(0.73)\,(0.37)^{1/2}}{(0.71)} = 0.63 \text{ atm}^{1/2}$$

61. $N_2(g) + 3\,H_2\,(g) \rightleftharpoons 2\,NH_3(g)$ $K_p = \dfrac{(P_{NH_3})^2}{(P_{N_2})\,(P_{H_2})^3} = 6.5 \times 10^{-3} \text{ atm}^{-2}$

<u>1.0 atm</u> $N_2(g)$ + $3\,H_2(g)$ $\rightleftharpoons$ $2\,NH_3(g)$

Initial   0.25 atm   0.75 atm   0
Equil.   0.25 - x   0.75 - 3x   2x

$$\frac{(2x)^2}{(0.75 - 3x)^3\,(0.25 - x)} = 6.5 \times 10^{-3}; \ \text{Using successive approximations:}$$

$x = 1.2 \times 10^{-2}; \ \ P_{NH_3} = 2x = 0.024 \text{ atm}$

<u>10 atm</u> $N_2(g)$ + $3\,H_2(g)$ $\rightleftharpoons$ $2\,NH_3(g)$

Initial   2.5 atm   7.5 atm   0
Equil.   2.5 - x   7.5 - 3x   2x

$$\frac{(2x)^2}{(7.5 - 3x)^3\,(2.5 - x)} = 6.5 \times 10^{-3}; \ \text{Using successive approximations:}$$

$x = 0.69 \text{ atm}; \ \ P_{NH_3} = 1.4 \text{ atm}$

<u>100 atm</u>   Using the same setup as above: $\dfrac{4x^2}{(75 - 3x)^3\,(25 - x)} = 6.5 \times 10^{-3}$

Solving by successive approximations: $x = 16 \text{ atm}; \ \ P_{NH_3} = 32 \text{ atm}$

<u>1000 atm</u>

$$N_2(g) \quad + \quad 3\,H_2(g) \quad \rightleftharpoons \quad 2\,NH_3(g)$$

Initial   250 atm   750 atm   0

Let 250 atm N_2 react completely.

New Initial   0   0 5.0×10^2

Equil. x $3x$ 5.0×10^2 - $2x$

$$\frac{(5.0 \times 10^2 - 2x)^2}{(3x)^3 x} = 6.5 \times 10^{-3}; \text{ Assume } x \text{ is small, then:}$$

$$\frac{(5.0 \times 10^2)^2}{(3x)^3 x} \approx 6.5 \times 10^{-3}, \ x = 35$$

Assumption is poor (14% error).

Solving by successive approximations:

$x = 32$

$P_{NH_3} = 5.0 \times 10^2$ - $2x = 440$ atm

The results are plotted as
log P_{NH_3} vs. log P_{tot}. The
plot will asymptotically
approach the line given by
log P_{NH_3} = log P at the
upper limit.

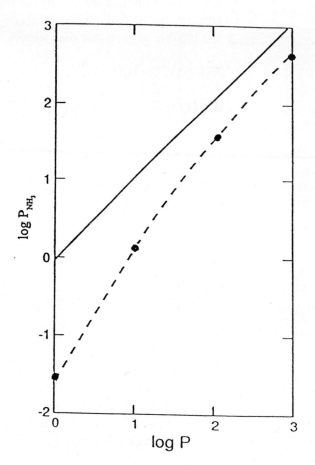

CHAPTER SEVEN

ACIDS AND BASES

Nature of Acids and Bases

3. Except for water, these are the conjugate bases of the acids in the previous exercise. The stronger the acid, the weaker the conjugate base. NO_3^- is the conjugate base of a strong acid. It is a terrible base (worse than water).

    $NH_3 > OCl^- > H_2O > NO_3^-$

5. a. H_2O b. ClO_2^- c. CN^-

    Note: The stronger the acid, the weaker the conjugate base (K_b decreases).

7. $H^-(aq) + H_2O(l) \rightarrow H_2(g) + OH^-(aq)$; $OCH_3^-(aq) + H_2O(l) \rightarrow CH_3OH(aq) + OH^-(aq)$

9. a. H_2O and $CH_3CO_2^-$

    b. $CH_3CO_2^-$, since the equilibrium favors acetic acid ($K_a < 1$).

    c. Acetate ion is a better base than water and produces basic solutions in water. When we put acetate ion into solution as the only major basic species, the reaction is:

    $$CH_3CO_2^- + H_2O \rightleftharpoons CH_3CO_2H + OH^-$$

    Now the competition is between $CH_3CO_2^-$ and OH^- for the proton. Hydroxide ion is the strongest base possible in water. The above equilibrium favors acetate plus water resulting in a K_b value less than one. Those species we specifically call weak bases ($10^{-14} < K_b < 1$) lie between H_2O and OH^- in base strength. Weak bases are stronger bases than water but are weaker bases than OH^-.

Autoionization of Water and pH Scale

11. a. Since the value of the equilibrium constant increases as the temperature increases, the reaction is endothermic.

b. $H_2O \rightleftharpoons H^+ + OH^-$ $K_w = 5.47 \times 10^{-14} = [H^+][OH^-]$

In pure water $[H^+] = [OH^-]$, so $5.47 \times 10^{-14} = [H^+]^2$, $[H^+] = 2.34 \times 10^{-7}\ M$
pH $= - \log [H^+] = - \log (2.34 \times 10^{-7}) = 6.631$

A neutral solution of water at 50.°C has:

   $[H^+] = [OH^-]$; $[H^+] = 2.34 \times 10^{-7}\ M$; pH = 6.631

Obviously, the condition that $[H^+] = [OH^-]$ is the most general definition of a neutral solution.

c. | Temp (°C) | Temp (K) | 1/T | K_w | $\ln K_w$ |
|---|---|---|---|---|
| 0 | 273 | 3.66×10^{-3} | 1.14×10^{-15} | -34.408 |
| 25 | 298 | 3.36×10^{-3} | 1.00×10^{-14} | -32.236 |
| 35 | 308 | 3.25×10^{-3} | 2.09×10^{-14} | -31.499 |
| 40. | 313 | 3.19×10^{-3} | 2.92×10^{-14} | -31.165 |
| 50. | 323 | 3.10×10^{-3} | 5.47×10^{-14} | -30.537 |

From the graph: $37°C = 310.\ K$; $1/T = 3.23 \times 10^{-3}$

$\ln K_w = -31.38$; $K_w = 2.35 \times 10^{-14}$

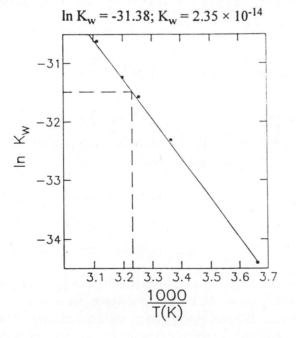

d.   At 37°C, $2.35 \times 10^{-14} = [H^+][OH^-] = [H^+]^2$, $[H^+] = 1.53 \times 10^{-7}$; pH = 6.815

Solutions of Acids

14.   If we just take the negative log of 10^{-12} we get pH = 12. This can't be. We can't add a tiny amount of acid to a neutral solution and get a strongly basic (pH = 12) solution. There are two sources of H^+: water and the HCl. So far we've considered the acid we add to water as the major source of H^+. In this case that is not true. The major source of H^+ is water (10^{-7} M) and not the HCl (10^{-12} M). So the $[H^+] \approx 10^{-7} + 10^{-12} \approx 10^{-7}$ M and pH = 7.00. This makes sense. If we add a minute amount of acid to a neutral solution we would still expect to have a roughly neutral solution.

16.   In all four parts of this problem, the major species are the weak acid and water. We will consider the weak acid to be the major source of H^+, i.e., ignore H^+ contribution from H_2O.

CH_3COOH

   a. $HC_2H_3O_2$ + H_2O $\rightleftharpoons$ H_3O^+ + $C_3H_3O_2^-$

   Initial   0.20 M   0(10^{-7})   0
                 x mol/L $HC_2H_3O_2$ dissociates to reach equilibrium
   Change $-x$ $\rightarrow$ $+x$ $+x$
   Equl.   0.20 - x x x

   $$K_a = 1.8 \times 10^{-5} = \frac{[H^+][C_2H_3O_2^-]}{[HC_2H_3O_2]} = \frac{x^2}{0.20 - x} \approx \frac{x^2}{0.20}$$

   $x = [H^+] = 1.9 \times 10^{-3}$ M

   We have made two assumptions which we must check.

   1. 0.20 - $x \approx$ 0.20

       0.20 - x = 0.20 - 0.002 = 0.198 = 0.20; Good assumption (1% error). If the percent error in the assumption is < 5%, assumption is valid.

   2. Acetic acid is the major source of H^+, i.e., we can ignore 10^{-7} M H^+ already present in neutral H_2O.

       $[H^+]$ from $HC_2H_3O_2$ = 2 × 10^{-3} >> 10^{-7};   This assumption is valid.

       In future problems we will always begin the problem solving process by making these assumptions and we will always check them. However, we may not explicitly state that the assumptions are valid. We will <u>always</u> state when the assumptions are <u>not</u> valid and we have to use other techniques to solve the problem. Remember, anytime we make an assumption, we must check its validity before the solution to the problem is complete. Answering the question:

       $[H^+] = [C_2H_3O_2^-] = 1.9 \times 10^{-3}$ M; $[OH^-] = 5.3 \times 10^{-12}$ M

       $[HC_2H_3O_2] = 0.20 - x = 0.198 \approx 0.20$ M

       pH = -log (1.9 × 10^{-3}) = 2.72

b. HNO_2 $\rightleftharpoons$ H^+ + NO_2^- $K_a = 4.0 \times 10^{-4}$

Initial   1.5 M $0(10^{-7})$ 0
               x mol/L HNO_2 dissociates to reach equilibrium
Change $-x$ $\rightarrow$ $+x$ $+x$
Equl.   1.5 - x x x

$$K_a = 4.0 \times 10^{-4} = \frac{[H^+][NO_2^-]}{[HNO_2]} = \frac{x^2}{1.5 - x} \approx \frac{x^2}{1.5} \quad (\text{assuming } x \ll 1.5)$$

$x = [H^+] = 2.4 \times 10^{-2}\ M;$ Assumptions good: $10^{-7} \ll 2.4 \times 10^{-2} \ll 1.5$

$[H^+] = [NO_2^-] = 2.4 \times 10^{-2}\ M;$ $[OH^-] = 4.2 \times 10^{-13}\ M$

$[HNO_2] = 1.5 - x = 1.48 \approx 1.5\ M;$ pH = 1.62

c.   HF $\rightleftharpoons$ H^+ + F^- $K_a = 7.2 \times 10^{-4}$

Initial   0.020 M $0(10^{-7})$ 0
               x mol/L HF dissociates to reach equilibrium
Change $-x$ $\rightarrow$ $+x$ $+x$
Equl.   0.020 - x x x

$$K_a = 7.2 \times 10^{-4} = \frac{[H^+][F^-]}{[HF]} = \frac{x^2}{0.020 - x} \approx \frac{x^2}{0.020} \quad (\text{assuming } x \ll 0.020)$$

$x = [H^+] = 3.8 \times 10^{-3};$ Check assumptions.

0.020 - x = 0.020 - 0.004 = 0.016, x is 20% of 0.020.

The assumption $x \ll 0.020$ is not good (x is more than 5% of 0.020). We must continue.
We can solve the equation by using the quadratic formula or by the method of successive
approximations (see Appendix 1.4 of text). Using the successive approximations, we let
0.016 M be a new approximation for [HF]. That is, try $x = 0.004$, so 0.020 - 0.004 = 0.016,
then solve for a new value of x.

$$\frac{x^2}{0.020 - x} \approx \frac{x^2}{0.016} = 7.2 \times 10^{-4},\ x = 3.4 \times 10^{-3}$$

We use this new value of x to further refine our estimate of [HF], i.e., 0.020 - x = 0.020 -
0.0034 = 0.0166 (carry extra significant figure).

$$\frac{x^2}{0.020 - x} \approx \frac{x^2}{0.0166} = 7.2 \times 10^{-4},\ x = 3.5 \times 10^{-3}$$

We repeat, until we get a self-consistent answer. In this case it will be: $x = 3.5 \times 10^{-3}$

So: $[H^+] = [F^-] = x = 3.5 \times 10^{-3}\ M;$ $[OH^-] = 2.9 \times 10^{-12}\ M$

$[HF] = 0.020 - x = 0.020 - 0.0035 = 0.017\ M;$ pH = 2.46

d.

$$\underset{\underset{HLac}{}}{\overset{\overset{OH}{|}}{CH_3CHCO_2H}} \rightleftharpoons \underset{\underset{Lac^-}{}}{\overset{\overset{OH}{|}}{CH_3CHCO_2^-}} + H^+$$

$$HLac \; \rightleftharpoons \; Lac^- \; + \; H^+ \quad K_a = 1.38 \times 10^{-4}$$

Initial	0.10 M	0	0(10^{-7})

x mol/L HLac dissociates to reach equilibrium

Change	-x $\rightarrow$	+x	+x
Equil.	0.10 - x	x	x

$$K_a = 1.38 \times 10^{-4} = \frac{[H^+][Lac^-]}{[HLac]} = \frac{x^2}{0.10 - x} \approx \frac{x^2}{0.10}$$

$x = [H^+] = 3.7 \times 10^{-3}$; Assumptions good (3.7% error): $10^{-7} \ll 3.7 \times 10^{-3} \ll 0.10$

$[H^+] = [Lac^-] = 3.7 \times 10^{-3}\ M$; $[OH^-] = 2.7 \times 10^{-12}\ M$

$[HLac] = 0.10 - 3.7 \times 10^{-3} = 0.10\ M$; pH = 2.43

18.   Major species: HIO_3, H_2O; Major source of H^+: HIO_3

$$HIO_3 \; \rightleftharpoons \; H^+ \; + \; IO_3^-$$

Initial	0.20 M	0(10^{-7})	0

x mol/L HIO_3 dissociates to reach equilibrium

Change	-x $\rightarrow$	+x	+x
Equil.	0.20 - x	x	x

$$K_a = 0.17 = \frac{[H^+][IO_3^-]}{[HIO_3]} = \frac{x^2}{0.20 - x} \approx \frac{x^2}{0.20}, \quad x = 0.18; \quad \text{Check assumption.}$$

Assumption is horrible (90% error). When the assumption is this poor, it is generally quickest to solve exactly using the quadratic formula (see Appendix 1.4 in text). The method of successive approximations will require many trials to finally converge on the answer. For this problem, 5 trials were required. Using the quadratic formula:

$$0.17 = \frac{x^2}{0.20 - x}, \; x^2 = 0.17\,(0.20 - x), \; x^2 + 0.17\,x - 0.034 = 0$$

$$x = \frac{-0.17 \pm [(0.17)^2 - 4(1)(-0.034)]^{1/2}}{2(1)} = \frac{-0.17 \pm 0.406}{2}, \; x = 0.12 \text{ or } -0.29$$

Only $x = 0.12$ makes sense. $x = 0.12$ M = [H$^+$]; pH = -log (0.12) = 0.92

20.   0.56 g $C_6H_5CO_2H(HBz) \times \dfrac{1 \text{ mol HBz}}{122.1 \text{ g}} = 4.6 \times 10^{-3}$ mol; $[HBz]_o = 4.6 \times 10^{-3}$ M

$$HBz \quad \rightleftharpoons \quad H^+ \quad + \quad Bz^-$$

Initial	4.6×10^{-3} M	$0(10^{-7})$	0

x mol/L HBz dissociates to reach equilibrium

Change	$-x$	$\rightarrow$	$+x$	$+x$
Equil.	$4.6 \times 10^{-3} - x$		x	x

$$K_a = 6.4 \times 10^{-5} = \dfrac{[H^+][Bz^-]}{[HBz]} = \dfrac{x^2}{4.6 \times 10^{-3} - x} \approx \dfrac{x^2}{4.6 \times 10^{-3}}$$

$x = [H^+] = 5.4 \times 10^{-4}$;   Check assumptions.

$0.0046 - x = 0.0046 - 0.0005 = 0.0041$

Assumption is not good (0.0005 is greater than 5% of 0.0046). When assumption(s) fail, we must solve exactly using the quadratic formula or the method of successive approximations (see Appendix 1.4 of text). Using successive approximations:

$$\dfrac{x^2}{0.0041} = 6.4 \times 10^{-5}, \ x = 5.1 \times 10^{-4}$$

$$\dfrac{x^2}{(0.0046 - 0.00051)} = \dfrac{x^2}{0.0041} = 6.4 \times 10^{-5}, \ x = 5.1 \times 10^{-4}$$

So: $x = [H^+] = [Bz^-] = 5.1 \times 10^{-4}$ M; $[HBz] = 4.6 \times 10^{-3} - x = 4.1 \times 10^{-3}$ M

pH = 3.29; pOH = 10.71; [OH$^-$] = $10^{-10.71} = 1.9 \times 10^{-11}$ M

22.   Let HX symbolize the weak acid.

$$HX \quad \rightleftharpoons \quad H^+ \quad + \quad X^-$$

Initial	0.15	$0(10^{-7})$	0

x mol/L HX dissociates to reach equilibrium

Change	$-x$	$\rightarrow$	$+x$	$+x$
Equil.	$0.15 - x$		x	x

If the acid is 3.0% dissociated, then x is 3.0% of 0.15. $x = 0.030 (0.15) = 4.5 \times 10^{-3}$

$$K_a = \dfrac{[H^+][X^-]}{[HX]} = \dfrac{(4.5 \times 10^{-3})^2}{0.15 - 4.5 \times 10^{-3}} = 1.4 \times 10^{-4}$$

23.   20.0 mL glacial acetic acid $\times \dfrac{1.05 \text{ g}}{\text{mL}} \times \dfrac{1 \text{ mol}}{60.05 \text{ g}} = 0.350$ mol

Initial concentration of $HC_2H_3O_2 = \dfrac{0.350 \text{ mol}}{0.2500 \text{ L}} = 1.40 \ M$

A common abbreviation used by chemists for acetic acid, $HC_2H_3O_2$, is HOAc. The abbreviation for $C_2H_3O_2^-$ is OAc^-.

$$HOAc \quad \rightleftharpoons \quad H^+ \quad + \quad OAc^- \quad K_a = 1.8 \times 10^{-5}$$

Initial   1.40 M $0(10^{-7})$ 0
               x mol/L $HC_2H_3O_2$ dissociates to reach equilibrium
Change $-x$ $\rightarrow$ $+x$ $+x$
Equil. $1.40 - x$ x x

$$K_a = 1.8 \times 10^{-5} = \frac{[H^+][OAc^-]}{[HOAc]} = \frac{x^2}{1.40 - x} \approx \frac{x^2}{1.40}$$

$x = [H^+] = 5.0 \times 10^{-3} \ M; \ \ pH = 2.30$ Assumptions good.

25.   Both are strong acids.

0.050 mmol/mL $\times$ 50.0 mL = 2.5 mmol HCl

0.10 mmol/mL $\times$ 150.0 mL = 15 mmol HNO_3

$$[H^+] = \frac{2.5 \text{ mmol} + 15 \text{ mmol}}{200.0 \text{ mL}} = 0.088 \ M; \ \ [OH^-] = \frac{K_w}{[H^+]} = 1.1 \times 10^{-13} \ M$$

$$[Cl^-] = \frac{2.5 \text{ mmol}}{200.0 \text{ mL}} = 0.0125 \text{ mol/L} \approx 0.013 \ M; \ \ [NO_3^-] = \frac{15 \text{ mmol}}{200.0 \text{ mL}} = 0.075 \ M$$

27.   The conductivity of the solution is a measure of the number of ions. In addition the colligative properties, which will be discussed in Chapter 17, depend on the number of particles. So measurements of osmotic pressure, vapor pressure lowering, freezing point depression or boiling point elevation will also allow us to determine the extent of ionization.

29.   a. $HOAc \quad \rightleftharpoons \quad H^+ \ + \ OAc^-$

        Initial   0.50 M $0(10^{-7})$ 0
                       x mol/L HOAc ($HC_2H_3O_2$) dissociates to reach equilibrium
        Change $-x$ $\rightarrow$ $+x$ $+x$
        Equil. $0.50 - x$ x x

$$K_a = 1.8 \times 10^{-5} = \frac{[H^+][OAc^-]}{[HOAc]} = \frac{x^2}{(0.50 - x)} \approx \frac{x^2}{0.50}$$

$x = [H^+] = [OAc^-] = 3.0 \times 10^{-3} \ M$ Assumptions good.

% ionized $= \dfrac{[OAc^-]}{0.50 \ M} \times 100 = \dfrac{3.0 \times 10^{-3}}{0.50} \times 100 = 0.60\%$

b. The set-up for (b) and (c) is similar to (a) except the final equation is slightly different.

$K_a = 1.8 \times 10^{-5} = \dfrac{x^2}{0.050 - x} \approx \dfrac{x^2}{0.050}$

$x = [H^+] = [OAc^-] = 9.5 \times 10^{-4} \ M$ Assumptions good.

% ionized $= \dfrac{9.5 \times 10^{-4}}{0.050} \times 100 = 1.9\%$

c. $K_a = 1.8 \times 10^{-5} = \dfrac{x^2}{0.0050 - x} \approx \dfrac{x^2}{0.0050}$

$x = [H^+] = [OAc^-] = 3.0 \times 10^{-4} \ M;$ Check assumptions.

Assumption that x is negligible is borderline (6% error). We should solve exactly. Using the method of successive approximations (Appendix 1.4 of text):

$1.8 \times 10^{-5} = \dfrac{x^2}{0.0047}, \ x = 2.9 \times 10^{-4};$ Next trial gives $x = 2.9 \times 10^{-4}$.

% ionized $= \dfrac{2.9 \times 10^{-4}}{5.0 \times 10^{-3}} \times 100 = 5.8\%$

d. As we dilute a solution, all concentrations are decreased by the same function. Dilution will shift the equilibrium to the side with the greater number of particles. For example, suppose we double the volume of an equilibrium mixture of a weak acid by adding water, then:

$$Q = \dfrac{\left(\dfrac{[H^+]_{eq}}{2}\right)\left(\dfrac{[X^-]_{eq}}{2}\right)}{\left(\dfrac{[HX]_{eq}}{2}\right)} = \dfrac{1}{2}K_a$$

$Q < K_a$, equilibrium shifts to the right or towards a greater percent dissociation.

e. $[H^+]$ depends on the initial concentration of weak acid and on how much weak acid dissociates. For solutions a-c the initial concentration of acid decreases more rapidly than the percent dissociation increases. Thus, $[H^+]$ decreases.

31. $HOBr \rightleftharpoons H^+ + OBr^-$

From normal weak acid problem: $[H^+] = [OBr^-]$ and $[HOBr] = 0.063 - [H^+]$

$pH = 4.95, \ [H^+] = 10^{-4.95} = 1.1 \times 10^{-5} \ M$

$$K_a = \frac{[H^+][OBr^-]}{[HOBr]} = \frac{(1.1 \times 10^{-5})^2}{(0.063 - 1.1 \times 10^{-5})} = 1.9 \times 10^{-9}$$

33.   The reactions are:

$$H_3PO_4 \rightleftharpoons H^+ + H_2PO_4^- \quad K_{a_1} = 7.5 \times 10^{-3}$$

$$H_2PO_4^- \rightleftharpoons H^+ + HPO_4^{2-} \quad K_{a_2} = 6.2 \times 10^{-8}$$

$$HPO_4^{2-} \rightleftharpoons H^+ + PO_4^{3-} \quad K_{a_3} = 4.8 \times 10^{-13}$$

We will deal with the reactions in order of importance, beginning with the largest K_a.

$$H_3PO_4 \quad \rightleftharpoons \quad H^+ \; + \; H_2PO_4^- \quad K_{a_1} = 7.5 \times 10^{-3} = \frac{[H^+][H_2PO_4^-]}{[H_3PO_4]}$$

Initial	0.100 M	0(10^{-7})	0
Equil.	0.100 - x	x	x

$$7.5 \times 10^{-3} = \frac{x^2}{0.100 - x}, \; x = 2.4 \times 10^{-2} \, M \qquad \text{(By using successive approximation or the quadratic formula.)}$$

$[H^+] = [H_2PO_4^-] = 2.4 \times 10^{-2} \, M; \; [H_3PO_4] = 0.100 - 0.024 = 0.076 \, M$

Since $K_{a_2} = \dfrac{[H^+][HPO_4^{2-}]}{[H_2PO_4^-]} = 6.2 \times 10^{-8}$ is much smaller than the K_{a_1} value, very little of the

second (and third) reactions occur as compared to the first reaction. Therefore, $[H^+]$ and

$[H_2PO_4^-]$ will not change significantly by the second reaction. Using the above concentrations of

H^+ and $H_2PO_4^-$ to calculate the concentration of HPO_4^{2-}:

$$6.2 \times 10^{-8} = \frac{(2.4 \times 10^{-2})[HPO_4^{2-}]}{2.4 \times 10^{-2}}, \; [HPO_4^{2-}] = 6.2 \times 10^{-8} \, M$$

Assumption that second reaction does not change $[H^+]$ and $[H_2PO_4^-]$ is good. We repeat the
process using K_{a_3} to get $[PO_4^{3-}]$.

$$K_{a_3} = 4.8 \times 10^{-13} = \frac{[H^+][PO_4^{3-}]}{[HPO_4^{2-}]} = \frac{(2.4 \times 10^{-2})[PO_4^{3-}]}{(6.2 \times 10^{-8})}$$

$[PO_4^{3-}] = 1.2 \times 10^{-18} \, M$ Assumptions good.

So in 0.100 M analytical concentration of H_3PO_4:

$[H_3PO_4] = 7.6 \times 10^{-2} \, M; \; [H^+] = [H_2PO_4^-] = 2.4 \times 10^{-2} \, M$

$[HPO_4^{2-}] = 6.2 \times 10^{-8}\ M;\ [PO_4^{3-}] = 1.2 \times 10^{-18}\ M$

$[OH^-] = 1.0 \times 10^{-14}/[H^+] = 4.2 \times 10^{-13}\ M$

Solutions of Bases

35. NO_3^-: $K_b \approx 0$ since HNO_3 is a strong acid. H_2O: $K_b = K_w = 10^{-14}$

NH_3: $K_b = 1.8 \times 10^{-5}$; CH_3NH_2: $K_b = 4.38 \times 10^{-4}$

$CH_3NH_2 > NH_3 > H_2O > NO_3^-$ (As K_b increases, base strength increases.)

37.   a. NH_3 b. NH_3 c. OH^- d. CH_3NH_2

The base with the largest K_b value is the strongest base.

39. 2.48 g TlOH $\times \dfrac{1\ \text{mol TlOH}}{221.4\ \text{g}} = 1.12 \times 10^{-2}$ mol

TlOH is a strong base, so $[OH^-] = \dfrac{1.12 \times 10^{-2}\ \text{mol}}{\text{L}}$

$pOH = -\log[OH^-] = 1.951$; $pH = 14.000 - pOH = 12.049$

41.   Nitrogen

43.   The N-atom is protonated in each case.

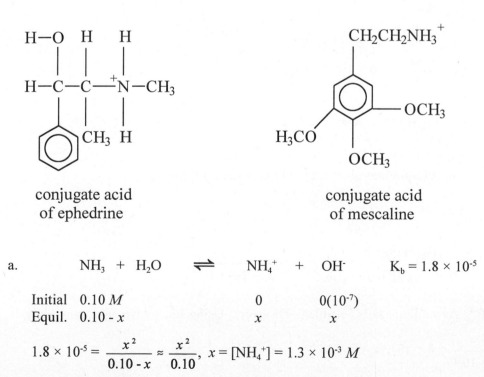

conjugate acid
of ephedrine

conjugate acid
of mescaline

46.   a. $NH_3\ +\ H_2O\ \rightleftharpoons\ NH_4^+\ +\ OH^-$ $K_b = 1.8 \times 10^{-5}$

Initial $0.10\ M$ 0 $0(10^{-7})$
Equil. $0.10 - x$ x x

$1.8 \times 10^{-5} = \dfrac{x^2}{0.10 - x} \approx \dfrac{x^2}{0.10}$, $x = [NH_4^+] = 1.3 \times 10^{-3}\ M$

$$\% \text{ ionized} = \frac{1.3 \times 10^{-3}\ M}{0.10\ M} \times 100 = 1.3\% \qquad \text{Assumptions good.}$$

b. $\qquad NH_3 + H_2O \rightleftharpoons NH_4^+ + OH^-$

Equil. $0.010 - x \qquad\qquad\qquad x \qquad\qquad x$

$$1.8 \times 10^{-5} = \frac{x^2}{0.010 - x} \approx \frac{x^2}{0.010}, \ x = [NH_4^+] = 4.2 \times 10^{-4};\ \text{Assumptions good.}$$

$$\% \text{ ionized} = \frac{4.2 \times 10^{-4}}{0.010} \times 100 = 4.2\%$$

c. $\qquad CH_3NH_2 + H_2O \rightleftharpoons CH_3NH_3^+ + OH^- \qquad K_b = 4.38 \times 10^{-4}$

Equil. $0.10 - x \qquad\qquad\qquad x \qquad\qquad x$

$$4.38 \times 10^{-4} = \frac{x^2}{0.10 - x} \approx \frac{x^2}{0.10}, \ x = 6.6 \times 10^{-3};\ \text{Assumption fails the 5\% rule (6.6\% error).}$$

Using successive approximations:

$$\frac{x^2}{0.093} = 4.38 \times 10^{-4},\ x = 6.4 \times 10^{-3}$$

$$\frac{x^2}{0.094} = 4.38 \times 10^{-4},\ x = 6.4 \times 10^{-3}\ M = [CH_3NH_3^+]$$

$$\% \text{ ionized} = \frac{6.4 \times 10^{-3}}{0.10} \times 100 = 6.4\%$$

48. $\dfrac{1.0\ g}{1.9\ L} \times \dfrac{1\ \text{mol quinine}}{324.4\ g} = 1.6 \times 10^{-3}\ M$ in quinine

$\qquad\qquad Q + H_2O \rightleftharpoons QH^+ + OH^- \qquad K_b = 10^{-5.1} = 8 \times 10^{-6}$

Initial $1.6 \times 10^{-3}\ M \qquad\qquad 0 \qquad 0(10^{-7})$
            x mol/L quinine reacts with H_2O to reach equilibrium
Change $-x \qquad\qquad\qquad \rightarrow \qquad +x \qquad +x$
Equil. $1.6 \times 10^{-3} - x \qquad\qquad\qquad x \qquad\qquad x$

$$K_b = 8 \times 10^{-6} = \frac{[QH^+][OH^-]}{[Q]} = \frac{x^2}{1.6 \times 10^{-3} - x} \approx \frac{x^2}{1.6 \times 10^{-3}}$$

$x = 1 \times 10^{-4}$; Assumption fails 5% rule (~7% error). Using successive approximations:

$$\frac{x^2}{1.5 \times 10^{-3}} = 8 \times 10^{-6},\ x = 1 \times 10^{-4}$$

$x = [OH^-] = 1 \times 10^{-4} \, M; \quad pOH = 4.0; \quad pH = 10.0$

50.   pyr = pyrrolidine, C_4H_8NH

$pyr + H_2O \rightleftharpoons pyrH^+ + OH^- \qquad K_b = \dfrac{[OH^-][pyrH^+]}{[pyr]}$

From normal setup: $[OH^-] = [pyrH^+]; \quad [pyr] = 1.00 \times 10^{-3} - [OH^-]$

$pH = 10.82; \quad pOH = 3.18; \quad [OH^-] = 10^{-3.18} = 6.6 \times 10^{-4}$

$K_b = \dfrac{(6.6 \times 10^{-4})^2}{1.00 \times 10^{-3} - 6.6 \times 10^{-4}} = 1.3 \times 10^{-3}$

Acid-Base Properties of Salts

52.   a. $KCl \rightarrow K^+ + Cl^-$ Neither K^+ nor Cl^- can change the pH of water. neutral

In general, +1 and +2 metal ions have no acidic/basic properties and all conjugate bases of strong acids have no basic properties.

b. $NaNO_3 \rightarrow Na^+ + NO_3^-$ neutral; Neither species have any acidic/basic properties.

c. $NaNO_2 \rightarrow Na^+ + NO_2^-$ basic

NO_2^- is a weak base. It is the conjugate base of the weak acid, HNO_2. Ignore Na^+.

$NO_2^- + H_2O \rightleftharpoons HNO_2 + OH^-$

d. $NH_4NO_3 \rightarrow NH_4^+ + NO_3^-$ acidic

NH_4^+, weak acid: $NH_4^+ \rightleftharpoons H^+ + NH_3$. NO_3^- has no basic (or acidic) properties.

e. $NH_4NO_2 \rightarrow NH_4^+ + NO_2^-$

NH_4^+ is a weak acid and NO_2^- is a weak base.

$NH_4^+ \rightleftharpoons NH_3 + H^+ \qquad K_a = \dfrac{K_w}{K_b} = \dfrac{1.0 \times 10^{-14}}{1.8 \times 10^{-5}} = 5.6 \times 10^{-10}$

$NO_2^- + H_2O \rightleftharpoons HNO_2 + OH^- \qquad K_b = \dfrac{K_w}{K_a} = \dfrac{1.0 \times 10^{-14}}{4.0 \times 10^{-4}} = 2.5 \times 10^{-11}$

NH_4^+ is stronger as an acid in water than NO_2^- is as a base. Therefore, the solution is acidic.

f. $NaHCO_3 \rightarrow Na^+ + HCO_3^-$

HCO_3^- can be either an acid or a base. Ignore Na^+.

$$HCO_3^- \rightleftharpoons H^+ + CO_3^{2-} \qquad K_{a_2} = 5.6 \times 10^{-11}$$

$$HCO_3^- + H_2O \rightleftharpoons H_2CO_3 + OH^- \qquad K_b = \frac{K_w}{K_{a_1}} = 2.3 \times 10^{-8}$$

HCO_3^- is a stronger base than an acid. The solution is basic.

g. $NH_4C_2H_3O_2 \rightleftharpoons NH_4^+ + C_2H_3O_2^-$
$$\qquad\qquad\quad weak \qquad weak$$
$$\qquad\qquad\quad acid \qquad\, base$$

$$NH_4^+ \rightleftharpoons NH_3 + H^+ \qquad K_a = \frac{K_w}{K_b} = \frac{1.0 \times 10^{-14}}{1.8 \times 10^{-5}} = 5.6 \times 10^{-10}$$

$$C_2H_3O_2^- + H_2O \rightleftharpoons HC_2H_3O_2 + OH^- \qquad K_b = \frac{K_w}{K_a} = \frac{1.0 \times 10^{-14}}{1.8 \times 10^{-5}} = 5.6 \times 10^{-10}$$

The acid and base are equal in strengths. The solution is neutral.

h. $NaF \rightarrow Na^+ + F^-$; $F^- = $ weak base; $F^- + H_2O \rightleftharpoons HF + OH^-$; Solution is basic.

54.   KOH: strong base; KBr: neutral, K^+ and Br^- have no acidic/basic properties.

KCN: CN^- is weak base, $K_b = 1.0 \times 10^{-14}/6.2 \times 10^{-10} = 1.6 \times 10^{-5}$.

NH_4Br: NH_4^+ is weak acid, $K_a = 5.6 \times 10^{-10}$.

NH_4CN: slightly basic, CN^- is a stronger base compared to NH_4^+ as an acid.

HCN: weak acid, $K_a = 6.2 \times 10^{-10}$

Most acidic $\rightarrow$ most basic: $HCN > NH_4Br > KBr > NH_4CN > KCN > KOH$

56.   Solution is acidic from $HSO_4^- \rightleftharpoons H^+ + SO_4^{2-}$.

$$HSO_4^- \qquad\rightleftharpoons\qquad H^+ \quad + \quad SO_4^{2-} \qquad K_a = 1.2 \times 10^{-2}$$

Initial	0.10 M	0(10^{-7})	0
Equil.	0.10 - x	x	x

$$1.2 \times 10^{-2} = \frac{[H^+][SO_4^{2-}]}{[HSO_4^-]} = \frac{x^2}{0.10-x} \approx \frac{x^2}{0.10}, \; x = 0.035$$

Assumption is not good (35% error). Using successive approximations:

$$\frac{x^2}{0.10-x} \approx \frac{x^2}{0.10-0.035} = 1.2 \times 10^{-2}, \; x = 0.028$$

$$\frac{x^2}{0.10 - 0.028} = 1.2 \times 10^{-2}, \ x = 0.029$$

$$\frac{x^2}{0.10 - 0.029} = 1.2 \times 10^{-2}, \ x = 0.029 \qquad \text{(consistent answers)}$$

$x = [H^+] = 0.029 \ M; \ pH = 1.54$

If we add Na_2CO_3 to a solution of $NaHSO_4$, the base CO_3^{2-} can react with the acid HSO_4^-. Depending on relative amounts, two reactions are possible.

$$CO_3^{2-}(aq) \ + \ HSO_4^-(aq) \rightleftharpoons HCO_3^-(aq) + SO_4^{2-}(aq)$$
or
$$CO_3^{2-}(aq) \ + \ 2 \ HSO_4^-(aq) \rightleftharpoons 2 \ SO_4^{2-}(aq) + H_2O(l) + CO_2(g)$$

58.   From the K_a values, acetic acid is a stronger acid than hypochlorous acid. Conversely, the conjugate base of acetic acid, $C_2H_3O_2^-$, is a weaker base than the conjugate base of hypochlorous acid, OCl^-. Thus, the hypochlorite ion, OCl^-, is a stronger base than the acetate ion, $C_2H_3O_2^-$.

Additional Exercises

61. $H_3Cit + HCO_3^- \rightarrow H_2Cit^- + H_2CO_3 \ (H_2O + CO_2)$

$$K_{eq} = \frac{[H_2Cit^-] \, [H_2CO_3]}{[H_3Cit] \, [HCO_3^-]} \times \frac{[H^+]}{[H^+]} = \frac{K_{a_1} \text{ (citric acid)}}{K_{a_1} \text{ (carbonic acid)}}$$

$$K_{eq} = \frac{8.4 \times 10^{-4}}{4.3 \times 10^{-7}} = 1950 = 2.0 \times 10^3$$

$H_3Cit + 3 \ HCO_3^- \rightleftharpoons Cit^{3-} + 3 \ H_2CO_3 \ (3 \ H_2O + 3 \ CO_2)$

$$K_{eq} = \frac{[Cit^{3-}] \, [H_2CO_3]^3}{[H_3Cit] \, [HCO_3^-]^3} \times \frac{[H^+]^3}{[H^+]^3} = \frac{K_{a_1} K_{a_2} K_{a_3} \text{ (citric acid)}}{K_{a_1}^3 \text{ (carbonic acid)}}$$

$$K_{eq} = \frac{(8.4 \times 10^{-4}) \, (1.8 \times 10^{-5}) \, (4.0 \times 10^{-6})}{(4.3 \times 10^{-7})^3} = 7.6 \times 10^5$$

63.   a. $HCO_3^- + HCO_3^- \rightleftharpoons H_2CO_3 + CO_3^{2-}$

$$K_{eq} = \frac{[H_2CO_3] \, [CO_3^{2-}]}{[HCO_3^-] \, [HCO_3^-]} \times \frac{[H^+]}{[H^+]} = \frac{K_{a_2}}{K_{a_1}} = \frac{5.6 \times 10^{-11}}{4.3 \times 10^{-7}} = 1.3 \times 10^{-4}$$

b. $[H_2CO_3] = [CO_3^{2-}]$ if the reaction in (a) is considered to be the only reaction.

c. $H_2CO_3 \rightleftharpoons 2\,H^+ + CO_3^{2-}$ $K_{eq} = \dfrac{[H^+]^2\,[CO_3^{2-}]}{[H_2CO_3]} = K_{a_1}K_{a_2}$

Since, $[H_2CO_3] = [CO_3^{2-}]$ from part b, $[H^+]^2 = K_{a_1}K_{a_2}$

$[H^+] = (K_{a_1}K_{a_2})^{1/2}$; $pH = \dfrac{pK_{a_1} + pK_{a_2}}{2}$

d. $[H^+] = [(4.3 \times 10^{-7})\,(5.6 \times 10^{-11})]^{1/2}$, $[H^+] = 4.9 \times 10^{-9}$; $pH = 8.31$

65.   a.   In the lungs, there is a lot of O_2 and the equilibrium favors $Hb(O_2)_4$. In the cells there is a deficiency of O_2 and the equilibrium favors HbH_4^{4+}.

b. CO_2 is a weak acid, $CO_2 + H_2O \rightleftharpoons HCO_3^- + H^+$. Removing CO_2 essentially decreases H^+. $Hb(O_2)_4$ is then favored and O_2 is not released by hemoglobin in the cells. Breathing into a paper bag increases CO_2 in the blood.

c. CO_2 builds up in the blood and it becomes too acidic, driving the equilibrium to the left. Hemoglobin can't bind O_2 as strongly in the lungs. Bicarbonate ion acts as a base in water and neutralizes the excess acidity.

69. HIO_3 $\rightleftharpoons$ H^+ + IO_3^-

Initial	0.010 M	0(10^{-7})	0
Equil.	0.010 - x	x	x

$\dfrac{x^2}{(0.010 - x)} = 1.7 \times 10^{-1} \approx \dfrac{x^2}{0.0100}$, $x = 0.041$; Assumption is horrible.

Using the quadratic formula: $x^2 + (1.7 \times 10^{-1})x - 1.7 \times 10^{-3} = 0$

$x = 9.5 \times 10^{-3}\,M = [H^+]$; $pH = -\log\,[H^+] = 2.02$

71. B^- is a weak base.

B^- + H_2O $\rightleftharpoons$ HB + OH^-

Initial	0.050 M	0	0(10^{-7})
Equil.	0.050 - x	x	x

$pH = 9.00$, $pOH = 5.00$, and $[OH^-] = 1.0 \times 10^{-5} = x$

$K_b = \dfrac{[HB]\,[OH^-]}{[B^-]} = \dfrac{(1.0 \times 10^{-5})^2}{(0.050 - 1.0 \times 10^{-5})} = 2.0 \times 10^{-9}$

Alternate Method: Mass balance for B⁻

$0.050 = [B^-] + [HB]$ and $[HB] = [OH^-]$ from the reaction

$$K_b = \frac{[HB][OH^-]}{[B^-]} = \frac{[OH^-]^2}{0.050 - [OH^-]} = \frac{(1.00 \times 10^{-5})^2}{0.050 - 1.0 \times 10^{-5}} = 2.0 \times 10^{-9}$$

Since B⁻ is a weak base, then HB is a weak acid.

$$HB \rightleftharpoons H^+ + B^-$$

Initial   0.010 M 0(10⁻⁷)   0
Equil.   0.010 - x x x

$$K_a = \frac{K_w}{K_b} = \frac{(1.0 \times 10^{-14})}{2.0 \times 10^{-9}} = 5.0 \times 10^{-6} = \frac{x^2}{(0.010 - x)} \approx \frac{x^2}{0.010}$$

$x = [H^+] = 2.2 \times 10^{-4} M$; pH = 3.66   Assumptions good.

73. $d = \dfrac{PM}{RT}$, $M = \dfrac{dRT}{P} = \dfrac{5.11 \text{ g/L} \times \dfrac{0.08206 \text{ L atm}}{\text{mol K}} \times 298 \text{ K}}{1.00 \text{ atm}} = 125$ g/mol

$$\frac{1.50 \text{ g} \times \dfrac{1 \text{ mol}}{125 \text{ g}}}{0.100 \text{ L}} = 0.120 \ M; \ \text{pH} = 1.80; \ [H^+] = 10^{-1.80} = 1.6 \times 10^{-2} \ M$$

$HA \rightarrow H^+ + A^-$; $[H^+] = [A^-]$, $0.120 = [HA] + [A^-]$ (mass balance)

$$K_a = \frac{[H^+][A^-]}{[HA]} = \frac{(1.6 \times 10^{-2})^2}{0.120 - 0.016} = 2.5 \times 10^{-3}$$

75.   For this problem we will abbreviate $CH_2=CHCO_2H$ as Hacr and $CH_2=CHCO_2^-$ as acr⁻.

a.   Hacr $\rightleftharpoons$ H^+ + acr⁻

Initial   0.10 M 0(10⁻⁷)   0
Equil.   0.10 - x x x

$$\frac{x^2}{0.10 - x} = 5.6 \times 10^{-5} \approx \frac{x^2}{0.10}, \ x = [H^+] = 2.4 \times 10^{-3} \ M; \ \text{pH} = 2.62 \quad \text{Assumptions good.}$$

b.   % dissociation = $\dfrac{2.4 \times 10^{-3}}{0.10} \times 100 = 2.4\%$

c.   For 0.010% dissociation: $[acr^-] = 1.0 \times 10^{-4} (0.10) = 1.0 \times 10^{-5} M$

$$K_a = \frac{[H^+][acr^-]}{[Hacr]} = 5.6 \times 10^{-5} = \frac{[H^+](1.0 \times 10^{-5})}{0.10 - 1.0 \times 10^{-5}}, \quad [H^+] = 0.56 M$$

d. acr^- is a weak base and the major source of OH^- in this solution.

	acr^-	+	H_2O	$\rightleftharpoons$	$Hacr$	+	OH^-
Initial	0.050 M				0		0(10^{-7})
Equil.	0.050 - x				x		x

$$K_b = \frac{K_w}{K_a} = \frac{1.0 \times 10^{-14}}{5.6 \times 10^{-5}}$$

$$K_b = 1.8 \times 10^{-10}$$

$$K_b = \frac{[OH^-][Hacr]}{[acr^-]} = 1.8 \times 10^{-10} = \frac{x^2}{0.050 - x} \approx \frac{x^2}{0.050}$$

$x = [OH^-] = 3.0 \times 10^{-6}$; pOH = 5.52; pH = 8.48   Assumptions good.

77.   Major species: BH^+, X^-, H_2O; If BH^+ is the best acid and X^- is the best base in solution, then the principal equilibrium is:

$$BH^+ + X^- \rightleftharpoons B + HX$$

$$K_{eq} = \frac{K_a(BH^+)}{K_a(HX)} = \frac{[B][HX]}{[BH^+][X^-]} \quad \text{where } [B] = [HX] \text{ and } [BH^+] = [X^-]$$

$$\frac{K_a(BH^+)}{K_a(HX)} = \frac{[HX]^2}{[X^-]^2}; \quad K_a(HX) = \frac{[H^+][X^-]}{[HX]}, \quad \frac{[HX]}{[X^-]} = \frac{[H^+]}{K_a(HX)}$$

$$\frac{K_a(BH^+)}{K_a(HX)} = \frac{[HX]^2}{[X^-]^2} = \left(\frac{[H^+]}{K_a(HX)}\right)^2, \quad [H^+]^2 = K_a(BH^+) \times K_a(HX)$$

Taking the -log of both sides: $pH = \dfrac{pK_a(BH^+) + pK_a(HX)}{2}$

$$K_b(B) = 1.0 \times 10^{-3}; \quad K_a(BH^+) = \frac{K_w}{K_b} = 1.0 \times 10^{-11}$$

$$8.00 = \frac{11.00 + pK_a}{2}, \quad pK_a = 5.00 \text{ and } K_a(HX) = 1.0 \times 10^{-5}$$

79.   At a pH = 0.00, the $[H^+] = 10^{-0.00} = 1.0\ M$. Begin with 1.0 L × 2.0 mol/L NaOH = 2.0 mol OH^-. We will need 2.0 mol HCl to neutralize the OH^- plus an additional 1.0 mol excess to reduce to a pH of 0.00. Need 3.0 mol HCl total.

81. HA $\rightleftharpoons$ H^+ $+$ A^-

Initial C $0(10^{-7})$ 0 $C = [HA]_o$
Equil. $(C-10^{-4})$ 10^{-4} 10^{-4} (Write 10^{-4} for brevity, really 1.00×10^{-4}.)

$$\frac{(10^{-4})^2}{C-10^{-4}} = 1.00 \times 10^{-6}, \ C = 0.0101 \ M$$

Solution initially contains $0.0101 \ mmol/mL \times 50.0 \ mL = 0.505 \ mmol$ HA. Dilute to total volume, V. The resulting pH = 5.000, $[H^+] = 1.00 \times 10^{-5}$. From normal setup:

                        HA $\rightleftharpoons$ H^+ $+$ A^-

Equil. $(0.505/V - 1.00 \times 10^{-5})$ 1.00×10^{-5} 1.00×10^{-5}

$$\frac{(1.00 \times 10^{-5})^2}{0.505/V - 1.00 \times 10^{-5}} = 1.00 \times 10^{-6}, \ 1.00 \times 10^{-4} = 0.505/V - 1.00 \times 10^{-5}$$

V = 4590 mL; 50.0 mL are present, so we need to add 4540 mL of water.

83. $\dfrac{0.135 \, mol \ CO_2}{2.50 \ L} = 5.40 \times 10^{-2} \ mol \ CO_2/L = 5.40 \times 10^{-2} \ M \ H_2CO_3; \ 0.105 \ M \, CO_3^{2-}$

$H_2CO_3 + CO_3^{2-} \rightarrow 2 \ HCO_3^-$ $K = \dfrac{1}{1.3 \times 10^{-4}} = 7.7 \times 10^3$ (See Exercise 63)

From large size of K, assume all CO_2 (H_2CO_3) is converted into HCO_3^-, i.e., 5.40×10^{-2} mol/L CO_3^{2-} converted into HCO_3^-.

$[HCO_3^-] = 2(5.40 \times 10^{-2}) = 0.108 \ M; \ [CO_3^{2-}] = 0.105 - 0.0540 = 0.051 \ M$

To solve for the $[H^+]$ in equilibrium with HCO_3^- and CO_3^{2-}, use the K_a expression for HCO_3^-.

$HCO_3^- \rightleftharpoons H^+ + CO_3^{2-}$ $K_a = 5.6 \times 10^{-11}$

$$5.6 \times 10^{-11} = \frac{[H^+][CO_3^{2-}]}{[HCO_3^-]} \approx [H^+] \left(\frac{0.051}{0.108} \right)$$

$[H^+] = 1.2 \times 10^{-10}; \ pH = 9.92$ Assumptions good.

85. HCN $\rightleftharpoons$ H^+ $+$ CN^-

Initial $5.0 \times 10^{-4} \ M$ $0(10^{-7})$ 0
Equil. $5.0 \times 10^{-4} - x$ x x

$$\frac{x^2}{5.0 \times 10^{-4} - x} \approx \frac{x^2}{5.0 \times 10^{-4}} = 6.2 \times 10^{-10}, \ x = 5.6 \times 10^{-7} \ M \quad \text{Check assumptions.}$$

The assumption that the H^+ contribution from water is negligible is poor. Whenever the calculated pH is greater than 6.0 for a weak acid, water contribution to $[H^+]$ must be considered. From Section 7.9 in text:

if $\dfrac{[H^+]^2 - K_w}{[H^+]} \ll [HCN]_0 = 5.0 \times 10^{-4}$ then we can use: $[H^+] = (K_a[HCN]_0 + K_w)^{1/2}$.

Using this formula: $[H^+] = [(6.2 \times 10^{-10})(5.0 \times 10^{-4}) + (1.0 \times 10^{-14})]^{1/2}$, $[H^+] = 5.7 \times 10^{-7}\ M$

Checking assumptions: $\dfrac{[H^+]^2 - K_w}{[H^+]} = 5.5 \times 10^{-7} \ll 5.0 \times 10^{-4}$

Assumptions good. pH $= -\log 5.7 \times 10^{-7} = 6.24$

87.   Major species: H_2O, Na^+, NO_2^-; NO_2^- is a weak base.

$NO_2^- + H_2O \rightleftharpoons HNO_2 + OH^-$

Since this is a very dilute solution of a weak base, OH^- contribution from H_2O must be considered. The analogous weak base equations from the weak acid equations are:

For $A^- + H_2O \rightleftharpoons HA + OH^-$

I. $K_b = \dfrac{[OH^-]^2 - K_w}{[A^-]_0 - \dfrac{[OH^-]^2 - K_w}{[OH^-]}}$

II.   When $[A^-]_0 \gg \dfrac{[OH^-]^2 - K_w}{[OH^-]}$, then $K_b = \dfrac{[OH^-]^2 - K_w}{[A^-]_0}$

and $[OH^-] = (K_b[A^-]_0 + K_w)^{1/2}$

Try $[OH^-] = \left(\dfrac{1.0 \times 10^{-14}}{4.0 \times 10^{-4}} \times (6.0 \times 10^{-4}) + 1.0 \times 10^{-14} \right)^{1/2} = 1.6 \times 10^{-7}\ M$

Checking assumption: $6.0 \times 10^{-4} \gg \dfrac{(1.6 \times 10^{-7})^2 - 1.0 \times 10^{-14}}{1.6 \times 10^{-7}} = 9.8 \times 10^{-8}$

Assumption good. $[OH^-] = 1.6 \times 10^{-7}\ M$; pOH $= 6.80$; pH $= 7.20$

89.   0.50 M HA, $K_a = 1.0 \times 10^{-3}$; 0.20 M HB, $K_a = 1.0 \times 10^{-10}$; 0.10 M HC, $K_a = 1.0 \times 10^{-12}$

Major source of H^+ is HA since its K_a value is significantly larger than other K_a values.

$$HA \rightleftharpoons H^+ + A^-$$

	HA	H$^+$	A$^-$
Initial	0.50 M	0(10^{-7})	0
Equil.	0.50 - x	x	x

$$\frac{x^2}{0.50 - x} = 1.0 \times 10^{-3} \approx \frac{x^2}{0.50}, \ x \approx 0.022 \ M = [H^+], \ \frac{0.022}{0.50} \times 100 = 4.4 \ \% \ error$$

Assumptions good. Let's check out the assumption that only HA is an important source of H$^+$.

For HB: $1.0 \times 10^{-10} = \dfrac{(0.022) \ [B^-]}{(0.20)}$, $[B^-] = 9.1 \times 10^{-10} \ M$

At <u>most</u>, HB will produce an additional $9.1 \times 10^{-10} \ M$ H$^+$. Even less will be produced by HC. Thus, our original assumption was good. [H$^+$] = 0.022 M.

91. $Ca(OH)_2 (s) \rightarrow Ca^{2+} (aq) + 2 \ OH^- (aq); \ [OH^-]_o = 6.0 \times 10^{-7} \ M$

We can't ignore the OH$^-$ contribution from H$_2$O. From dissociation of Ca(OH)$_2$ alone, 2[Ca^{2+}] = [OH$^-$]. Including H$_2$O dissociation, the overall charge balance is:

$$2[Ca^{2+}] + [H^+] = [OH^-]$$

$$6.0 \times 10^{-7} \ M + K_w/[OH^-] = [OH^-], \ [OH^-]^2 = 6.0 \times 10^{-7} \ [OH^-] + K_w$$

$$[OH^-]^2 - (6.0 \times 10^{-7}) \ [OH^-] - 1.0 \times 10^{-14} = 0; \ Using \ quadratic \ formula: \ [OH^-] = 6.2 \times 10^{-7} \ M$$

93. $[H^+]_o = 1.0 \times 10^{-2} + 1.0 \times 10^{-2} = 2.0 \times 10^{-2} \ M$ from strong acids HCl and H$_2$SO$_4$.

HSO$_4^-$ is a good weak acid (K$_a$ = 0.012). However, HCN is a poor weak acid (K$_a$ = 6.2 $\times$ 10^{-10}) and can be ignored. Calculating the H$^+$ contribution from HSO$_4^-$:

$$HSO_4^- \rightleftharpoons H^+ + SO_4^{2-} \quad K_a = 0.012$$

	HSO$_4^-$	H$^+$	SO$_4^{2-}$
Initial	0.010 M	0.020 M	0
Equil.	0.010 - x	0.020 + x	x

$$\frac{x(0.020 + x)}{(0.010 - x)} = 0.012 \approx \frac{x(0.020)}{(0.010)}, \ x = 0.0060; \ Assumption \ poor \ (60\% \ error).$$

Using the quadratic formula: $x^2 + 0.032 \ x - 1.2 \times 10^{-4} = 0, \ x = 3.4 \times 10^{-3}$

$[H^+] = 0.020 + x = 0.020 + 3.4 \times 10^{-3} = 0.023 \ M; \ pH = 1.64$

95.   a. $HOAc \rightleftharpoons H^+ + OAc^-$

	HOAc	H$^+$	OAc$^-$
Initial	0.100 M	5.00 $\times$ 10^{-4} M	0
Equil.	0.100 - x	5.00 $\times$ 10^{-4} + x	x

$$1.8 \times 10^{-5} = \frac{x(5.00 \times 10^{-4} + x)}{(0.100 - x)} \approx \frac{x(5.00 \times 10^{-4})}{0.100}$$

$x = 3.6 \times 10^{-3}$; Assumption is horrible. Using the quadratic formula:

$x = 1.1 \times 10^{-3}$ M; $[H^+] = 5.00 \times 10^{-4} + x = 1.6 \times 10^{-3}$ M; pH = 2.80

b. $x = [OAc^-] = 1.1 \times 10^{-3}$ M

CHAPTER EIGHT

APPLICATIONS OF AQUEOUS EQUILIBRIA

Common Ions: Buffers

1. A buffered solution must contain both a weak acid and a weak base. Buffer solutions are useful for controlling the pH of a solution since they resist pH change.

3. The capacity of a buffer is a measure of how much strong acid or base the buffer can neutralize. All the buffers listed have the same pH. The 1.0 M buffer has the greatest capacity; the 0.01 M buffer the least capacity.

5. a. This is a weak acid problem. Let $CH_3CH_2CO_2H = HOPr$ and $CH_3CH_2CO_2^- = OPr^-$.

$$HOPr \rightleftharpoons H^+ + OPr^- \qquad K_a = 1.3 \times 10^{-5}$$

Initial	0.100 M	~0	0

x mol/L HOPr dissociates to reach equilibrium

Change	-x	$\rightarrow$	+x	+x
Equil.	0.100 - x		x	x

$$K_a = 1.3 \times 10^{-5} = \frac{[H^+][OPr^-]}{[HOPr]} = \frac{x^2}{0.100 - x} \approx \frac{x^2}{0.100}$$

$x = [H^+] = 1.1 \times 10^{-3}\ M;\ pH = 2.96$ Assumptions good by the 5% rule.

b. This is a weak base problem.

$$OPr^- + H_2O \rightleftharpoons HOPr + OH^- \qquad K_b = \frac{K_w}{K_a} = 7.7 \times 10^{-10}$$

Initial	0.100 M	0	0

x mol/L OPr$^-$ reacts with H$_2$O to reach equilibrium

Change	-x	$\rightarrow$	+x	+x
Equil.	0.100 - x		x	x

$$K_b = 7.7 \times 10^{-10} = \frac{[HOPr][OH^-]}{[OPr^-]} = \frac{x^2}{0.100 - x} \approx \frac{x^2}{0.100}$$

$x = [OH^-] = 8.8 \times 10^{-6} \ M; \quad pOH = 5.06; \quad pH = 8.94 \qquad$ Assumptions good.

c. pure H_2O, $[H^+] = [OH^-] = 1.0 \times 10^{-7} \ M; \quad pH = 7.00$

d. This solution contains a weak acid and its conjugate base. This is a buffer solution. Solve for the pH through the normal set-up.

$$HOPr \quad \rightleftharpoons \quad H^+ \quad + \quad OPr^- \qquad K_a = 1.3 \times 10^{-5}$$

Initial	0.100 M	~0	0.100 M

x mol/L HOPr dissociates to reach equilibrium

Change	-x $\rightarrow$	+x	+x
Equil.	0.100 - x	x	0.100 + x

$$1.3 \times 10^{-5} = \frac{(0.100 + x)(x)}{0.100 - x} \approx \frac{(0.100)(x)}{0.100} = x = [H^+]$$

$[H^+] = 1.3 \times 10^{-5} \ M; \quad pH = 4.89 \quad$ Assumptions good.

Alternately, we can use the Henderson-Hasselbalch equation to calculate the pH of buffer solutions.

$$pH = pK_a + \log \frac{[Base]}{[Acid]} = pK_a + \log \frac{(0.100)}{(0.100)} = pK_a = -\log(1.3 \times 10^{-5}) = 4.89$$

The Henderson-Hasselbalch equation will be valid when an assumption of the type, $0.1 + x \approx 0.1$, that we just made in this problem is valid. From a practical standpoint, this will almost always be true for useful buffer solutions. If the assumption is not valid, the solution will have such a low buffering capacity it will not be of any use to control the pH. Note: The Henderson-Hasselbalch equation can only be used to solve for the pH of buffer solutions.

7.   a. OH$^-$ will react completely with the best acid present, HOPr.

$$HOPr \quad + \quad OH^- \quad \rightarrow \quad OPr^- \quad + \quad H_2O$$

Before	0.100 M	0.020 M	0
Change	-0.020	-0.020 $\rightarrow$	+0.020
After	0.080	0	0.020

Reacts completely

A buffer solution results after the reaction. Using the Henderson-Hasselbalch equation:

$$pH = pK_a + \log \frac{[Base]}{[Acid]} = 4.89 + \log \frac{(0.020)}{(0.080)} = 4.29$$

b. $\qquad$ OPr^- + H_2O $\rightleftharpoons$ $HOPr$ + OH^- $\qquad$ $K_b = 7.7 \times 10^{-10}$

Before $\quad$ 0.100 M $\qquad\qquad\qquad$ 0 $\quad$ 0.020 M

x mol/L OPr^- reacts with H_2O to reach equilibrium

Change $\quad$ -x $\qquad\qquad \rightarrow \qquad$ +x $\qquad$ +x

Equil. $\quad$ 0.100 - x $\qquad\qquad\qquad$ x $\qquad$ 0.020 + x

$[OH^-] = 0.020 + x \approx 0.020$ M; pOH = 1.70; pH = 12.30 $\qquad$ Assumption good.

Note: OH^- contribution from the weak base OPr^- was negligible ($x = 3.9 \times 10^{-9}$). pH can be determined by only considering the amount of strong base present.

c. $[OH^-] = 0.020$ M; pOH = 1.70; pH = 12.30

d. OH^- will react completely with HOPr, the best acid present.

$\qquad\qquad$ $HOPr$ + OH^- $\rightarrow$ OPr^- + H_2O

Initial $\quad$ 0.100 M $\qquad$ 0.020 M $\qquad$ 0.100 M

Change $\quad$ -0.020 $\qquad$ -0.020 $\qquad \rightarrow \qquad$ +0.020 $\qquad$ Reacts completely

After $\quad$ 0.080 $\qquad\quad$ 0 $\qquad\qquad$ 0.120

Using Henderson-Hasselbalch equation to solve for the pH of the resulting buffer solution:

$$pH = pK_a + \log \frac{[Base]}{[Acid]} = 4.89 + \log \frac{(0.120)}{(0.080)} = 5.07$$

8. Consider all of the results to Exercises 8.5, 6, and 7.

Solution	Initial pH	after added acid	after added base
a	2.96	1.70	4.29
b	8.94	5.49	12.30
c	7.00	1.70	12.30
d	4.89	4.71	5.07

The solution in (d) is a buffer; it contains both a weak acid (HOPr) and a weak base (OPr^-). It resists a change in pH when strong acid or strong base is added.

10. $NH_4^+ \rightleftharpoons H^+ + NH_3$ $\quad$ $K_a = \dfrac{K_w}{K_b} = 5.6 \times 10^{-10}$; $pK_a = -\log(5.6 \times 10^{-10}) = 9.25$

a. $9.00 = 9.25 + \log \dfrac{[NH_3]}{[NH_4^+]}$ $\qquad\qquad$ b. $8.80 = 9.25 + \log \dfrac{[NH_3]}{[NH_4^+]}$

$\log \dfrac{[NH_3]}{[NH_4^+]} = -0.25$ $\qquad\qquad\qquad\qquad$ $\dfrac{[NH_3]}{[NH_4^+]} = 10^{-0.45} = 0.35$

$\dfrac{[NH_3]}{[NH_4^+]} = 10^{-0.25} = 0.56$

c. $10.00 = 9.25 + \log \dfrac{[NH_3]}{[NH_4^+]}$ d. $9.60 = 9.25 + \log \dfrac{[NH_3]}{[NH_4^+]}$

$\dfrac{[NH_3]}{[NH_4^+]} = 10^{0.75} = 5.6$ $\dfrac{[NH_3]}{[NH_4^+]} = 10^{0.35} = 2.2$

12. $75.0 \text{ g } CH_3CO_2Na \times \dfrac{1 \text{ mol}}{82.03 \text{ g}} = 0.914 \text{ mol NaOAc}; \quad [OAc^-] = \dfrac{0.914 \text{ mol}}{0.5000 \text{ L}} = 1.83 \ M$

$pH = pK_a + \log \dfrac{[OAc^-]}{[HOAc]} = 4.74 + \log\left(\dfrac{1.83}{0.64}\right) = 5.20$

14. $pH = pK_a + \log \dfrac{[Base]}{[Acid]}, \quad 7.41 = 6.37 + \log \dfrac{[HCO_3^-]}{[H_2CO_3]}$

$\dfrac{[HCO_3^-]}{[H_2CO_3]} = 10^{1.04} = 11, \quad \dfrac{[CO_2]}{[HCO_3^-]} = 0.091$

16.   a.   No, A strong acid and neutral salt do not constitute a buffer solution.

b.   Yes, HNO_2 = weak acid, NO_2^- = weak base

c.   Yes; $250 \text{ mL} \times 0.10 \text{ mmol/mL} = 25 \text{ mmol } CH_3CO_2H$

$500 \text{ mg KOH} \times 1 \text{ mmol}/56.1 \text{ mg} = 9 \text{ mmol OH}^-$

$OH^- + CH_3CO_2H \rightarrow CH_3CO_2^- + H_2O$ Reacts completely. After this reaction goes to completion, both a weak acid and weak base are present: 16 mmol CH_3CO_2H and 9 mmol $CH_3CO_2^-$ ion. This is a buffer solution.

d.   No, both the CO_3^{2-} and PO_4^{3-} ions are weak bases. No weak acid is present.

Acid-Base Titrations

18.   At the beginning of the titration, only the weak acid HLac is present:

	HLac	$\rightleftharpoons$	H^+	+	Lac^-	$K_a = 1.4 \times 10^{-4}$ HLac: $HC_3H_5O_3$
						Lac$^-$: $C_3H_5O_3^-$
Initial	0.100 M		~0		0	

x mol/L HLac dissociates to reach equilibrium

	HLac		H^+		Lac^-
Change	$-x$	$\rightarrow$	$+x$		$+x$
Equil.	0.100 - x		x		x

$1.4 \times 10^{-4} = \dfrac{x^2}{0.100 - x} = \dfrac{x^2}{0.100}, \quad x = [H^+] = 3.7 \times 10^{-3} \ M; \quad pH = 2.43$ Assumptions good.

Up to the stoichiometric point, we calculate the pH using the Henderson-Hasselblach equation. This is the buffer region. For example, 4.0 mL of NaOH added:

$$\text{initial mmol HLac} = 25.0 \text{ mL} \times \frac{0.100 \text{ mmol}}{\text{mL}} = 2.50 \text{ mmol HLac}$$

$$\text{mmol OH}^- \text{ added} = 4.0 \text{ mL} \times \frac{0.100 \text{ mmol}}{\text{mL}} = 0.40 \text{ mmol OH}^-$$

Note: The units mmol are usually easier numbers to work with. The units for molarity are moles/L but are also equal to mmoles/mL.

The OH⁻ converts 0.40 mmoles HLac to 0.40 mmoles Lac⁻ according to the equation:

$$\text{HLac} + \text{OH}^- \rightarrow \text{Lac}^- + \text{H}_2\text{O} \qquad \text{Reacts completely}$$

mmol HLac remaining = 2.50 - 0.40 = 2.10 mmol; mmol Lac⁻ produced = 0.40 mmol

We have a buffer solution. Using the Henderson-Hasselbalch equation:

$$\text{pH} = \text{pK}_a + \log \frac{[\text{Lac}^-]}{[\text{HLac}]} = 3.86 + \log \frac{(0.40)}{(2.10)} \qquad \begin{array}{l}\text{(Total volume cancels, so} \\ \text{we can use the ratio of moles.)}\end{array}$$

pH = 3.86 - 0.72 = 3.14

Other points in the buffer region are calculated in a similar fashion. Do a stoichiometry problem first, followed by a buffer problem. The buffer region includes all points up to 24.9 mL OH⁻ added.

At the stoichiometric point (25.0 mL OH⁻ added), we have added enough OH⁻ to convert all of the HLac (2.50 mmol) into its conjugate base, Lac⁻. All that is present is a weak base. To determine the pH, we perform a weak base calculation.

$$[\text{Lac}^-] = \frac{2.50 \text{ mmol}}{50.0 \text{ mL}} = 0.0500 \, M$$

	Lac⁻ + H₂O	⇌	HLac + OH⁻	$K_b = \dfrac{1.0 \times 10^{-14}}{1.4 \times 10^{-4}} = 7.1 \times 10^{-11}$
Initial	0.0500 M		0 0	

x mol/L Lac⁻ reacts with H₂O to reach equilibrium

| Change | $-x$ | $\rightarrow$ | $+x$ $+x$ | |
| Equil. | 0.0500 - x | | x x | |

$$\frac{x^2}{0.0500 - x} = \frac{x^2}{0.0500} = 7.1 \times 10^{-11}$$

$x = [\text{OH}^-] = 1.9 \times 10^{-6} \, M$; pOH = 5.72; pH = 8.28   Assumptions good.

Past the stoichiometric point, we have added more than 2.50 mmol of NaOH. The pH will be determined by the excess OH^- ion present.

At 25.1 mL: OH^- added = 25.1 mL $\times$ $\dfrac{0.100 \text{ mmol}}{\text{mL}}$ = 2.51 mmol OH^-

excess OH^- = 2.51 - 2.50 = 0.01 mmol

$[OH^-]$ = $\dfrac{0.01 \text{ mmol}}{50.1 \text{ mL}}$ = 2×10^{-4} M; pOH = 3.7; pH = 10.3

All results are summarized in Table 8.1 and plotted at the end of the solution to Exercise 8.20.

20.   Initially, a weak base problem:

$$\text{py} \quad + \quad H_2O \quad \rightleftharpoons \quad Hpy^+ \quad + \quad OH^- \qquad \text{py is pyridine}$$

Equil.   0.100 - x x x

K_b = $\dfrac{[Hpy^+][OH^-]}{[py]}$ = $\dfrac{x^2}{0.100 - x}$ = $\dfrac{x^2}{0.100}$ = 1.7×10^{-9}

x = $[OH^-]$ = 1.3×10^{-5}; pOH = 4.89; pH = 9.11   Assumptions good.

Buffer region (4-24.5) mL: Added acid converts: py + $H^+ \rightarrow Hpy^+$. Determine moles of py and Hpy^+ after reaction and use the Henderson-Hasselbalch equation to solve for the pH.

K_a = $\dfrac{K_w}{K_b}$ = $\dfrac{1.0 \times 10^{-14}}{1.7 \times 10^{-9}}$ = 5.9×10^{-6}; pK_a = 5.23; pH = 5.23 + log $\dfrac{[py]}{[Hpy^+]}$

At stoichiometric point (25.0 mL), this is a weak acid problem where $[Hpy^+]_0 = 0.0500$ M.

$$Hpy^+ \quad \rightleftharpoons \quad \text{py} \quad + \quad H^+ \qquad K_a = 5.9 \times 10^{-6}$$

Equil.   0.0500 - x x x

5.9×10^{-6} = $\dfrac{x^2}{0.0500 - x}$ = $\dfrac{x^2}{0.0500}$, x = $[H^+]$ = 5.4×10^{-4}; pH = 3.27   Assumptions good.

Beyond the stoichiometric point, the pH is determined by the excess H^+.

At 28.0 mL: H^+ added = 28.0 mL $\times$ $\dfrac{0.100 \text{ mmol}}{\text{mL}}$ = 2.80 mmol H^+

Excess H^+ = 2.80 mmol - 2.50 mmol = 0.30 mmol excess H^+

$[H^+]$ = $\dfrac{0.30 \text{ mmol}}{53.0 \text{ mL}}$ = 5.7×10^{-3} M; pH = 2.24

All results are summarized in the following table and titration curve.

Table 8.1: Summary of pH Results for Exercises 8.18 and 8.20   (Graph follows)

titrant mL	Exercise 8.18	Exercise 8.20
0.0	2.43	9.11
4.0	3.14	5.95
8.0	3.53	5.56
12.5	3.86	5.23
20.0	4.46	4.63
24.0	5.24	3.85
24.5	5.6	3.5
24.9	6.3	-
25.0	8.28	3.27
25.1	10.3	-
26.0	11.29	2.71
28.0	11.75	2.24
30.0	11.96	2.04

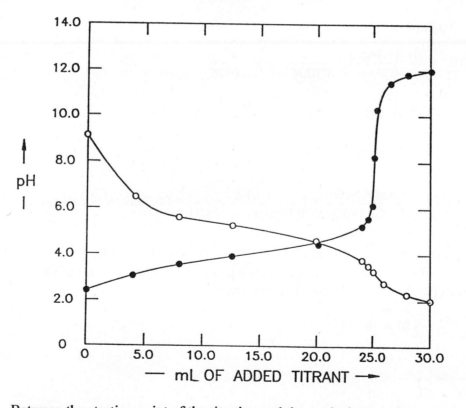

22. Between the starting point of the titration and the equivalence point, we are dealing with a buffer solution. The Henderson-Hasselbalch equation can be used to determine pH.

$$pH = pK_a + \log \frac{[Base]}{[Acid]}$$

At the halfway point to equivalence:

$[Base] = [Acid]$ so $pH = pK_a + \log 1 = pK_a$

24.   a. $0.104 \text{ g NaC}_2\text{H}_3\text{O}_2 \times \dfrac{1 \text{ mol NaC}_2\text{H}_3\text{O}_2}{82.03 \text{ g}} = 1.27 \times 10^{-3} \text{ mol} = 1.27 \text{ mmol NaC}_2\text{H}_3\text{O}_2$

$1.27 \text{ mmol NaC}_2\text{H}_3\text{O}_2 \times \dfrac{1 \text{ mmol HCl}}{\text{mmol NaC}_2\text{H}_3\text{O}_2} \times \dfrac{1 \text{ mL}}{0.0996 \text{ mmol HCl}} = 12.8 \text{ mL}$

Added H^+ reacts with the acetate ion to completion: $H^+ + C_2H_3O_2^- \rightarrow HC_2H_3O_2$. The titration converts acetate ion into acetic acid. At the equivalence point, there is a solution of acetic acid with a concentration of:

$$\dfrac{1.27 \text{ mmol}}{25.0 + 12.8 \text{ mL}} = 3.36 \times 10^{-2} \, M$$

The acetic acid partially dissociates, making the equivalence point acidic.

	HOAc	$\rightleftharpoons$	H^+	+	OAc^-
Initial	0.0336 M		0		0
	x mol/L HOAc dissociates to reach equilibrium				
Change	$-x$	$\rightarrow$	$+x$		$+x$
Equil.	0.0336 - x		x		x

$K_a = 1.8 \times 10^{-5} = \dfrac{[H^+][OAc^-]}{[HOAc]} = \dfrac{x^2}{0.0336 - x} \approx \dfrac{x^2}{0.0336}$

$x = [H^+] = 7.8 \times 10^{-4} \, M; \quad pH = 3.11 \quad$ Assumptions good.

b. $50.00 \text{ mL} \times \dfrac{0.0426 \text{ mmol HOCl}}{\text{mL}} = 2.13 \text{ mmol HOCl}$

$2.13 \text{ mmol HOCl} \times \dfrac{1 \text{ mmol NaOH}}{\text{mmol HOCl}} \times \dfrac{1 \text{ mL}}{0.1028 \text{ mmol NaOH}} = 20.7 \text{ mL of NaOH soln.}$

Added OH^- reacts with HOCl to completion: $OH^- + HOCl \rightarrow OCl^- + H_2O$. The titration converts HOCl into OCl^- ion. At the equivalence point, there are 2.13 mmol of OCl^- in 70.7 mL of solution (50.0 mL + 20.7 mL). The concentration of OCl^- is:

$$\dfrac{2.13 \text{ mmol}}{70.7 \text{ mL}} = 3.01 \times 10^{-2} \, M$$

The OCl^- reacts with H_2O to produce a basic solution.

	OCl^-	+	H_2O	$\rightleftharpoons$	HOCl	+	OH^-
Initial	0.0301 M				0		0
	x mol/L OCl^- reacts with H_2O to reach equilibrium						
Change	$-x$			$\rightarrow$	$+x$		$+x$
Equil.	0.0301 - x				x		x

$$K_b = \frac{K_w}{K_a} = \frac{1.0 \times 10^{-14}}{3.5 \times 10^{-8}} = 2.9 \times 10^{-7} = \frac{[HOCl][OH^-]}{[OCl^-]} = \frac{x^2}{0.0301 - x}$$

$$2.9 \times 10^{-7} \approx \frac{x^2}{0.0301}, \quad x = [OH^-] = 9.3 \times 10^{-5} \ M; \quad pOH = 4.03; \quad pH = 9.97 \quad \text{Assumptions good.}$$

c. HBr is a strong acid; NaOH is a strong base. At the equivalence point we will have an aqueous solution of NaBr. Neither Na^+ nor Br^- reacts with water; $pH = 7.00$.

26. $pH > 5$ for bromcresol green to be blue. $pH < 8$ for thymol blue to be yellow. pH is between 5 and 8.

28. a. yellow   b. yellow

c. green (Both yellow and blue forms are present.)   d. colorless

32.

Exercise	pH at eq. pt.	Indicator	
8.18	8.28	phenolphthalein	
8.20	3.27	2,4-dinitrophenol	(The titration in 8.20 is not feasible. The pH break is too small.)

35. From results of the bromcresol green indicator, $pH \approx 5$.

$HX \rightleftharpoons H^+ + X^-$; From normal weak acid setup: $[H^+] = [X^-] \approx 1 \times 10^{-5} \ M$ and $[HX] \approx 0.01 \ M$

$$K_a = \frac{[H^+][X^-]}{[HX]} \approx \frac{(1 \times 10^{-5})^2}{0.01} = 1 \times 10^{-8}$$

Solubility Equilibria

37. In all setups, s = solubility of solid in mol/L. Note: Since solids do not appear in the K_{sp} expression, we do not need to worry about their initial or equilibrium amounts.

a.

	$Al(OH)_3(s)$	$\rightleftharpoons$	Al^{3+}	+	$3 \ OH^-$
Initial			0		$10^{-7} \ M$ from water
	s mol/L dissolves to reach equilibrium				
Change	-s	$\rightarrow$	+s		+3s
Equil.			s		$10^{-7} + 3s$

$$K_{sp} = 2 \times 10^{-32} = [Al^{3+}][OH^-]^3 = (s)(10^{-7} + 3s)^3 \approx s(10^{-7})^3$$

$$s = \frac{2 \times 10^{-32}}{1 \times 10^{-21}} = 2 \times 10^{-11} \ mol/L \qquad \text{Assumption good } (10^{-7} + 3s \approx 10^{-7}).$$

$$\frac{2 \times 10^{-11} \ mol}{L} \times \frac{78.00 \ g}{mol} = 2 \times 10^{-9} \ g/L$$

b. $Be(IO_4)_2(s)$ $\rightleftharpoons$ Be^{2+} + $2 IO_4^-$

Initial		0	0

s mol/L dissolves to reach equilibrium

Change	-s	$\rightarrow$	+s	+2s
Equil.			s	2s

$K_{sp} = 1.57 \times 10^{-9} = [Be^{2+}] [IO_4^-]^2 = (s) (2s)^2 = 4s^3, \ s = \left(\dfrac{1.57 \times 10^{-9}}{4} \right)^{\frac{1}{3}}$

$s = 7.32 \times 10^{-4} \ mol/L; \ \dfrac{7.32 \times 10^{-4} \ mol}{L} \times \dfrac{390.8 \ g}{mol} = 0.286 \ g/L$

c. $CaSO_4(s)$ $\rightleftharpoons$ Ca^{2+} + SO_4^{2-}

Initial	0	0
Equil.	s	s

$K_{sp} = 6.1 \times 10^{-5} = [Ca^{2+}] [SO_4^{2-}] = s^2, \ s = (6.1 \times 10^{-5})^{1/2}$

$s = 7.8 \times 10^{-3} \ mol/L; \ \dfrac{7.8 \times 10^{-3} \ mol}{L} \times \dfrac{136.2 \ g}{mol} = 1.1 \ g/L$

Note: This ignores any reaction between SO_4^{2-} (a very weak base) and water.

d. $CaCO_3(s)$ $\rightleftharpoons$ Ca^{2+} + CO_3^{2-}

Initial	0	0
Equil.	s	s

$K_{sp} = 8.7 \times 10^{-9} = [Ca^{2+}] [CO_3^{2-}] = s^2$

$s = 9.3 \times 10^{-5} \ mol/L; \ \dfrac{9.3 \times 10^{-5} \ mol}{L} \times \dfrac{100.1 \ g}{mol} = 9.3 \times 10^{-3} \ g/L$

Note: This ignores any reaction between CO_3^{2-} and H_2O to form HCO_3^-.

e. $Mg(NH_4)PO_4(s)$ $\rightleftharpoons$ Mg^{2+} + NH_4^+ + PO_4^{3-}

Initial	0	0	0
Equil.	s	s	s

$K_{sp} = 3 \times 10^{-13} = [Mg^{2+}] [NH_4^+] [PO_4^{3-}] = s^3$

$s = 7 \times 10^{-5} \ mol/L; \ \dfrac{7 \times 10^{-5} \ mol}{L} \times \dfrac{137.3 \ g}{mol} = 1 \times 10^{-2} \ g/L$

Note: We are ignoring any reaction between NH_4^+ and PO_4^{3-}.

f. $Hg_2Cl_2(s) \rightleftharpoons Hg_2^{2+} + 2 Cl^-$

Initial   0   0
Equil.   s   2s

$K_{sp} = 1.1 \times 10^{-18} = [Hg_2^{2+}][Cl^-]^2 = (s)(2s)^2 = 4s^3, \; s = 6.5 \times 10^{-7} \text{ mol/L}$

$$\frac{6.5 \times 10^{-7} \text{ mol}}{L} \times \frac{472.1 \text{ g}}{mol} = \frac{3.1 \times 10^{-4} \text{ g}}{L}$$

g. $SrSO_4(s) \rightleftharpoons Sr^{2+} + SO_4^{2-}$

s mol/L $\rightarrow$ s   s
dissolves

$K_{sp} = 3.2 \times 10^{-7} = [Sr^{2+}][SO_4^{2-}] = s^2, \; s = 5.7 \times 10^{-4} \text{ mol/L}$

$$\frac{5.7 \times 10^{-4} \text{ mol}}{L} \times \frac{183.7 \text{ g}}{mol} = \frac{0.10 \text{ g}}{L}$$

Note: This ignores any reaction between SO_4^{2-} and H_2O.

h. $Ag_2CO_3(s) \rightleftharpoons 2 Ag^+ + CO_3^{2-}$ (ignoring $CO_3^{2-} + H_2O \rightleftharpoons HCO_3^- + OH^-$)

s mol/L $\rightarrow$ 2s   s
dissolves

$K_{sp} = 8.1 \times 10^{-12} = [Ag^+]^2 [CO_3^{2-}] = (2s)^2 (s) = 4s^3$

$s = 1.3 \times 10^{-4} \text{ mol/L}; \quad \dfrac{1.3 \times 10^{-4} \text{ mol}}{L} \times \dfrac{275.8 \text{ g}}{mol} = \dfrac{3.6 \times 10^{-2} \text{ g}}{L}$

i. $Ag_2Cl_2O_7(s) \rightleftharpoons 2 Ag^+ + Cl_2O_7^{2-}$

s mol/L $\rightarrow$ 2s   s
dissolves

$K_{sp} = 2 \times 10^{-7} = [Ag^+]^2 [Cl_2O_7^{2-}] = (2s)^2 (s) = 4s^3$

$s = 3.7 \times 10^{-3} \text{ mol/L} \approx 4 \times 10^{-3} \text{ mol/L}; \quad \dfrac{4 \times 10^{-3} \text{ mol}}{L} \times \dfrac{398.7 \text{ g}}{mol} = 1.6 \text{ g/L} \approx 2 \text{ g/L}$

j. $Cu_2S(s) \rightleftharpoons 2 Cu^+ + S^{2-}$ (ignoring any HS^- formation)

s mol/L $\rightarrow$ 2s   s
dissolves

$$K_{sp} = 2 \times 10^{-47} = [Cu^+]^2 [S^{2-}] = (2s)^2(s) = 4s^3$$

$$s = 1.7 \times 10^{-16} \text{ mol/L} \approx 2 \times 10^{-16} \text{ mol/L}; \quad \frac{2 \times 10^{-16} \text{ mol}}{L} \times \frac{159.2 \text{ g}}{\text{mol}} = 3 \times 10^{-14} \text{ g/L}$$

39.   a. $Fe(OH)_3(s) \rightleftharpoons \quad Fe^{3+} \quad + \quad 3 \text{ OH}^-$

Initial		0	$1 \times 10^{-7} M$

s mol/L dissolves to reach equilibrium

Change	$-s$	$\rightarrow$	$+s$	$+3s$
Equil.			s	$3s + 1 \times 10^{-7}$

$$K_{sp} = 4 \times 10^{-38} = [Fe^{3+}] [OH^-]^3 = (s)(3s + 1 \times 10^{-7})^3 \approx s(1 \times 10^{-7})^3$$

$s = 4 \times 10^{-17} \text{ mol/L}$ Assumption good (s $\ll$ 1 $\times$ 10^{-7}).

b. $Fe(OH)_3(s) \rightleftharpoons \quad Fe^{3+} \quad + \quad 3 \text{ OH}^- \quad pH = 5.0$ so $[OH^-] = 1 \times 10^{-9} M$

Initial		0	$1 \times 10^{-9} M$	(buffered)

s mol/L dissolves to reach equilibrium

Change	$-s$	$\rightarrow$	$+s$	-----	(assume no pH change in buffer)
Equil.			s	1×10^{-9}	

$$K_{sp} = 4 \times 10^{-38} = [Fe^{3+}] [OH^-]^3 = (s)(1 \times 10^{-9})^3, \quad s = 4 \times 10^{-11} \text{ mol/L}$$

c. $Fe(OH)_3(s) \rightleftharpoons \quad Fe^{3+} \quad + \quad 3 \text{ OH}^- \quad\quad pH = 11.0$ so $[OH^-] = 1 \times 10^{-3} M$

Initial		0	$0.001 M$	(buffered)

s mol/L dissolves to reach equilibrium

Change	$-s$	$\rightarrow$	$+s$	-----	(assume no pH change)
Equil.			s	0.001	

$$K_{sp} = 4 \times 10^{-38} = [Fe^{3+}] [OH^-]^3 = (s)(0.001)^3, \quad s = 4 \times 10^{-29} \text{ mol/L}$$

42.   a. $PbI_2(s) \quad\rightleftharpoons\quad Pb^{2+} \quad + \quad 2 I^-$

s mol/L	$\rightarrow$	s	2s

dissolves

$$K_{sp} = 1.4 \times 10^{-8} = [Pb^{2+}] [I^-]^2 = 4s^3, \quad s = 1.5 \times 10^{-3} \text{ mol/L}$$

b. $PbI_2(s) \rightleftharpoons \quad Pb^{2+} \quad + \quad 2 I^-$

Initial	$\rightarrow$	$0.10 M$	0
Equil.		$0.10 + s$	2s

$$1.4 \times 10^{-8} = (0.10 + s)(2s)^2 \approx (0.10)(2s)^2 = 0.40s^2$$

$s = 1.9 \times 10^{-4} \text{ mol/L}$ Assumption good.

c. $PbI_2(s)$ $\rightleftharpoons$ Pb^{2+} + $2\,I^-$

Initial $\rightarrow$ 0 $0.010\;M$
Equil.   s $0.010 + 2s$

$1.4 \times 10^{-8} = (s)\,(0.010 + 2s)^2 \approx (s)\,(0.010)^2,\;\; s = 1.4 \times 10^{-4}\;mol/L$ Assumption good.

45.   After mixing: $[Pb^{2+}]_0 = [Cl^-]_0 = 0.010\;M$

$[Pb^{2+}]_0[Cl^-]_0^2 = (0.010)\,(0.010)^2 = 1.0 \times 10^{-6} < K_{sp}\;(1.6 \times 10^{-5});$ No precipitate will form.

Thus, $[Pb^{2+}] = [Na^+] = [Cl^-] = 0.010\;M;\;\; [NO_3^-] = 2(0.010) = 0.020\;M$

Complex Ion Equilibria

49. $\dfrac{65\;g\;KI}{0.500\;L} \times \dfrac{1\;mol}{166.0\;g} = \dfrac{0.78\;mol}{L}$

Hg^{2+} + $4\,I^-$ $\rightleftharpoons$ HgI_4^{2-} $K_f = 1.0 \times 10^{30}$

Before $0.010\;M$ $0.78\;M$ 0
Change -0.010 -0.040 $\rightarrow$ $+0.010$ Reacts completely (K large)
After   0   0.74   0.010   New initial
                x mol/L HgI_4^{2-} dissociates to reach equilibrium
Change $+x$ $+4x$ $\leftarrow$ $-x$
Equil. x $0.74 + 4x$ $0.010 - x$

$K_f = 1.0 \times 10^{30} = \dfrac{[HgI_4^{2-}]}{[Hg^{2+}]\,[I^-]^4} = \dfrac{(0.010 - x)}{(x)\,(0.74 + 4x)^4}$

$1.0 \times 10^{30} \approx \dfrac{(0.010)}{(x)\,(0.74)^4},\;\; x = [Hg^{2+}] = 3.3 \times 10^{-32}\;M$ Assumptions good.

Note: 3.3×10^{-32} mol/L corresponds to one Hg^{2+} ion per 5×10^7 L. It is very reasonable to approach the equilibrium in two steps. The reaction essentially goes to completion.

52. $AgBr(s) \rightleftharpoons Ag^+ + Br^-$ $K_{sp} = 5.0 \times 10^{-13}$
            $Ag^+ + 2\,S_2O_3^{2-} \rightleftharpoons Ag(S_2O_3)_2^{3-}$ $K_f = 2.9 \times 10^{13}$

$AgBr(s) + 2\,S_2O_3^{2-} \rightleftharpoons Ag(S_2O_3)_2^{3-} + Br^-$ $K = K_{sp}K_f = 14.5$ (Carry extra S.F.)

$$AgBr(s) \;+\; 2\,S_2O_3^{3-} \;\rightleftharpoons\; Ag(S_2O_3)_2^{3-} \;+\; Br^-$$

Initial		0.500 M	0	0

s mol/L AgBr dissolves to reach equilibrium

Change	-s	-2s	$\rightarrow$	+s	+s
Equil.		0.500 - 2s		s	s

$$\frac{s^2}{0.500 - 2s} = 14.5; \;\; \text{Using the quadratic equation since s is not small:}$$

$$s^2 = 7.25 - 29.0\,s, \;\; s^2 + 29.0\,s - 7.25 = 0$$

$$s = \frac{-29.0 + \sqrt{(29.0)^2 + 4(7.25)}}{2} = 0.248 \text{ mol/L}$$

$$1.00 \text{ L} \times \frac{0.248 \text{ mol AgBr}}{L} \times \frac{187.8 \text{ g AgBr}}{\text{mol AgBr}} = 46.6 \text{ g AgBr} = 47 \text{ g AgBr}$$

Additional Exercises

55.   a. $$\frac{28.6 \text{ g borax}}{L} \times \frac{1 \text{ mol}}{381.4 \text{ g}} = \frac{0.0750 \text{ mol borax}}{L}$$

$$\frac{0.0750 \text{ mol borax}}{L} \times \frac{2 \text{ mol B(OH)}_3}{\text{mol borax}} = 0.150 \; M$$

The concentration of $B(OH)_4^-$ is also 0.150 M.

$$B(OH)_3 + H_2O \rightleftharpoons B(OH)_4^- + H^+ \quad K_a = 5.8 \times 10^{-10}$$

$$pH = pK_a + \log \frac{[\text{Base}]}{[\text{Acid}]} = pK_a + \log 1.00 = pK_a = 9.24$$

b. $100. \text{ mL} \times \dfrac{0.10 \text{ mmol}}{\text{mL}} = 10. \text{ mmol NaOH added or } 0.010 \text{ mol NaOH}$

For $B(OH)_3$: $\dfrac{0.150 \text{ mol B(OH)}_3}{L} \times 1.0 \text{ L} = 0.15 \text{ mol B(OH)}_3$

Added OH^- converts $B(OH)_3$ to $B(OH)_4^-$: $B(OH)_3 + OH^- \rightarrow B(OH)_4^-$

mol $B(OH)_3$ = 0.15 - 0.010 = 0.14 mol; mol $B(OH)_4^-$ = 0.15 + 0.010 = 0.16 mol

$[B(OH)_3] = \dfrac{0.14 \text{ mol}}{1.1 \text{ L}}$; Similarly $[B(OH)_4^-] = \dfrac{0.16 \text{ mol}}{1.1 \text{ L}}$

$$pH = pK_a + \log \frac{[\text{Base}]}{[\text{Acid}]} = 9.24 + \log \frac{[B(OH)_4^-]}{[B(OH)_3]} = 9.24 + \log \frac{(0.16)}{(0.14)} = 9.30$$

57. $pH = pK_a + \log \dfrac{[(CH_3)_2AsO_2^-]}{[(CH_3)_2AsO_2H]}$, $6.60 = 6.19 + \log \dfrac{[Cac^-]}{[HCac]}$

$\dfrac{[Cac^-]}{[HCac]} = 10^{0.41} = 2.6$, $[Cac^-] = 2.6\,[HCac]$

$[Cac^-] + [HCac] = 0.25$; $3.6[HCac] = 0.25$, $[HCac] = 0.069\ M$ and $[Cac^-] = 0.18\ M$

$0.500\ L \times \dfrac{0.069\ mol\ (CH_3)_2AsO_2H}{L} \times \dfrac{138.0\ g}{mol} = 4.8\ g$ cacodylic acid

$0.500\ L \times \dfrac{0.18\ mol\ (CH_3)_2AsO_2^-}{L} \times \dfrac{160.0\ g\ (CH_3)_2AsO_2Na}{mol} = 14\ g$ sodium cacodylate

59. a. $pH = pK_a = 4.19$

b. $[Bz^-]$ will increase to $0.120\ M$. $[HBz]$ will decrease to $0.080\ M$.

$pH = pK_a + \log \dfrac{[Bz^-]}{[HBz]}$, $pH = 4.19 + \log \dfrac{(0.120)}{(0.080)} = 4.37$

c.

| | Bz⁻ | + | H₂O | ⇌ | HBz | + | OH⁻ |

$$Bz^- + H_2O \rightleftharpoons HBz + OH^-$$

Initial $0.120\ M$ $0.080\ M$ 0
Equil. $0.120 - x$ $0.080 + x$ x

$K_b = \dfrac{K_w}{K_a} = \dfrac{1.0 \times 10^{-14}}{6.4 \times 10^{-5}} = \dfrac{(0.080 + x)\,(x)}{(0.120 - x)} \approx \dfrac{(0.080)\,(x)}{0.120}$

$x = [OH^-] = 2.34 \times 10^{-10}\ M$ (carry extra S.F.); Assumptions good.

$pOH = 9.63$; $pH = 4.37$

d. We get the same answer. Both equilibria involve the two major species, benzoic acid and benzoate anion. Both equilibria must hold true. K_b is related to K_a by K_w. $[OH^-]$ is also related to $[H^+]$ by K_w.

61. a. The predominate equilibrium is:

$NH_4^+ + X^- \rightleftharpoons NH_3 + HX$ $K_{eq} = \dfrac{[NH_3]\,[HX]}{[NH_4^+]\,[X^-]} = \dfrac{K_a(NH_4^+)}{K_a(HX)}$

From the reaction, $[NH_4^+] = [X^-]$ and $[NH_3] = [HX]$.

Therefore, $K_{eq} = \dfrac{K_a(NH_4^+)}{K_a(HX)} = \dfrac{[HX]^2}{[X^-]^2}$

The K_a expression for HX is: $K_a (HX) = \dfrac{[H^+][X^-]}{[HX]}$, $\dfrac{[HX]}{[X^-]} = \dfrac{[H^+]}{K_a(HX)}$

Substituting into the K_{eq} expression: $K_{eq} = \dfrac{K_a(NH_4^+)}{K_a(HX)} = \dfrac{[HX]^2}{[X^-]^2} = \left(\dfrac{[H^+]}{K_a(HX)} \right)^2$

Rearranging: $[H^2]^2 = K_a(NH_4^+) \times K_a (HX)$ or taking the -log of both sides:

$$pH = \dfrac{pK_a(NH_4^+) + pK_a(HX)}{2}$$

b.   Ammonium formate $= NH_4(HCO_2)$

$$K_a(NH_4^+) = \dfrac{1.0 \times 10^{-14}}{1.8 \times 10^{-5}} = 5.6 \times 10^{-10}; \ K_a(HCO_2H) = 1.8 \times 10^{-4}$$

$$pH = \dfrac{pK_a(NH_4^+) + pK_a(HCO_2H)}{2} = \dfrac{9.25 + 3.74}{2} = 6.50$$

Ammonium acetate $= NH_4(CH_3CO_2)$; $pK_a(CH_3CO_2H) = 4.74$

$$pH = \dfrac{9.25 + 4.74}{2} = 7.00$$

Ammomium bicarbonate $= NH_4(HCO_3)$; $K_a(H_2CO_3) = 4.3 \times 10^{-7}$; $pK_a = 6.37$

$$pH = \dfrac{9.25 + 6.37}{2} = 7.81$$

c. $NH_4^+ + OH^- \rightarrow NH_3 + H_2O$; $CH_3CO_2^- + H^+ \rightarrow CH_3CO_2H$

63.   At the equivalence point, $C_6H_4(CO_2)_2^{2-} = P^{2-}$ is the major species. It is a weak base in water.

	P^{2-}	+	H_2O	$\rightleftharpoons$	HP^-	+	OH^-

Initial $\dfrac{0.5 \text{ g}}{0.1 \text{ L}} \times \dfrac{1 \text{ mol}}{204.2 \text{ g}} = 0.024 \ M$ 0   0   (carry extra sig. fig.)

Equil. $0.024 - x$ x x

$$K_b = \dfrac{[HP^-][OH^-]}{[P^{2-}]} = \dfrac{K_w}{K_{a_2}} = \dfrac{1.0 \times 10^{-14}}{10^{-5.51}} = 3.2 \times 10^{-9} = \dfrac{x^2}{0.024 - x} \approx \dfrac{x^2}{0.024}$$

$x = [OH^-] = 8.8 \times 10^{-6}$; $pH = 8.9$ Assumptions good.

Phenolphthalein would be the best indicator for this titration since it changes color at pH ~ 9.

64.
$$Cr^{3+} + H_2EDTA^{2-} \rightleftharpoons CrEDTA^- + 2 H^+$$

Before	0.0010 M	0.050 M	0	1.0 × 10⁻⁶ M (buffer-[H⁺] constant)

Before   0.0010 M 0.050 M 0 1.0×10^{-6} M (buffer-[H⁺] constant)
Change   -0.0010   -0.0010   →   +0.0010   No change   Reacts completely
After   0   0.049   0.0010 1.0×10^{-6} New initial

x mol/L CrEDTA⁻ dissociates to reach equilibrium

Change   +x +x ←   -x ---
Equil. x 0.049 + x 0.0010 - x 1.0×10^{-6} (buffer)

$$K_f = 1.0 \times 10^{23} = \frac{[CrEDTA^-][H^+]^2}{[Cr^{3+}][H_2EDTA^{2-}]} = \frac{(0.0010 - x)(1.0 \times 10^{-6})^2}{(x)(0.049 + x)}$$

$$1.0 \times 10^{23} \approx \frac{(0.0010)(1.0 \times 10^{-12})}{x(0.049)}, \quad x = [Cr^{3+}] = 2.0 \times 10^{-37} M \quad \text{Assumptions good.}$$

66. $Fe(OH)_3 \rightleftharpoons Fe^{3+} + 3 OH^-$ $K_{sp} = [Fe^{3+}][OH^-]^3 = 4 \times 10^{-38}$

pH = 7.41; pOH = 6.59; $[OH^-] = 2.6 \times 10^{-7} M$; $[Fe^{3+}] = \dfrac{4 \times 10^{-38}}{(2.6 \times 10^{-7})^3} = 2 \times 10^{-18} M$

The lowest level of iron in serum: $\dfrac{60 \times 10^{-6} \text{ g}}{0.1 \text{ L}} \times \dfrac{1 \text{ mol}}{55.85 \text{ g}} = 1 \times 10^{-5} M$

The actual concentration of iron is much greater than expected when considering only the solubility of $Fe(OH)_3$. There must be complexing agents present to increase the solubility.

68. $Cu(OH)_2(s) + 4 NH_3 \rightleftharpoons Cu(NH_3)_4^{2+} + 2 OH^-$

Initial   5.0 M 0   0.010 M
s mol/L $Cu(OH)_2$ dissolves to reach equilibrium
Equil.   5.0 - 4s s 0.010 + 2s

$$1.6 \times 10^{-6} = \frac{[Cu(NH_3)_4^{2+}][OH^-]^2}{[NH_3]^4} = \frac{s(0.010 + 2s)^2}{(5.0 - 4s)^4}$$

If s is small: $1.6 \times 10^{-6} = \dfrac{s(0.010)^2}{(5.0)^4}$, $s = 10.$ mol/L

Assumptions are not good. We will solve the problem by successive approximations.

$$s_{calc} = \frac{1.6 \times 10^{-6}(5.0 - 4s_{guess})^4}{(0.010 + 2s_{guess})^2}, \quad \text{The results from six trials are:}$$

s_{guess}:   0.10, 0.050, 0.060, 0.055, 0.058, 0.056

s_{calc}: 1.6×10^{-2}, 0.070, 0.049, 0.058, 0.052, 0.056

Thus, the solubility is 0.056 mol/L.

70.   The solubility of SiO_2 will equal the sum of the concentrations of H_4SiO_4 and $H_3SiO_4^-$.

$$SiO_2(s) + 2\ H_2O \rightleftharpoons H_4SiO_4(aq)   K = 2 \times 10^{-3}\ M = [H_4SiO_4]$$

$$H_4SiO_4 \rightleftharpoons H_3SiO_4^- + H^+   K_a = 10^{-9.46} = 3.5 \times 10^{-10} = \frac{[H_3SiO_4^-]\,[H^+]}{[H_4SiO_4]}$$

At pH = 7.0: $3.5 \times 10^{-10} = \dfrac{[H_3SiO_4^-]\,(1 \times 10^{-7})}{2 \times 10^{-3}}$, $[H_3SiO_4^-] = 7 \times 10^{-6}\ M$

Solubility = $2 \times 10^{-3} + 7 \times 10^{-6} \approx 2 \times 10^{-3}$ mol/L at pH = 7.0

At pH = 10.0: $3.5 \times 10^{-10} = \dfrac{[H_3SiO_4^-]\,(1 \times 10^{-10})}{2 \times 10^{-3}}$, $[H_3SiO_4^-] = 7 \times 10^{-3}\ M$

Solubility = $2 \times 10^{-3} + 7 \times 10^{-3} = 9 \times 10^{-3}$ mol/L at pH = 10.0

72. $AgC_2H_3O_2(s) \rightleftharpoons Ag^+ + C_2H_3O_2^-$ $K_{sp} = 2.5 \times 10^{-3}$; $HC_2H_3O_2 \rightleftharpoons H^+ + C_2H_3O_2^-$ $K_a = 1.8 \times 10^{-5}$

Solubility = $[Ag^+]$ = total $C_2H_3O_2^-$ concentration = $[C_2H_3O_2^-] + [HC_2H_3O_2]$

$$K_a = \frac{(1.0 \times 10^{-3})\,[C_2H_3O_2^-]}{[HC_2H_3O_2]} = 1.8 \times 10^{-5}$$

$$\frac{[C_2H_3O_2^-]}{[HC_2H_3O_2]} = 1.8 \times 10^{-2},\ [HC_2H_3O_2] = 56\,[C_2H_3O_2^-]$$

$[Ag^+] = [C_2H_3O_2^-] + [HC_2H_3O_2] = [C_2H_3O_2^-] + 56\,[C_2H_3O_2^-]$, $[C_2H_3O_2^-] = \dfrac{[Ag^+]}{57}$

$$K_{sp} = [Ag^+]\,[C_2H_3O_2^-] = 2.5 \times 10^{-3} = [Ag^+]\left(\frac{[Ag^+]}{57}\right),\ [Ag^+] = \text{solubility} = 0.38\ \text{mol/L}$$

0.38 mol of silver acetate will dissolve per liter of pH = 3.00 buffer.

75.   For HOCl, $K_a = 3.5 \times 10^{-8}$; $pH = pK_a + \log \dfrac{[OCl^-]}{[HOCl]}$

$8.00 = 7.46 + \log \dfrac{[OCl^-]}{[HOCl]}$, $\dfrac{[OCl^-]}{[HOCl]} = 10^{0.54} = 3.5$

1.00 L × 0.0500 M = 0.0500 mol HOCl initially. Added OH^- converts HOCl into OCl^-.

$n_{OCl^-} + n_{HOCl} = 0.0500$ and $n_{OCl^-} = 3.5\ n_{HOCl}$

4.5 $n_{HOCl} = 0.0500$, $n_{HOCl} = 0.011$ mol; $n_{OCl^-} = 0.039$ mol

Need to add 0.039 mol NaOH to produce 0.039 mol OCl⁻.

0.039 mol = 0.0100 M × V, V = 3.9 L NaOH

77. a. $NH_3 + H_2O \rightleftharpoons OH^- + NH_4^+$; pH = 8.95; pOH = 5.05

$K_b = 1.8 \times 10^{-5} = \dfrac{(10^{-5.05})(x)}{(0.500)}$, $x = [NH_4^+] = 1.0\ M$

b. 4.00 g NaOH × $\dfrac{1\ mol}{40.00\ g}$ = 0.100 mol; OH⁻ converts NH_4^+ into NH_3.

$NH_4^+ + OH^- \rightarrow NH_3 + H_2O$; After this reaction goes to completion, a buffer solution still exists.

pH = 9.26 + log $\dfrac{0.600}{0.9}$ = 9.26 - 0.18 = 9.08 = 9.1

79. a. 1.00 L × 0.100 mol/L = 0.100 mol HCl added to reach stoichiometric point.

The 10.0 g sample must have contained 0.100 mol of NaA. $\dfrac{10.0\ g}{0.100\ mol}$ = 100. g/mol

b. 500.0 mL of HCl added represents the halfway point to equivalence. So, pH = pK_a = 5.00 and $K_a = 1.0 \times 10^{-5}$.

$[HA]_0 = \dfrac{0.100\ mol}{1.10\ L}$ = 0.0909 M

	HA	$\rightleftharpoons$	H⁺	+	A⁻	$K_a = 1.0 \times 10^{-5}$
Initial	0.0909 M		0		0	
Equil.	0.0909 - x		x		x	

$1.0 \times 10^{-5} = \dfrac{x^2}{0.0909 - x} \approx \dfrac{x^2}{0.0909}$

$x = 9.5 \times 10^{-4}\ M = [H^+]$; pH = 3.02   Assumptions good.

81. Aniline = $C_6H_5NH_2$; $K_b = 3.8 \times 10^{-10}$; Titration reaction: $C_6H_5NH_2 + H^+ \rightleftharpoons C_6H_5NH_3^+$

100.0 mL × 0.250 mmol/mL = 25.0 mmol aniline; Need 25.0 mmol HCl to reach the stoichiometric point.

$V_{HCl} = \dfrac{25.0\ mmol}{0.500\ mmol/mL}$ = 50.0 mL

At stoichiometric point:

$$C_6H_5NH_3^+ \quad \rightleftharpoons \quad H^+ \; + \; C_6H_5NH_2$$

Initial $\quad \dfrac{25.0 \text{ mmol}}{150.0 \text{ mL}} = 0.167 \, M \qquad 0 \qquad \quad 0$

Equil. $\quad 0.167 - x \qquad\qquad\qquad\quad x \qquad\quad x$

$$K_a = \frac{K_w}{3.8 \times 10^{-10}} = 2.6 \times 10^{-5} = \frac{x^2}{0.167 - x} \approx \frac{x^2}{0.167}$$

$x = [H^+] = 2.1 \times 10^{-3} \, M; \quad pH = 2.68 \qquad$ Assumptions good.

83. $HX \rightleftharpoons H^+ + X^-$;   At equil., $[H^+] = [X^-]$ and $[HX] = C_o - [H^+]$ where $C_o = [HX]_o$.

$$K_a = \frac{[H^+][X^-]}{[HX]} = 1.5 \times 10^{-4} = \frac{[H^+]^2}{C_o - [H^+]}; \quad [H^+] = 10^{-3.58} = 2.6 \times 10^{-4} \, M$$

$$1.5 \times 10^{-4} = \frac{(2.6 \times 10^{-4})^2}{C_o - 2.6 \times 10^{-4}}, \quad C_o = 7.1 \times 10^{-4} \, M$$

$75.0 \text{ mL} \times 7.1 \times 10^{-4} \text{ mmol/mL} = 5.3 \times 10^{-2} \text{ mmol HX}$

Need 5.3×10^{-2} mmol NaOH $= 9.5 \times 10^{-2}$ mmol/mL $\times$ V, $V_{NaOH} = 0.56$ mL

85. In the final solution: $[H^+] = 10^{-2.15} = 7.1 \times 10^{-3} \, M$

Beginning mmol HCl $= 500.0 \text{ mL} \times 0.200 \text{ mmol/mL} = 100.$ mmol HCl

Amount of HCl that reacts with NaOH $= 1.50 \times 10^{-2}$ mmol/mL $\times$ V

$$\frac{7.1 \times 10^{-3} \text{ mmol}}{\text{mL}} = \frac{\text{final mmol H}^+}{\text{total vol soln}} = \frac{100. - 0.0150 \, V}{500.0 + V}$$

$3.6 + 7.1 \times 10^{-3} \, V = 100. - 1.50 \times 10^{-2} \, V, \quad 2.21 \times 10^{-2} \, V = 100. - 3.6$

$V = 4.36 \times 10^3 \text{ mL} = 4.36 \text{ L} = 4.4 \text{ L NaOH}$

87. $50.0 \text{ mL} \times 0.100 \, M = 5.00 \text{ mmol H}_2SO_4$; $30.0 \text{ mL} \times 0.10 \, M = 3.0 \text{ mmol HOCl}$

$25.0 \text{ mL} \times 0.20 \, M = 5.0 \text{ mmol NaOH}$; $25.0 \text{ mL} \times 0.10 \, M = 2.5 \text{ mmol Ca(OH)}_2 = 5.00 \text{ mmol OH}^-$

$10.0 \text{ mL} \times 0.15 \, M = 1.5 \text{ mmol KOH}$; We've added 11.5 mmol OH$^-$ total.

$10.0 \text{ mmol OH}^- + 5.00 \text{ mmol H}_2SO_4 \rightarrow 5.0 \text{ mmol H}_2O + 5.0 \text{ mmol SO}_4^{2-}$

The remaining 1.5 mmol OH^- will convert 1.5 mmol HOCl to OCl^-, leaving 1.5 mmol OCl^- and 1.5 mmol HOCl. Major species at this point: HOCl, OCl^-, SO_4^{2-}, H_2O plus cations that don't affect pH. SO_4^{2-} is an extremely weak base ($K_b = 8.3 \times 10^{-13}$). Major equilibrium affecting pH: $HOCl \rightleftharpoons H^+ + OCl^-$. Since [HOCl] = [$OCl^-$]:

$$[H^+] = K_a = 3.5 \times 10^{-8}\ M;\ \ pH = 7.46$$

89.   50.0 mL $\times$ 0.100 M = 5.00 mmol NaOH initially

at pH = 10.50, pOH = 3.50, $[OH^-] = 10^{(-3.50)} = 3.2 \times 10^{-4}\ M$

mmol OH^- remaining = 3.2×10^{-4} mmol/mL $\times$ 73.75 mL = 2.4×10^{-2} mmol

mmol OH^- that reacted = 5.00 - 0.024 = 4.98 mmol

Assuming the weak acid is monoprotic, then 23.75 mL of the weak acid solution contains 4.98 mmol HA.

$$C_o(HA) = \frac{4.98\ mmol}{23.75\ mL} = 0.210\ M$$

91.   a.   Since $K_{a1} > K_{a2}$ and K_{a3}, then initial pH is determined by H_3A. Consider only the first dissociation:

$$H_3A \quad \rightleftharpoons \quad H^+ \quad + \quad H_2A^-$$

Initial	0.100 M	~0	0
Equil.	0.100 - x	x	x

$$K_{a1} = \frac{[H^+][H_2A^-]}{[H_3A]} = \frac{x^2}{0.100 - x} = 1.5 \times 10^{-4} \approx \frac{x^2}{0.100},\ x = 3.9 \times 10^{-3}$$

$[H^+] = 3.9 \times 10^{-3}\ M;\ pH = 2.41$ Assumptions good.

b. $H_3A \rightleftharpoons 3\ H^+ + A^{3-}$ $K = K_{a1} \cdot K_{a2} \cdot K_{a3} = 2.3 \times 10^{-23} = \dfrac{[H^+]^3 [A^{3-}]}{[H_3A]}$

From (a), $[H^+] = 3.9 \times 10^{-3}\ M$ and $[H_3A] = 0.100 - 3.9 \times 10^{-3}\ M$, so

$$[A^{3-}] = \frac{2.3 \times 10^{-23}\ (0.100 - 3.9 \times 10^{-3})}{(3.9 \times 10^{-3})^3} = 3.7 \times 10^{-17}\ M$$

c.   10.0 mL $\times$ 1.00 M = 10.0 mmol NaOH. Began with 100.0 mL $\times$ 0.100 M = 10.0 mmol H_3A. This is at the 1st stoichiometric point where H_2A^- is the major species present.

$$pH = \frac{pK_{a1} + pK_{a2}}{2} = \frac{3.82 + 7.52}{2} = 5.67$$

d. 25.0 mL × 1.00 M = 25.0 mmol NaOH added. Mixture contains 5.00 mmol A^{3-} and 5.00 mmol HA^{2-}.

$$K_{a3} = \frac{[H^+][A^{3-}]}{[HA^{2-}]}; \quad \text{Since } [A^{3-}] = [HA^{2-}], \text{ then } [H^+] = K_{a3}; \quad pH = pK_{a3} = 11.30$$

Assumptions good.

93. 50.0 mL × 0.00200 M = 0.100 mmol Ag^+; 50.0 mL × 0.0100 M = 0.500 mmol IO_3^-

Assume $AgIO_3$ precipitates completely. After reaction, 0.400 mmol IO_3^- is remaining. Now, let some $AgIO_3$ dissolve in solution with excess IO_3^- to reach equilibrium.

	$AgIO_3$	$\rightleftharpoons$	Ag^+	$+$	IO_3^-
Initial			0		$\dfrac{0.400 \text{ mmol}}{100.0 \text{ mL}} = 4.00 \times 10^{-3}\ M$
Equil.			s		$4.00 \times 10^{-3} + s$

$$K_{sp} = [Ag^+][IO_3^-] = 3.0 \times 10^{-8} = s(4.00 \times 10^{-3} + s) \approx s(4.00 \times 10^{-3})$$

$s = 7.5 \times 10^{-6}\ M = [Ag^+]$ Assumptions good.

95. $MX\ (s) \rightleftharpoons M^+ + X^-$

$X^- + H_2O \rightleftharpoons HX + OH^-$ $K_b = \dfrac{1.00 \times 10^{-14}}{1.00 \times 10^{-15}} = 10.0$

$$K_b = 10.0 = \frac{1.00 \times 10^{-14}\ [HX]}{[X^-]}, \quad [X^-] = 1.00 \times 10^{-15}\ [HX]$$

$[M^+]$ = total X^- concentration = $[HX] + [X^-] \approx [HX]$ (since K_b is large)

Thus $[X^-] = 1.00 \times 10^{-15}\ [M^+]$ and $[M^+]$ = solubility = $3.17 \times 10^{-8}\ M$.

$[X^-] = (1.00 \times 10^{-15})(3.17 \times 10^{-8}) = 3.17 \times 10^{-23}\ M$

$K_{sp} = [M^+][X^-] = (3.17 \times 10^{-8})\ (3.17 \times 10^{-23}) = 1.00 \times 10^{-30}$

When MX dissolves in H_2O, the reaction is:

	$MX(s) + H_2O \rightleftharpoons$	M^+	$+$	HX	$+$	OH^-		$K = K_{sp}\ (K_b) = 1.00 \times 10^{-30}\ (10.) = 1.00 \times 10^{-29}$
Equil.		s		s		$1.00 \times 10^{-7} + s$		

$$1.00 \times 10^{-29} = [M^+]\ [HX]\ [OH^-] = (s)\ (s)\ (1.00 \times 10^{-7} + s) \approx 1.00 \times 10^{-7}\ s^2$$

$$s^2 = \frac{1.00 \times 10^{-29}}{1.00 \times 10^{-7}} = 1.00 \times 10^{-22}, \quad s = 1.00 \times 10^{-11}\ mol/L \quad \text{Assumption good.}$$

99.   50.0 mL × 1.0 M = 50. mmol CH_3NH_2 initially

a.   50.0 mL × 0.50 M = 25. mmol HCl added. This is the halfway point to equivalence where $[CH_3NH_2] = [CH_3NH_3^+]$.

$$pH = pK_a + \log \frac{[CH_3NH_2]}{[CH_3NH_3^+]} = pK_a; \quad K_a = \frac{1.0 \times 10^{-14}}{4.0 \times 10^{-4}} = 2.5 \times 10^{-11}$$

$$pH = pK_a = -\log (2.5 \times 10^{-11}) = 10.60$$

b.   It will take 100. mL of HCl solution to reach the stoichiometric point.

$$[CH_3NH_3^+] = \frac{50. \text{ mmol}}{150. \text{ mL}} = 0.33 \, M$$

$$CH_3NH_3^+ \quad \rightleftharpoons \quad H^+ \quad + \quad CH_3NH_2 \qquad K_a = \frac{K_w}{K_b} = 2.5 \times 10^{-11}$$

Initial	0.33 M	0	0
Equil.	0.33 - x	x	x

$$2.5 \times 10^{-11} = \frac{x^2}{0.33 - x} \approx \frac{x^2}{0.33}, \quad x = 2.9 \times 10^{-6} \, M; \quad pH = 5.54 \qquad \text{Asumptions good.}$$

101.   100.0 mL × 0.100 M = 10.0 mmol NaF; 100.0 mL × 0.025 M = 2.5 mmol HCl

2.5 mmol H^+ converts 2.5 mmol F^- into 2.5 mmol HF. A buffer solution results containing 2.5 mmol HF and (10.0 - 2.5 =) 7.5 mmol F^- in 200.0 mL.

$$pH = pK_a + \log \frac{[F^-]}{[HF]} = 3.14 + \log 3.0 = 3.62 \qquad \text{Assumptions good.}$$

104. K_{a3} is so small that a break is not seen at the third stoichiometric point.

107.   At equivalence point: 16.00 mL × 0.125 mmol/mL = 2.00 mmol OH^- added; There must be 2.00 mmol HX present initially.

2.00 mL NaOH added = 2.00 mL × 0.125 mmol/mL = 0.250 mmol OH^-

0.250 mmol of OH^- added will convert 0.250 mmol HX into 0.250 mmol X^-.

Remaining HX = 2.00 - 0.250 = 1.75 mmol HX

This is a buffer solution where $[H^+] = 10^{-6.912} = 1.22 \times 10^{-7} \, M$.   Since total volume cancels:

$$K_a = \frac{[H^+][X^-]}{[HX]} = \frac{1.22 \times 10^{-7} (0.250)}{1.75} = 1.74 \times 10^{-8}$$

CHAPTER NINE

ENERGY, ENTHALPY AND THERMOCHEMISTRY

Potential and Kinetic Energy

2. $KE = \dfrac{1}{2}\, mv^2 = \dfrac{1}{2}\, (2.0\ kg) \left(\dfrac{1.0\ m}{s} \right)^2 = 1.0\ J;\ \ KE = \dfrac{1}{2}\, (1.0\ kg) \left(\dfrac{2.0\ m}{s} \right)^2 = 2.0\ J$

The 1.0 kg object with a velocity of 2.0 m/s has the greater kinetic energy.

3. $q = \dfrac{20.8\ J}{°C\ mol} \times 39.1\ mol \times (38.0 - 0.0)\ °C = 30,900\ J = 30.9\ kJ$

$w = -P\Delta V = -1.00\ atm\ (998\ L - 876\ L) = -122\ L\ atm$

$w = -122\ L\ atm \times \dfrac{101.3\ J}{L\ atm} = -12,400\ J = -12.4\ kJ$

$\Delta E = q + w = 30.9\ kJ + (-12.4\ kJ) = 18.5\ kJ$

5. $313\ g\ He \times \dfrac{1\ mol\ He}{4.003\ g\ He} = 78.2\ mol\ He$

$q = 78.2\ mol\ He \times \dfrac{20.8\ J}{mol\ °C} \times (-15\ °C) = -2.4 \times 10^4\ J\ or\ -24\ kJ$

$w = -P\Delta V = -1.00\ atm\ (1814 - 1910.)\ L = +96\ L\ atm$

$w = +96\ L\ atm \times \dfrac{101.3\ J}{L\ atm} = +9.7 \times 10^3\ J\ or\ +9.7\ kJ$

$\Delta E = q + w = -24\ kJ + 9.7\ kJ = -14.3\ kJ = -14\ kJ$

Properties of Enthalpy

7. a. $1.00\ g\ CH_4 \times \dfrac{1\ mol\ CH_4}{16.04\ g\ CH_4} \times \dfrac{-891\ kJ}{mol\ CH_4} = -55.5\ kJ$

b. $n = \dfrac{PV}{RT} = \dfrac{\dfrac{740.}{760}\ atm \times (1.00 \times 10^3\ L)}{\dfrac{0.08206\ L\ atm}{mol\ K} \times 298\ K} = 39.8\ mol;\ \ 39.8\ mol \times \dfrac{-891\ kJ}{mol} = -3.55 \times 10^4\ kJ$

The Thermodynamics of Ideal Gases

10.   Calculate the constant volume process first.

$n = 1.00 \times 10^3\ g \times \dfrac{1\ mol}{30.07\ g} = 33.3\ mol\ C_2H_6;\ \ C_v = \dfrac{44.60\ J}{K\ mol} = \dfrac{44.60\ J}{°C\ mol}$

$\Delta E = nC_v\Delta T = (33.3\ mol)\ (44.60\ J\ °C^{-1}\ mol^{-1})\ (75.0 - 25.0°C) = 74{,}300\ J = 74.3\ kJ$

$\Delta E = q + w;\ \ Since\ \Delta V = 0,\ w = 0;\ \ \Delta E = q_v = 74.3\ kJ$

$\Delta H = \Delta E + \Delta PV = \Delta E + nR\Delta T$

$\Delta H = 74.3\ kJ + (33.3\ mol)(8.3145\ J\ mol^{-1}\ K^{-1})\ (50.0\ K)(1\ kJ/1000\ J)$

$\Delta H = 74.3\ kJ + 13.8\ kJ = 88.1\ kJ$

Now consider the constant pressure process.

$q_p = \Delta H = nC_p\Delta T = (33.3\ mol)\ (52.92\ J\ mol^{-1}\ K^{-1})\ (50.0\ K)$

$q_p = 88{,}100\ J = 88.1\ kJ = \Delta H$

$w = -P\Delta V = -nR\Delta T = -(33.3\ mol)\ (8.3145\ J\ mol^{-1}\ K^{-1})\ (50.0\ K) = -13{,}800\ J = -13.8\ kJ$

$\Delta E = q + w = 88.1\ kJ - 13.8\ kJ = 74.3\ kJ$

Summary:	Constant V	Constant P
q	74.3 kJ	88.1 kJ
ΔE	74.3 kJ	74.3 kJ
ΔH	88.1 kJ	88.1 kJ
w	0	-13.8 kJ

12.   Pathway I:

Step 1: (5.00 mol, 3.00 atm, 15.0 L) → (5.00 mol, 3.00 atm, 55.0 L)

$w = -P\Delta V = -(3.00\ atm)\ (55.0 - 15.0\ L) = -120.\ L\ atm$

$$w = -120. \text{ L atm} \times \frac{101.3 \text{ J}}{\text{L atm}} \times \frac{1 \text{ kJ}}{1000 \text{ J}} = -12.2 \text{ kJ}$$

$$\Delta H = q_p = nC_p\Delta T = nC_p \frac{\Delta(PV)}{nR} = \frac{C_p\Delta(PV)}{R}; \quad \Delta(PV) = (P_2V_2 - P_1V_1)$$

For an ideal monatomic gas: $C_p = \frac{5}{2} R$

$$\Delta H = q_p = \frac{5}{2}\Delta(PV) = \frac{5}{2}(165 - 45.0) \text{ L atm} = 300. \text{ L atm}$$

$$\Delta H = q_p = 300. \text{ L atm} \times \frac{101.3 \text{ J}}{\text{L atm}} \times \frac{1 \text{ kJ}}{1000 \text{ J}} = 30.4 \text{ kJ}$$

$$\Delta E = q + w = 30.4 \text{ kJ} - 12.2 \text{ kJ} = 18.2 \text{ kJ}$$

Step 2: (5.00 mol, 3.00 atm, 55.0 L) → (5.00 mol, 6.00 atm, 20.0 L)

$$\Delta E = nC_v\Delta T = n\left(\frac{3}{2} R\right)\left(\frac{\Delta(PV)}{nR}\right) = \frac{3}{2}\Delta PV$$

$$\Delta E = \frac{3}{2}(120. - 165) \text{ L atm} = -67.5 \text{ L atm} \quad \text{(Carry extra significant figure.)}$$

$$\Delta E = -67.5 \text{ L atm} \times \frac{101.3 \text{ J}}{\text{L atm}} \times \frac{1 \text{ kJ}}{1000 \text{ J}} = -6.8 \text{ kJ}$$

$$\Delta H = nC_p\Delta T = n\left(\frac{5}{2} R\right)\left(\frac{\Delta(PV)}{nR}\right) = \frac{5}{2}\Delta(PV)$$

$$\Delta H = \frac{5}{2}(-45 \text{ L atm}) = -113 \text{ L atm} \quad \text{(Carry extra significant figure.)}$$

$$\Delta H = -113 \text{ L atm} \times \frac{101.3 \text{ J}}{\text{L atm}} \times \frac{1 \text{ kJ}}{1000 \text{ J}} = -11 \text{ kJ}$$

$$w = -P_{ext}\Delta V = -(6.00 \text{ atm}) (20.0 - 55.0)\text{L} = 210. \text{ L atm}$$

$$w = 210. \text{ L atm} \times \frac{101.3 \text{ J}}{\text{L atm}} \times \frac{1 \text{ kJ}}{1000 \text{ J}} = 21.3 \text{ kJ}$$

$$\Delta E = q + w, \; -6.8 \text{ kJ} = q + 21.3 \text{ kJ}, \; q = -28.1 \text{ kJ}$$

Summary:

Path I	Step 1	Step 2	Total
q	30.4 kJ	-28.1 kJ	2.3 kJ
w	-12.2 kJ	21.3 kJ	9.1 kJ
ΔE	18.2 kJ	-6.8 kJ	11.4 kJ
ΔH	30.4 kJ	-11 kJ	19 kJ

Pathway II:

Step 3: (5.00 mol, 3.00 atm, 15.0 L) $\rightarrow$ (5.00 mol, 6.00 atm, 15.0 L)

$$\Delta E = q_v = \frac{3}{2}\Delta(PV) = \frac{3}{2}(90.0 - 45.0)\text{L atm} = 67.5 \text{ L atm}$$

$$\Delta E = q_v = 67.5 \text{ L atm} \times \frac{101.3 \text{ J}}{\text{L atm}} \times \frac{1 \text{ kJ}}{1000 \text{ J}} = 6.84 \text{ kJ}$$

$w = -P\Delta V = 0$ since $\Delta V = 0$

$\Delta H = \Delta E + \Delta(PV) = 67.5 \text{ L atm} + 45.0 \text{ L atm} = 112.5 \text{ L atm} = 11.40 \text{ kJ}$

Step 4: (5.00 mol, 6.00 atm, 15.0 L) $\rightarrow$ (5.00 mol, 6.00 atm, 20.0 L)

$$\Delta H = q_p = nC_p\Delta T = n\left(\frac{5}{2}R\right)\left(\frac{\Delta(PV)}{nR}\right) = \frac{5}{2}\Delta PV$$

$$\Delta H = \frac{5}{2}(120. - 90.0) \text{ L atm} = 75 \text{ L atm}$$

$$\Delta H = q_p = 75 \text{ L atm} \times \frac{101.3 \text{ J}}{\text{L atm}} \times \frac{1 \text{ kJ}}{1000 \text{ J}} = 7.6 \text{ kJ}$$

$w = -P\Delta V = -(6.00 \text{ atm})(20.0 - 15.0)\text{L} = -30. \text{ L atm}$

$$w = -30. \text{ L atm} \times \frac{101.3 \text{ J}}{\text{L atm}} \times \frac{1 \text{ kJ}}{1000 \text{ J}} = -3.0 \text{ kJ}$$

$\Delta E = q + w = 7.6 \text{ kJ} - 3.0 \text{ kJ} = 4.6 \text{ kJ}$

Summary:	Path II	Step 3	Step 4	Total
q		6.84 kJ	7.6 kJ	14.4 kJ
w		0	-3.0 kJ	-3.0 kJ
ΔE		6.84 kJ	4.6 kJ	11.4 kJ
ΔH		11.40 kJ	7.6 kJ	19.0 kJ

Note that ΔE and ΔH are the same for both pathways. They are state functions.

Calorimetry and Heat Capacity

16.   Specific heat capacity $= \dfrac{78.2 \text{ J}}{45.6 \text{ g} \times 13.3°C} = \dfrac{0.129 \text{ J}}{\text{g °C}}$

Molar heat capacity $= \dfrac{0.129 \text{ J}}{\text{g °C}} \times \dfrac{207.2 \text{ g}}{\text{mol}} = \dfrac{26.7 \text{ J}}{\text{mol °C}}$

18.   Heat lost by solution = Heat gained by KBr

Note: Sign errors are common with calorimetry problems. However, the correct sign for ΔH can easily be obtained from the ΔT data. When working calorimetry problems, keep all quantities positive (ignore signs). When finished, deduce the correct sign for ΔH. For this problem, T decreases so ΔH is positive.

Heat lost by solution $= \dfrac{4.18 \text{ J}}{\text{g °C}} \times 136 \text{ g} \times 3.1°C = 1800 \text{ J}$

Heat gained by KBr $= \dfrac{1800 \text{ J}}{10.5 \text{ g}} = \dfrac{170 \text{ J}}{\text{g}} = \Delta H$

$\Delta H = \dfrac{170 \text{ J}}{\text{g KBr}} \times \dfrac{119.0 \text{ g KBr}}{\text{mol KBr}} \times \dfrac{1 \text{ kJ}}{1000 \text{ J}} = \dfrac{20. \text{ kJ}}{\text{mol}}$

20. $50.0 \times 10^{-3} \text{ L} \times 0.100 \text{ mol/L} = 5.00 \times 10^{-3}$ mol of both $AgNO_3$ and HCl are reacted. Thus, 5.00×10^{-3} mol of AgCl will be produced.

Heat lost by chemicals = Heat gained by water

Heat gain $= \dfrac{4.18 \text{ J}}{\text{g °C}} \times 100.0 \text{ g} \times 0.80°C = 330 \text{ J}$

Heat loss = 330 J; This is the heat evolved (exothermic reaction) when 5.00×10^{-3} mol of AgCl is produced. So ΔH is negative with a value of:

$\Delta H = \dfrac{-330 \text{ J}}{5.00 \times 10^{-3} \text{ mol}} \times \dfrac{1 \text{ kJ}}{1000 \text{ J}} = -66 \text{ kJ/mol}$

22.   Heat gain by calorimeter = $\dfrac{1.56 \text{ kJ}}{\text{°C}} \times 3.2\text{°C} = 5.0$ kJ = heat loss by quinone

Heat loss = 5.0 kJ which is the heat evolved (exothermic reaction) by the combustion of 0.1964 g of quinone.

$\Delta E_{comb} = \dfrac{-5.0 \text{ kJ}}{0.1964 \text{ g}} = -25$ kJ/g; $\dfrac{-25 \text{ kJ}}{\text{g}} \times \dfrac{108.1 \text{ g}}{\text{mol}} = -2700$ kJ/mol

24. $V = 10.0 \text{ m} \times 4.0 \text{ m} \times 3.0 \text{ m} = 1.2 \times 10^2 \text{ m}^3 \times (100 \text{ cm/m})^3 = 1.2 \times 10^8 \text{ cm}^3$

Mass of water = 1.2×10^8 g since the density of water is 1.0 g/cm^3.

Heat required = $\dfrac{4.18 \text{ J}}{\text{g °C}} \times (1.2 \times 10^8 \text{ g}) \times 9.8\text{°C} = 4.9 \times 10^9 \text{ J} = 4.9 \times 10^6$ kJ

Hess's Law

27. $S + 3/2\ O_2 \rightarrow SO_3$ $\qquad\qquad$ $\Delta H° = -395.2$ kJ
$\qquad$ $SO_3 \rightarrow SO_2 + 1/2\ O_2$ $\qquad$ $\Delta H° = +198.2$ kJ/2 = +99.1 kJ

$S(s) + O_2(g) \rightarrow SO_2(g)$ $\qquad\qquad$ $\Delta H° = -296.1$ kJ

29. $\qquad\qquad$ $4\ HNO_3 \rightarrow 2\ N_2O_5 + 2\ H_2O$ $\qquad$ $\Delta H° = 2(+76.6$ kJ)
$2\ N_2 + 6\ O_2 + 2\ H_2 \rightarrow 4\ HNO_3$ $\qquad$ $\Delta H° = 4(-174.1$ kJ)
$\qquad\qquad\qquad$ $2\ H_2O \rightarrow 2\ H_2 + O_2$ $\qquad$ $\Delta H° = 2(+285.8$ kJ)

$2\ N_2(g) + 5\ O_2(g) \rightarrow 2\ N_2O_5(g)$ $\qquad$ $\Delta H° = 28.4$ kJ

31.   Information given:

$\qquad\qquad$ $C(s) + O_2(g) \rightarrow CO_2(g)$ $\qquad\qquad$ $\Delta H° = -393.7$ kJ
$\qquad$ $CO(g) + 1/2\ O_2(g) \rightarrow CO_2(g)$ $\qquad$ $\Delta H° = -283.3$ kJ

So:

$\qquad\qquad$ $2\ C + 2\ O_2 \rightarrow 2\ CO_2$ $\qquad\qquad$ $\Delta H° = 2(-393.7$ kJ)
$\qquad\qquad$ $2\ CO_2 \rightarrow 2\ CO + O_2$ $\qquad\qquad$ $\Delta H° = 2(+283.3$ kJ)

$2\ C(s) + O_2(g) \rightarrow 2\ CO(g)$ $\qquad\qquad$ $\Delta H° = -220.8$ kJ

33. $NO + O_3 \rightarrow NO_2 + O_2$ $\qquad\qquad$ $\Delta H° = -199$ kJ
$\qquad\qquad$ $3/2\ O_2 \rightarrow O_3$ $\qquad\qquad$ $\Delta H° = +427$ kJ/2
$\qquad\qquad\qquad$ $O \rightarrow 1/2\ O_2$ $\qquad\qquad$ $\Delta H° = -495$ kJ/2

$NO(g) + O(g) \rightarrow NO_2(g)$ $\qquad\qquad$ $\Delta H° = -233$ kJ

35. $1/2\ O_2 + 1/2\ H_2 \rightarrow OH$ $\Delta H° = 77.9\ kJ/2$
                  $O \rightarrow 1/2\ O_2$ $\Delta H° = -495\ kJ/2$
                  $H \rightarrow 1/2\ H_2$ $\Delta H° = -435.9\ kJ/2$
       _____
       $O(g) + H(g) \rightarrow OH(g)$ $\Delta H° = -427\ kJ$

37. $2\ N_2(g) + 6\ H_2(g) \rightarrow 4\ NH_3(g)$ $\Delta H° = 4(-46\ kJ)$
                  $6\ H_2O(g) \rightarrow 6\ H_2(g) + 3\ O_2(g)$ $\Delta H° = 3(484\ kJ)$
       _____
       $2\ N_2(g) + 6\ H_2O(g) \rightarrow 3\ O_2(g) + 4\ NH_3(g)$ $\Delta H° = +1268\ kJ$

No, since the reaction is very endothermic (requires a lot of heat), it would not be a practical way of making ammonia.

Standard Enthalpies of Formation

40.   a. $4\ NH_3(g) + 5\ O_2(g) \rightarrow 4\ NO(g) + 6\ H_2O(g);\ \ \Delta H° = \Sigma\Delta H_f°\ \text{(products)} - \Sigma\Delta H_f°\ \text{(reactants)}$

$$\Delta H° = \left[4\ mol\left(\frac{90\ kJ}{mol}\right) + 6\ mol\left(\frac{-242\ kJ}{mol}\right)\right] - 4\ mol\left(\frac{-46\ kJ}{mol}\right) = -908\ kJ$$

$2\ NO(g) + O_2(g) \rightarrow 2\ NO_2(g)$

$$\Delta H° = 2\ mol\left(\frac{34\ kJ}{mol}\right) - 2\ mol\left(\frac{90\ kJ}{mol}\right) = -112\ kJ$$

$3\ NO_2(g) + H_2O(l) \rightarrow 2\ HNO_3(aq) + NO(g)$

$$\Delta H° = 2\ mol\left(\frac{-207\ kJ}{mol}\right) + 1\ mol\left(\frac{90\ kJ}{mol}\right)$$

$$- \left[3\ mol\left(\frac{34\ kJ}{mol}\right) + 1\ mol\left(\frac{-286\ kJ}{mol}\right)\right] = -140.\ kJ$$

       b. $12\ NH_3(g) + 15\ O_2(g) \rightarrow 12\ NO(g) + 18\ H_2O(g)$
                  $12\ NO(g) + 6\ O_2(g) \rightarrow 12\ NO_2(g)$
            $12\ NO_2(g) + 4\ H_2O(l) \rightarrow 8\ HNO_3(aq) + 4\ NO(g)$
                       $4\ H_2O(g) \rightarrow 4\ H_2O(l)$
       _____
       $12\ NH_3(g) + 21\ O_2(g) \rightarrow 8\ HNO_3(aq) + 4\ NO(g) + 14\ H_2O(g)$

The overall reaction is exothermic since each step is exothermic.

42. $3 Al(s) + 3 NH_4ClO_4(s) \rightarrow Al_2O_3(s) + AlCl_3(s) + 3 NO(g) + 6 H_2O(g)$

$$\Delta H° = \left[6 \text{ mol} \left(\frac{-242 \text{ kJ}}{\text{mol}} \right) + 3 \text{ mol} \left(\frac{90 \text{ kJ}}{\text{mol}} \right) + 1 \text{ mol} \left(\frac{-704 \text{ kJ}}{\text{mol}} \right) + 1 \text{ mol} \left(\frac{-1676 \text{ kJ}}{\text{mol}} \right) \right]$$

$$- \left[3 \text{ mol} \left(\frac{-295 \text{ kJ}}{\text{mol}} \right) \right] = -2677 \text{ kJ}$$

45.   a. $\Delta H° = 3 \text{ mol} (227 \text{ kJ/mol}) - 1 \text{ mol} (49 \text{ kJ/mol}) = 632 \text{ kJ}$

       b.   Since $3 C_2H_2(g)$ is higher in energy than $C_6H_6(l)$, then acetylene will release more energy per gram when burned in air.

47. $2 ClF_3(g) + 2 NH_3(g) \rightarrow N_2(g) + 6 HF(g) + Cl_2(g)$

$$\Delta H° = 6 \Delta H_f° (HF) - [2 \Delta H_f° (ClF_3) + 2 \Delta H_f° (NH_3)]$$

$$-1196 \text{ kJ} = 6 \text{ mol} \left(\frac{-271 \text{ kJ}}{\text{mol}} \right) - 2 \Delta H_f° - 2 \text{ mol} \left(\frac{-46 \text{ kJ}}{\text{mol}} \right)$$

$$-1196 \text{ kJ} = -1626 \text{ kJ} - 2 \Delta H_f° + 92 \text{ kJ}, \quad \Delta H_f° = \frac{(-1626 + 92 + 1196) \text{ kJ}}{2 \text{ mol}} = \frac{-169 \text{ kJ}}{\text{mol}}$$

Energy Consumption and Sources

49. $CH_4(g) + O_2(g) \rightarrow CO_2(g) + 2 H_2O(l)$ $\Delta H° = -891 \text{ kJ}$

       Need 4.9×10^6 kJ of energy (from Exercise 24).

$$4.9 \times 10^6 \text{ kJ} \times \frac{1 \text{ mol CH}_4}{891 \text{ kJ}} = 5.5 \times 10^3 \text{ mol CH}_4; \quad 5.5 \times 10^3 \text{ mol} \times \frac{22.4 \text{ L}}{\text{mol}} \text{ at STP} = 1.2 \times 10^5 \text{ L}$$

       Or using the ideal gas law: $V = \dfrac{5.5 \times 10^3 \text{ mol} \times \dfrac{0.08206 \text{ L atm}}{\text{mol K}} \times 273 \text{ K}}{1.0 \text{ atm}} = 1.2 \times 10^5 \text{ L}$

51. $CO(g) + 2 H_2(g) \rightarrow CH_3OH(l) \quad \Delta H° = (-239 \text{ kJ}) - (-110.5 \text{ kJ}) = -129 \text{ kJ}$

53. $C_3H_8(g) + 5 O_2(g) \rightarrow 3 CO_2(g) + 4 H_2O(l)$

$$\Delta H° = [3(-393.5 \text{ kJ}) + 4(-286 \text{ kJ})] - (-104 \text{ kJ}) = -2221 \text{ kJ/mol C}_3H_8$$

$$\frac{-2221 \text{ kJ}}{\text{mol}} \times \frac{1 \text{ mol}}{44.096 \text{ g}} = \frac{-50.37 \text{ kJ}}{\text{g}} \text{ vs. } -47.7 \text{ kJ/g for octane (Example 9.8)}$$

The fuel values of the fuels are very close. An advantage of propane is that it burns more cleanly. The boiling point of propane is -42°C. Thus, it is more difficult to store propane and there are extra safety hazards associated in using high pressure compressed gas tanks.

55.   Energy needed $= \dfrac{20. \times 10^3 \text{ g C}_{12}\text{H}_{22}\text{O}_{11}}{\text{hr}} \times \dfrac{1 \text{ mol C}_{12}\text{H}_{22}\text{O}_{11}}{342.3 \text{ g C}_{12}\text{H}_{22}\text{O}_{11}} \times \dfrac{5640 \text{ kJ}}{\text{mol}} = 3.3 \times 10^5 \text{ kJ/hr}$

Energy from sun $= 1.0 \text{ kW/m}^2 = 1000 \text{ W/m}^2 = \dfrac{1000 \text{ J}}{\text{s m}^2} = \dfrac{1.0 \text{ kJ}}{\text{s m}^2}$

$10{,}000 \text{ m}^2 \times \dfrac{1.0 \text{ kJ}}{\text{s m}^2} \times \dfrac{60 \text{ s}}{\text{min}} \times \dfrac{60 \text{ min}}{\text{hr}} = 3.6 \times 10^7 \text{ kJ/hr}$

% efficiency $= \dfrac{\text{Energy used per hour}}{\text{Total energy per hour}} \times 100 = \dfrac{3.3 \times 10^5 \text{ kJ}}{3.6 \times 10^7 \text{ kJ}} \times 100 = 0.92\%$

Additional Exercises

57.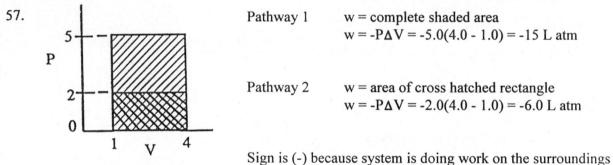

Pathway 1   w = complete shaded area
          $w = -P\Delta V = -5.0(4.0 - 1.0) = -15 \text{ L atm}$

Pathway 2   w = area of cross hatched rectangle
          $w = -P\Delta V = -2.0(4.0 - 1.0) = -6.0 \text{ L atm}$

Sign is (-) because system is doing work on the surroundings

No, since work depends on pathway it cannot be a state function.

59. $0.100 \text{ L} \times \dfrac{0.500 \text{ mol HCl}}{\text{L}} \times \dfrac{1 \text{ mol BaCl}_2}{2 \text{ mol HCl}} = 2.50 \times 10^{-2} \text{ mol BaCl}_2$

$0.300 \text{ L} \times \dfrac{0.500 \text{ mol Ba(OH)}_2}{\text{L}} \times \dfrac{1 \text{ mol BaCl}_2}{1 \text{ mol Ba(OH)}_2} = 1.50 \times 10^{-1} \text{ mol BaCl}_2$

Thus, HCl is limiting.

$2.50 \times 10^{-2} \text{ mol BaCl}_2 \times \dfrac{-118 \text{ kJ}}{\text{mol BaCl}_2} = -2.95 \text{ kJ of heat is evolved.}$

60. $400 \text{ kcal} \times \dfrac{4.18 \text{ kJ}}{\text{kcal}} = 1.67 \times 10^3 \text{ kJ} \approx 2 \times 10^3 \text{ kJ}$

$PE = mgz = \left(180 \text{ lb} \times \dfrac{1 \text{ kg}}{2.205 \text{ lb}} \right) \left(\dfrac{9.8 \text{ m}}{\text{s}^2} \right) \left(8 \text{ in} \times \dfrac{2.54 \text{ cm}}{\text{in}} \times \dfrac{1 \text{ m}}{100 \text{ cm}} \right) = 160 \text{ J} \approx 200 \text{ J}$

200 J of energy are needed to climb one step.

$$2 \times 10^6 \text{ J} \times \frac{1 \text{ step}}{200 \text{ J}} = 1 \times 10^4 \text{ steps}$$

63.   a.   Using Hess's Law and the equation $\Delta H = nC_p\Delta T$:

$CH_3Cl(248°C) + H_2(248°C) \rightarrow CH_4(248°C) + HCl(248°C)$ $\Delta H_1 = -83.3$ kJ

$CH_3Cl(25°C) \rightarrow CH_3Cl(248°C)$ $\Delta H_2 = 1$ mol (48.5 J °C^{-1} mol^{-1}) (223 °C)

                                              $\Delta H_2 = 10{,}800$ J $= 10.8$ kJ

$H_2(25°C) \rightarrow H_2(248°C)$ $\Delta H_3 = 1(28.9) (223) (1 \text{ kJ}/1000 \text{ J}) = 6.44$ kJ

$CH_4(248°C) \rightarrow CH_4(25°C)$ $\Delta H_4 = 1(41.3) (-223) (1/1000) = -9.21$ kJ

$HCl(248°C) \rightarrow HCl(25°C)$ $\Delta H_5 = 1(29.1) (-223) (1/1000) = -6.49$ kJ

$CH_3Cl(25°C) + H_2(25°C) \rightarrow CH_4(25°C) + HCl(25°C)$ $\Delta H° = \Delta H_1 + \Delta H_2 + \Delta H_3 + \Delta H_4 + \Delta H_5$

$\Delta H° = -83.3$ kJ $+ 10.8$ kJ $+ 6.44$ kJ $- 9.21$ kJ $- 6.49$ kJ $= -81.8$ kJ

    b. $\Delta H° = [\Delta H_f°(CH_4) + \Delta H_f°(HCl)] - [\Delta H_f°(CH_3Cl) + \Delta H_f°(H_2)]$

-81.8 kJ $= -75$ kJ $- 92$ kJ $- [\Delta H_f°(CH_3Cl) + 0]$, $\Delta H_f°(CH_3Cl) = -85$ kJ/mol

65. $w = -P\Delta V = -RT\Delta n_{gas}$, Δn_{gas} = gaseous product moles - gaseous reactant moles

$\Delta n < 0$, $w > 0$ and surroundings does work on system (a, c, and d).

$\Delta n > 0$, $w < 0$ and system does work on surroundings (e and f).

$\Delta n = 0$, $w = 0$ and no work is done (b).

66. $C_3H_8(g) + 5 O_2(g) \rightarrow 3 CO_2(g) + 4 H_2O(l)$

$\Delta H° = 4(-286$ kJ$) + 3(-393.5$ kJ$) - (-104$ kJ$) = -2221$ kJ

We need 1.3×10^8 J $= 1.3 \times 10^5$ kJ of energy. The mass of C_3H_8 required is:

$$1.3 \times 10^5 \text{ kJ} \times \frac{1 \text{ mol } C_3H_8}{2221 \text{ kJ}} \times \frac{44.1 \text{ g } C_3H_8}{\text{mol}} = 2600 \text{ g of } C_3H_8$$

CHAPTER TEN

SPONTANEITY, ENTROPY AND FREE ENERGY

Spontaneity and Entropy

3.   We draw all of the possible arrangements of the two particles in the three levels.

2 kJ	__	__	x	__	x	xx
1 kJ	__	x	__	xx	x	__
0 kJ	xx	x	x	__	__	__
Total E =	0 kJ	1 kJ	2 kJ	2 kJ	3 kJ	4 kJ

The most likely total energy is 2 kJ.

7.   There are more ways to roll a seven. We can consider all of the possible throws by constructing a table.

one die	1	2	3	4	5	6
1	2	3	4	5	6	7
2	3	4	5	6	7	8
3	4	5	6	7	8	9
4	5	6	7	8	9	10
5	6	7	8	9	10	11
6	7	8	9	10	11	12

sum of the two dice

There are six ways to get a seven, more than any other number. The seven is not favored by energy; rather it is favored by probability. To change the probability we would have to expend energy (do work).

9. $S = k \ln \Omega$; S has units of $J K^{-1} mol^{-1}$ and k has units of J/K

To make units match: $S (J K^{-1} mol^{-1}) = N_A k \ln \Omega$ when N_A = Avogadro's number

$$189 J K^{-1} mol^{-1} = 8.31 J K^{-1} mol^{-1} \ln \Omega_g$$
$$70. J K^{-1} mol^{-1} = 8.31 J K^{-1} mol^{-1} \ln \Omega_l$$

Subtracting: $119 J K^{-1} mol^{-1} = 8.31 J K^{-1} mol^{-1} (\ln \Omega_g - \ln \Omega_l)$

$14.3 = \ln(\Omega_g/\Omega_l)$, $\dfrac{\Omega_g}{\Omega_l} = e^{14.3} = 1.6 \times 10^6$

11.   a. N_2O; It is the more complex molecule, i.e., more parts, more disorder.

b. H_2 at 100°C and 0.5 atm; Higher temperature and lower pressure means greater volume and hence, greater positional entropy.

c. N_2 at STP has the greater volume.   d. $H_2O(l)$ is more disordered.

Entropy and the Second Law of Thermodynamics: Free Energy

15.   a. $C_{12}H_{22}O_{11}$; Larger molecule, more parts, more disorder

b. H_2O (0°C); Higher temp.; $S° = 0$ at 0 K

c. $H_2S(g)$; A gas has greater disorder than a liquid.   d.   He (10 K); $S = 0$ at 0 K

e. N_2O; More complicated molecule

f.   HCl; More electrons in HCl

16.   a.   Decrease in disorder; ΔS (-)   b.   Increase in disorder; ΔS (+)

c.   Decrease in disorder ($\Delta n < 0$); ΔS (-)   d.   Decrease in disorder ($\Delta n < 0$); ΔS (-)

e.   HCl(g) is more disordered. One mole of a gas will still be more disordered than two moles of ions in solution; ΔS (-)

f.   Increase in disorder; ΔS (+)

18. $CS_2(g) + 3 O_2(g) \rightarrow CO_2(g) + 2 SO_2(g)$; $\Delta S° = S°(CO_2) + 2 S°(SO_2) - [3 S°(O_2) + S°(CS_2)]$

-143 J/K = 214 J/K + 2(248 J/K) - 3(205 J/K) - (1 mol)S°, S° = 238 $J K^{-1} mol^{-1}$

20.   At the boiling point $\Delta G = 0$, so $\Delta H = T\Delta S$.

$\Delta S = \dfrac{\Delta H}{T} = \dfrac{31.4 \text{ kJ/mol}}{(273.2 + 61.7)K} = 9.38 \times 10^{-2} \text{ kJ mol}^{-1} K^{-1} = 93.8 J K^{-1} mol^{-1}$

22. $\Delta G = 0$ so $\Delta H = T\Delta S$, $\Delta S = \dfrac{\Delta H}{T} = \dfrac{35.2 \times 10^3 \text{ J/mol}}{3680 \text{ K}} = 9.57 \text{ J K}^{-1} \text{ mol}^{-1}$

Free Energy and Chemical Reactions

25.   a. $CH_4(g)$ + $2\,O_2(g)$ → $CO_2(g\,)$ + $2\,H_2O(g)$

$\Delta H_f^{\bullet}$	-75 kJ/mol	0	-393.5	-242
$\Delta G_f^{\bullet}$	-51 kJ/mol	0	-394	-229
S°	186 J K^{-1} mol^{-1}	205	214	189

Data from Appendix 4

$\Delta H^{\circ} = 2$ mol(-242 kJ/mol) + 1 mol (-393.5 kJ/mol) - [1 mol(-75 kJ/mol)] = -803 kJ

$\Delta S^{\circ} = 2$ mol(189 J K^{-1} mol^{-1}) + 1 mol(214 J K^{-1} mol^{-1})

$- [1 \text{ mol}(186 \text{ J K}^{-1} \text{ mol}^{-1}) + 2 \text{ mol}(205 \text{ J K}^{-1} \text{ mol}^{-1})] = -4 \text{ J/K}$

There are two ways to get ΔG°:

$\Delta G^{\circ} = \Delta H^{\circ} - T\Delta S^{\circ} = -803 \times 10^3$ J - 298 K(-4 J/K) = -8.018 × 10^5 J = -802 kJ

or from $\Delta G_f^{\bullet}$, we get:

$\Delta G^{\circ} = 2$ mol(- 229 kJ/mol) + 1 mol(-394 kJ/mol) - [1 mol(- 51 kJ/mol)]

$\Delta G^{\circ} = -801$ kJ   (Answers are the same within round off error)

   b. $6\,CO_2(g)$ + $6\,H_2O(l)$ → $C_6H_{12}O_6(s)$ + $6\,O_2(g)$

$\Delta H_f^{\bullet}$	-393.5 kJ/mol	-286	-1275	0
S°	214 J K^{-1} mol^{-1}	70	212	205

$\Delta H^{\circ} = -1275 - [6(-286) + 6(-393.5)] = +2802$ kJ

$\Delta S^{\circ} = 6(205) + 212 - [6(214) + 6(70)] = -262$ J/K

$\Delta G^{\circ} = 2802$ kJ - 298 K(-0.262 kJ/K) = 2880. kJ

c. $P_4O_{10}(s) + 6 H_2O(l) \rightarrow 4 H_3PO_4(s)$

ΔH_f° (kJ/mol)	-2984	-286	-1279
S° (J K^{-1} mol^{-1})	229	70	110

ΔH° = 4 mol (-1279 kJ/mol) - [1 mol(-2984 kJ/mol) + 6 mol(-286 kJ/mol)] = -416 kJ

ΔS° = 4(110) - [229 + 6(70)] = -209 J/K

$\Delta G^\circ = \Delta H^\circ - T\Delta S^\circ$ = -416 kJ - 298 K (-0.209 kJ/K) = -354 kJ

d. $HCl(g) + NH_3(g) \rightarrow NH_4Cl(s)$

ΔH_f° (kJ/mol)	-92	-46	-314
S° (J K^{-1} mol^{-1})	187	193	96

ΔH° = -314 - [-92 - 46] = -176 kJ; ΔS° = 96 - [187 + 193] = -284 J/K

$\Delta G^\circ = \Delta H^\circ - T\Delta S^\circ$ = -176 kJ - (298 K) (-0.284 kJ/K) = -91 kJ

27. $2 Al(OH)_3(s) \rightarrow Al_2O_3(s) + 3 H_2O(g)$

7 kJ = 3(-229 kJ) - 1582 kJ - (2 mol)ΔG_f°, ΔG_f° = -1138 kJ/mol

29. $C_2H_4(g) + H_2O(g) \rightarrow CH_3CH_2OH(l)$

ΔH° = -278 - (52 - 242) = -88 kJ; ΔS° = 161 - (219 + 189) = -247 J/K

When $\Delta G^\circ = 0$, $\Delta H^\circ = T\Delta S^\circ$, $T = \dfrac{\Delta H^\circ}{\Delta S^\circ} = \dfrac{-88 \times 10^3 \text{ J}}{-247 \text{ J/K}} = 360$ K

Since the signs of ΔH° and ΔS° are both negative, this reaction will be spontaneous at temperatures below 360 K (where the ΔH° term will dominate).

$C_2H_6(g) + H_2O(g) \rightarrow CH_3CH_2OH(l) + H_2(g)$

ΔH° = -278 - (-84.7 - 242) = +49 kJ; ΔS° = 131 + 161 - (229.5 + 189) = -127 J/K

This reaction will never be spontaneous because of the signs of ΔH° and ΔS°.

Thus the reaction $C_2H_4(g) + H_2O(g) \rightarrow C_2H_5OH(l)$ would be preferred.

31.   a.   A bond is broken: ΔH (+); Increase in disorder ($\Delta n > 0$): ΔS (+)

       b. $\Delta G = \Delta H - T\Delta S$; For the reaction to be spontaneous, the entropy term must dominate. The reaction will be spontaneous at higher temperatures.

33. $\Delta G° = -RT \ln K = -\dfrac{8.3145\ J}{K\ mol}$ (298 K) ln $(1.00 \times 10^{-14}) = 7.99 \times 10^4$ J $= 79.9$ kJ

35. $NO(g) + O_3(g) \rightleftharpoons NO_2(g) + O_2(g)$; $\Delta G° = \Sigma \Delta G_f°$ (Products) - $\Sigma \Delta G_f°$ (Reactants)

       $\Delta G° = 1$ mol(52 kJ/mol) - [1 mol(87 kJ/mol) + 1 mol(163 kJ/mol)] $= -198$ kJ

       $\Delta G° = -RT \ln K$, $K = \exp \dfrac{-\Delta G°}{RT} = \exp\left(\dfrac{+1.98 \times 10^5\ J}{8.3145\ J\ K^{-1}\ mol^{-1}\ (298\ K)} \right) = e^{79.912} = 5.07 \times 10^{34}$

37.   a. $\Delta G° = -RT \ln K$, $K = \exp(-\Delta G°/RT) = \exp\left(\dfrac{30,500\ J}{8.3145\ J\ K^{-1}\ mol^{-1} \times 298\ K} \right) = 2.22 \times 10^5$

       b. $C_6H_{12}O_6(s) + 6\ O_2(g) \rightarrow 6\ CO_2(g) + 6\ H_2O(l)$

            $\Delta G° = 6$ mol (-394 kJ/mol) + 6 mol (-237 kJ/mol) - 1 mol (-911 kJ/mol) $= -2875$ kJ

            $\dfrac{2875\ kJ}{mol\ glucose} \times \dfrac{1\ mol\ ATP}{30.5\ kJ} = 94.3$ mol ATP; 94.3 molecules ATP/molecule glucose

            This is an overstatement. The assumption that all of the free energy goes into this reaction is false. Actually only 38 moles of ATP are produced by metabolism of one mole of glucose.

39.   a. $\Delta G° = -RT \ln K$

            $\ln K = \dfrac{-\Delta G°}{RT} = \dfrac{-14,000\ J}{(8.3145\ J\ K^{-1}\ mol^{-1})\ (298\ K)} = -5.65$, $K = e^{-5.65} = 3.5 \times 10^{-3}$

       b.   Glutamic acid + $NH_3 \rightarrow$ Glutamine + H_2O $\Delta G° = 14$ kJ
                  $ATP + H_2O \rightarrow ADP + H_2PO_4^-$ $\Delta G° = -30.5$ kJ
            _____

            Glutamic acid + ATP + $NH_3 \rightarrow$ Glutamine + ADP + $H_2PO_4^-$ $\Delta G° = 14 - 30.5 = -17$ kJ

            $\ln K = \dfrac{-\Delta G°}{RT} = \dfrac{-(-17,000\ J)}{8.3145\ J\ K^{-1}\ mol^{-1}\ (298\ K)} = 6.86$, $K = e^{6.86} = 9.5 \times 10^2$

Free Energy and Pressure

41.   From Exercise 10.35 we get $\Delta G° = -198$ kJ. $\Delta G = \Delta G° + RT \ln \dfrac{P_{NO_2} P_{O_2}}{P_{NO} P_{O_3}}$

       $\Delta G = -198$ kJ $+ \dfrac{8.3145\ J\ K^{-1}\ mol^{-1}}{1000\ J/kJ}$ (298 K) ln $\dfrac{(1.00 \times 10^{-7})\ (1.00 \times 10^{-3})}{(1.00 \times 10^{-6})\ (2.00 \times 10^{-6})}$

       $\Delta G = -198$ kJ $+ 9.69$ kJ $= -188$ kJ

43. $N_2(g) + 3 H_2(g) \rightleftharpoons 2 NH_3(g)$

$\Delta H° = 2 \ \Delta H_f°(NH_3) = 2(-46) = -92 \text{ kJ}; \quad \Delta G° = 2 \ \Delta G_f°(NH_3) = 2(-17) = -34 \text{ kJ}$

$\Delta S° = 2(193 \text{ J/K}) - [192 \text{ J/K} + 3(131 \text{ J/K})] = -199 \text{ J/K}$

$K = \exp \dfrac{-\Delta G°}{RT} = \exp\left(\dfrac{34,000 \text{ J}}{(8.3145 \text{ J K}^{-1} \text{ mol}^{-1})(298 \text{ K})} \right) = e^{13.72} = 9.1 \times 10^5$

a. $\Delta G = \Delta G° + RT \ln \dfrac{P_{NH_3}^2}{P_{N_2} P_{H_2}^3} = -34 \text{ kJ} + \dfrac{(8.3145 \text{ J K}^{-1} \text{ mol}^{-1})(298 \text{ K})}{1000 \text{ J/kJ}} \ln \dfrac{(50.)^2}{(200.)(200.)^3}$

$\Delta G = -34 \text{ kJ} - 33 \text{ kJ} = -67 \text{ kJ}$

b. $\Delta G = -34 \text{ kJ} + \dfrac{(8.3145 \text{ J K}^{-1} \text{ mol}^{-1})(298 \text{ K})}{1000 \text{ J/kJ}} \ln \dfrac{(200.)^2}{(200.)(600.)^3}$

$\Delta G = -34 \text{ kJ} - 34.4 \text{ kJ} = -68 \text{ kJ}$

c.   Assume $\Delta H°$ and $\Delta S°$ are temperature independent.

$\Delta G_{100}° = \Delta H° - T\Delta S°, \quad \Delta G_{100}° = -92 \text{ kJ} - (100. \text{ K})(-0.199 \text{ kJ/K}) = -72 \text{ kJ}$

$\Delta G_{100} = \Delta G_{100}° + RT \ln Q = -72 \text{ kJ} + \dfrac{(8.3145 \text{ J K}^{-1} \text{ mol}^{-1})(100. \text{ K})}{1000 \text{ J/kJ}} \ln \dfrac{(10.)^2}{(50.)(200.)^3}$

$\Delta G_{100} = -72 \text{ kJ} - 13 \text{ kJ} = -85 \text{ kJ}$

d. $\Delta G_{700}° = -92 \text{ kJ} - (700. \text{ K})(-0.199 \text{ kJ/K}) = 47 \text{ kJ}$

$\Delta G_{700} = 47 \text{ kJ} + \dfrac{(8.3145 \text{ J K}^{-1} \text{ mol}^{-1})(700. \text{ K})}{1000 \text{ J/kJ}} \ln \dfrac{(10.)^2}{(50.)(200.)^3} = 47 \text{ kJ} - 88 \text{ kJ} = -41 \text{ kJ}$

Additional Exercises

46.   It appears that the sum of the two processes has no net change. This is not so, ΔS_{univ} has increased even though it looks as if we have gone through a cyclic process.

50.   S (rhombic) $\rightarrow$ S (monoclinic); $\Delta H° = 0.30 \text{ kJ}$; $\Delta S° = 32.55 - 31.88 = 0.67 \text{ J/K}$

For $\Delta G° = 0 = \Delta H° - T\Delta S°, \quad \Delta H° = T\Delta S°, \quad T = \dfrac{\Delta H°}{\Delta S°} = \dfrac{3.0 \times 10^2 \text{ J}}{0.67 \text{ J/K}} = 450 \text{ K}$

53. K^+ (blood) $\rightleftharpoons$ K^+ (muscle) $\Delta G° = 0$; $\Delta G = RT \ln \left(\dfrac{[K^+]_m}{[K^+]_b} \right)$; $\Delta G = w_{max}$

$\Delta G = \dfrac{8.3145 \text{ J}}{\text{K mol}} (310. \text{ K}) \ln \left(\dfrac{0.15}{0.0050} \right)$, $\Delta G = 8.8 \times 10^3$ J/mol $= 8.8$ kJ/mol

At least 8.8 kJ of work must be applied. $\dfrac{8.8 \text{ kJ}}{\text{mol K}^+} \times \dfrac{1 \text{ mol ATP}}{30.5 \text{ kJ}} = 0.29$ mol ATP

Other ions will have to be transported in order to maintain electroneutrality. Either anions must be transported into the cells, or cations (Na^+) in the cell must be transported to the blood. The latter is what happens: [Na^+] in blood is greater than [Na^+] in cells as a result of this pumping.

57. $q_v = \Delta E = C_v \Delta T = (12.47$ J K^{-1} mol^{-1}) (56.5 K) $= 705$ J/mol

15.0 g He $\times \dfrac{1 \text{ mol}}{4.003 \text{ g}} \times \dfrac{705 \text{ J}}{\text{mol}} = 2640$ J $= 2.64$ kJ

59.   Heat gained by water $= 4.18$ J g^{-1} °C^{-1} $\times$ 250.0 g $\times$ 2.5°C $= 2600$ J

Heat lost by Al = Heat gained by H_2O

2600 J $= S_{Al}$ (50.0 g) (85.0 - 27.5)°C, $S_{Al} = 0.90$ J g^{-1} °C^{-1}

61.   a. $q_v = \Delta E = C_v \Delta T = (28.95$ J mol^{-1} K^{-1}) (350.0 - 298.0 K) $= 1.51 \times 10^3$ J/mol $= 1.51$ kJ/mol

$q_p = \Delta H = C_p \Delta T = 37.27$ (350.0 - 298.0) $= 1.94 \times 10^3$ J/mol $= 1.94$ kJ/mol

b. $\Delta S = S_{350} - S_{298} = nC_p \ln (T_2/T_1)$

$S_{350} - 213.64$ J/K $= (1.000$ mol) (37.27 J mol^{-1} K^{-1}) $\ln$ (350.0/298.0)

$S_{350} = 213.64$ J/K $+ 5.994$ J/K $= 219.63$ J/K = molar entropy at 350.0 K and 1.000 atm

c. $\Delta S = nR \ln (V_2/V_1)$, $V = nRT/P$, $\Delta S = nR \ln (P_1/P_2) = S_{(350, 1.174)} - S_{(350, 1.000)}$

$\Delta S = S_{(350, 1.174)} - 219.63$ J/K $= (1.000$ mol) (8.3145 J mol^{-1} K^{-1}) $\ln$ (1.000/1.174)

$\Delta S = -1.334$ J/K $= S - 219.63$, $S = 218.30$ J K^{-1} mol^{-1} $= S_{(350, 1.174)}$

62.   It takes $nC_p \Delta T$ amount of energy to carry out this process. The internal energy of the system increases by $nC_v \Delta T$. So the fraction that goes into raising the internal energy is:

$\dfrac{nC_v \Delta T}{nC_p \Delta T} = \dfrac{C_v}{C_p} = \dfrac{20.8}{29.1} = 0.715$

The remainder of the energy ($nR\Delta T$) goes into expanding the gas against the constant pressure.

$$100.0 \text{ g N}_2 \times \frac{1 \text{ mol}}{28.014 \text{ g}} = 3.570 \text{ mol}$$

$$q_v = \Delta E = nC_v\Delta T = 3.570 \text{ mol } (20.8 \text{ J mol}^{-1} \text{ K}^{-1}) (60.0 \text{ K}) = 4.46 \times 10^3 \text{ J} = 4.46 \text{ kJ}$$

65.   a.   He(g, 0.100 mol, 25°C, 1.00 atm) → He(g, 0.100 mol, 25°C, 5.00 L)

$$\Delta S = nR \ln (V_2/V_1) = S_{final} - S_{initial}; \quad S_i = 0.100 \text{ mol } (126.1 \text{ J mol}^{-1} \text{ K}^{-1}) = 12.6 \text{ J/K}$$

$$V_1 = \frac{nRT}{P_1} = \frac{0.100 \text{ mol} \times \dfrac{0.08206 \text{ L atm}}{\text{mol K}} \times 298 \text{ K}}{1.00 \text{ atm}} = 2.45 \text{ L}$$

$$S_f - 12.6 \text{ J/K} = (0.100 \text{ mol}) (8.3145 \text{ J mol}^{-1} \text{ K}^{-1}) \ln (5.00 \text{ L}/2.45 \text{ L})$$

$$S_f = 12.6 \text{ J/K} + 0.593 \text{ J/K} = 13.2 \text{ J/K}$$

b.   He (3.00 mol, 25°C, 1.00 atm) → He (3.00 mol, 25°C, 3000.0 L)

$$\Delta S = nR \ln (V_2/V_1) = S_{final} - S_{initial}; \quad S_i = 3.00 \text{ mol } (126.1 \text{ J mol}^{-1} \text{ K}^{-1}) = 378 \text{ J/K}$$

$$V_1 = \frac{nRT}{P_1} = \frac{3.00 \text{ mol} \times \dfrac{0.08206 \text{ L atm}}{\text{mol K}} \times 298 \text{ K}}{1.00 \text{ atm}} = 73.4 \text{ L}$$

$$S_f - 378 \text{ J/K} = (3.00 \text{ mol}) (8.3145 \text{ J mol}^{-1} \text{ K}^{-1}) \ln \left(\frac{3000.0}{73.4} \right) = 92.6 \text{ J/K}$$

$$S_f = 378 + 92.6 = 471 \text{ J/K}$$

67. $\Delta S = \dfrac{q_{rev}}{T} = \dfrac{\Delta H_{vap}}{T}$;   For methane: $\Delta S = \dfrac{8.20 \times 10^3 \text{ J/mol}}{112 \text{ K}} = 73.2 \text{ J mol}^{-1} \text{ K}^{-1}$

For hexane: $\Delta S = \dfrac{28.9 \times 10^3 \text{ J/mol}}{342 \text{ K}} = 84.5 \text{ J mol}^{-1} \text{ K}^{-1}$

$$V_{met} = \frac{nRT}{P} = \frac{1.00 \text{ mol } (0.08206) (112 \text{ K})}{1.00 \text{ atm}} = 9.19 \text{ L}; \quad V_{hex} = \frac{nRT}{P} = R(342 \text{ K}) = 28.1 \text{ L}$$

$$\Delta S_{hex} - \Delta S_{met} = 84.5 - 73.2 = 11.3 \text{ J mol}^{-1} \text{ K}^{-1}; \quad R \ln (V_{hex}/V_{met}) = 9.29 \text{ J mol}^{-1} \text{ K}^{-1}$$

As the molar volume of a gas increases, ΔS_{vap} also increases. In the case of hexane and methane, the difference in molar volume accounts for 82% of the difference in the entropies.

69. $(3.00 \text{ mol})(75.3 \text{ J mol}^{-1} \text{ °C}^{-1})(T_f - 0°C) = (1.00 \text{ mol})(75.3 \text{ J mol}^{-1} \text{ °C}^{-1})(100.°C - T_f)$

Solving: $T_f = 25°C = 298 \text{ K};$ $\Delta S = nC_p \ln (T_2/T_1)$

Heat 3 mol H_2O: $\Delta S_1 = (3.00 \text{ mol})(75.3 \text{ J mol}^{-1} \text{ K}^{-1}) \ln (298/273) = 19.8 \text{ J/K}$

Cool 1 mol H_2O: $\Delta S_2 = (1.00 \text{ mol})(75.3 \text{ J mol}^{-1} \text{ K}^{-1}) \ln (298/373) = -16.9 \text{ J/K}$

$\Delta S_{tot} = 19.8 - 16.9 = 2.9 \text{ J/K}$

71. $q = (1.000 \text{ mol})(37.5 \text{ J mol}^{-1} \text{ K}^{-1})(30.0 \text{ K}) + 6010 \text{ J} + (1.000 \text{ mol})(75.3 \text{ J mol}^{-1} \text{ K}^{-1})(100.0 \text{ K})$

$$+ 40,700 \text{ J} + (1.000 \text{ mol})(36.4 \text{ J mol}^{-1} \text{ K}^{-1})(40.0 \text{ K})$$

$q = 1130 \text{ J} + 6010 \text{ J} + 7530 \text{ J} + 40,700 \text{ J} + 1460 \text{ J} = 56,800 \text{ J} = 56.8 \text{ kJ}$

At constant pressure: $q_p = \Delta H = 56.8 \text{ kJ}$

at 100.0°C: $V = \dfrac{nRT}{P} = \dfrac{1.000 \text{ mol} \times \dfrac{0.08206 \text{ L atm}}{\text{mol K}} \times 373.2 \text{ K}}{1.00 \text{ atm}} = 30.6 \text{ L}$

at 140.0°C: $V = \dfrac{nR(413.2 \text{ K})}{P} = 33.9 \text{ L}$

Work is only done when vaporization occurs and when the vapor expands as T is increased from 100.0°C to 140.0°C.

$w = -P\Delta V = -1.00 \text{ atm} (30.6 \text{ L} - 0.018 \text{ L}) - 1.00 \text{ atm} (33.9 - 30.6 \text{ L})$

$w = -30.6 \text{ L atm} - 3.3 \text{ L atm} = -33.9 \text{ L atm};$ $-33.9 \text{ L atm} \times \dfrac{101.3 \text{ J}}{\text{L atm}} = -3430 \text{ J} = -3.43 \text{ kJ}$

$\Delta E = q + w = 56.8 \text{ kJ} - 3.43 \text{ kJ} = 53.4 \text{ kJ};$ $\Delta S = nC_p \ln (T_2/T_1)$ or $\Delta S = \Delta H/T$ (phase change)

$\Delta S = (1.000 \text{ mol})(37.5 \text{ J mol}^{-1} \text{ K}^{-1}) \ln \left(\dfrac{273.2}{243.2} \right) + \dfrac{6010 \text{ J}}{273.2 \text{ K}}$

$$+ (1.000 \text{ mol}) (75.3 \text{ J mol}^{-1} \text{ K}^{-1}) \ln \left(\dfrac{373.2}{273.2} \right) + \dfrac{40,700 \text{ J}}{372.2 \text{ K}}$$

$$+ (1.000 \text{ mol}) (36.4 \text{ J mol}^{-1} \text{ K}^{-1}) \ln \left(\dfrac{413.2}{373.2} \right)$$

$\Delta S = 4.36 \text{ J/K} + 22.0 \text{ J/K} + 23.5 \text{ J/K} + 109 \text{ J/K} + 3.71 \text{ J/K} = 163 \text{ J/K}$

Summary: $q = 56.8 \text{ kJ};$ $\Delta H = 56.8 \text{ kJ};$ $w = -3.43 \text{ kJ};$ $\Delta E = 53.4 \text{ kJ};$ $\Delta S = 163 \text{ J/K}$

73. $P_i = \dfrac{1.00 \text{ mol} \times \dfrac{0.08206 \text{ L atm}}{\text{mol K}} \times 300. \text{ K}}{30.0 \text{ L}} = 0.821 \text{ atm}; \quad P_f = \dfrac{nRT}{40.0 \text{ L}} = 0.615 \text{ atm}$

a. free expansion

$w = 0$ since $P_{ext} = 0$; $\Delta E = nC_v\Delta T$, since $\Delta T = 0$, $\Delta E = 0$

$\Delta E = q + w$, $q = 0$; $\Delta H = nC_p\Delta T$, since $\Delta T = 0$, $\Delta H = 0$

$\Delta S = nR \ln\left(\dfrac{V_2}{V_1}\right) = (1.00 \text{ mol})(8.3145 \text{ J mol}^{-1} \text{ K}^{-1}) \ln\left(\dfrac{40.0}{30.0}\right) = 2.39 \text{ J/K}$

$\Delta G = \Delta H - T\Delta S = 0 - 300. \text{ K} (2.39 \text{ J/K}) = -717 \text{ J}$

b. reversible expansion

$\Delta E = 0$; $\Delta H = 0$; $\Delta S = 2.39 \text{ J/K}$; $\Delta G = -717 \text{ J}$; These are state functions.

$w_{rev} = -nRT \ln\left(\dfrac{V_2}{V_1}\right) = -(1.00 \text{ mol})(8.3145 \text{ J mol}^{-1} \text{ K}^{-1})(300. \text{ K}) \ln\left(\dfrac{40.0}{30.0}\right) = -718 \text{ J}$

$\Delta E = 0 = q + w$, $q_{rev} = -w_{rev} = 718 \text{ J}$

Summary:	a) free expansion	b) reversible
q	0	718 J
w	0	-718 J
ΔE	0	0
ΔH	0	0
ΔS	2.39 J/K	2.39 J/K
ΔG	-717 J	-717 J

77. $2 SO_2(g) \quad + \quad O_2(g) \quad \rightarrow \quad 2 SO_3(g)$

ΔH_f°	-297 kJ/mol	0	-396
S°	248 J mol^{-1} K^{-1}	205	257

$\Delta H_{298}^{\circ} = 2(-396) - 2(-297) = -198 \text{ kJ}$; $\Delta S_{298}^{\circ} = 2(257) - [205 + 2(248)] = -187 \text{ J/K}$

Set up a thermochemical cycle to convert to $T = 227°C = 500. \text{ K}$.

$$2 \text{ SO}_2 \text{ (g, 227°C)} \rightarrow 2 \text{ SO}_2 \text{ (g, 25°C)} \qquad\qquad \Delta H = nC_p \Delta T$$

$$O_2 \text{ (g, 227°C)} \rightarrow O_2 \text{ (g, 25°C)} \qquad\qquad \Delta H = nC_p \Delta T$$

$$2 \text{ SO}_2 \text{ (g, 25°C)} + O_2 \text{ (g, 25°C)} \rightarrow 2 \text{ SO}_3 \text{ (g, 25°C)} \qquad \Delta H° = -198 \text{ kJ}$$

$$2 \text{ SO}_3 \text{ (g, 25°C)} \rightarrow 2 \text{ SO}_3 \text{ (g, 227°C)} \qquad\qquad \Delta H = nC_p \Delta T$$

$$2 \text{ SO}_2 \text{ (g, 227°C)} + O_2 \text{ (g, 227°C)} \rightarrow 2 \text{ SO}_3 \text{ (g, 227°C)} \qquad \Delta H_{500}° = ?$$

$$\Delta H_{500}° = 2 \text{ mol} \times \frac{39.9 \text{ J mol}^{-1}\text{ K}^{-1}}{1000 \text{ J/kJ}} \times (-202 \text{ K}) + 1 \times \frac{29.4}{1000} \times (-202) - 198 \text{ kJ} + 2 \times \frac{50.7}{1000} \times 202$$

$$\Delta H_{500}° = -16.1 \text{ kJ} - 5.94 \text{ kJ} - 198 \text{ kJ} + 20.5 \text{ kJ} = -199.5 \text{ kJ} = -200. \text{ kJ}$$

For the same cycle using $\Delta S = nC_p \ln (T_2/T_1)$:

$$\Delta S_{500}° = 2(39.9) \ln (298 \text{ K}/500. \text{ K}) + 1(29.4) \ln (298/500.) - 187 + 2(50.7) \ln (500./298)$$

$$\Delta S_{500}° = -41.3 \text{ J/K} - 15.2 \text{ J/K} - 187 \text{ J/K} + 52.5 \text{ J/K} = -191 \text{ J/K}$$

79. $\Delta G° = 2(-371) - [2(-300)] = -142 \text{ kJ}; \quad \Delta G = \Delta G° + RT \ln Q = -142 \text{ kJ} + RT \ln \left(\dfrac{P_{SO_3}^2}{P_{SO_2}^2 P_{O_2}} \right)$

$$\Delta G = -142 \text{ kJ} + \frac{(8.3145 \text{ J mol}^{-1}\text{ K}^{-1})}{1000 \text{ J/kJ}} (298 \text{ K}) \ln \left(\frac{(10.0)^2}{(10.0)^2(10.0)} \right) = -148 \text{ kJ}$$

81.   Isothermal: $\Delta H = 0$ (assume ideal gas)

$$\Delta S = nR \ln \left(\frac{V_2}{V_1} \right) = (1.00 \text{ mol})(8.3145 \text{ J mol}^{-1}\text{ K}^{-1}) \ln \left(\frac{1.00 \text{ L}}{100.0 \text{ L}} \right) = -38.3 \text{ J/K}$$

$$\Delta G = \Delta H - T\Delta S = 0 - (300. \text{ K})(-38.3 \text{ J/K}) = +11,500 \text{ J} = 11.5 \text{ kJ}$$

83. $\ln K = \dfrac{-\Delta H°}{RT} + \dfrac{\Delta S°}{R}, \quad R = 8.3145 \text{ J mol}^{-1}\text{ K}^{-1}$

For K at two temperatures T_2 and T_1: $\ln \dfrac{K_2}{K_1} = \dfrac{\Delta H°}{R} \left(\dfrac{1}{T_1} - \dfrac{1}{T_2} \right)$

$$\ln (10.0) = \frac{\Delta H°}{8.3145} \left(\frac{1}{300.0 \text{ K}} - \frac{1}{350.0 \text{ K}} \right), \quad 2.30 = \frac{\Delta H°}{8.3145} (4.76 \times 10^{-4})$$

$$\Delta H° = 4.02 \times 10^4 \text{ J/mol} = 40.2 \text{ kJ/mol}$$

85.   We can set up 3 equations in 3 unknowns:

$$28.7262 = a + 300.0\,b + c(300.0)^2$$

$$29.2937 = a + 400.0\,b + c(400.0)^2$$

$$29.8545 = a + 500.0\,b + c(500.0)^2$$

These can be solved by several methods. One way involves setting up a matrix and solving with a calculator such as:

$$\begin{pmatrix} 1 & 300.0 & 90{,}000 \\ 1 & 400.0 & 160{,}000 \\ 1 & 500.0 & 250{,}000 \end{pmatrix} \begin{pmatrix} a \\ b \\ c \end{pmatrix} = \begin{pmatrix} 28.7262 \\ 29.2937 \\ 29.8545 \end{pmatrix}$$

The solution is: $a = 26.98$; $b = 5.91 \times 10^{-3}$; $c = -3.4 \times 10^{-7}$

At 900. K: $C_p = 26.98 + 5.91 \times 10^{-3}(900.) - 3.4 \times 10^{-7}(900.)^2 = 32.02$ J K^{-1} mol^{-1}

$$\Delta S = n \int_{T_1}^{T_2} \frac{C_p dT}{T} = n \int_{T_1}^{T_2} \frac{(a + bT + cT^2)}{T}\,dT, \quad n = 1.00 \text{ mol}$$

$$\Delta S = a \int_{T_1}^{T_2} \frac{dT}{T} + b \int_{T_1}^{T_2} dT + c \int_{T_1}^{T_2} T\,dT = a \ln\left(\frac{T_2}{T_1}\right) + b\,(T_2 - T_1) + \frac{c(T_2^2 - T_1^2)}{2}$$

Solving using $T_2 = 900.$ K and $T_1 = 100.$ K: $\Delta S = 59.3 + 4.73 - 0.14 = 63.9$ J/K

87.   a.   Isothermal: $\Delta E = 0$ and $\Delta H = 0$ if gas is ideal.

$\Delta S = nR \ln (P_1/P_2) = (1.00 \text{ mol})(8.3145 \text{ J mol}^{-1} \text{ K}^{-1}) \ln (5.00/2.00) = 7.62$ J/K

$T = \dfrac{PV}{nR} = \dfrac{5.00 \times 5.00}{1.00 \times 0.08206} = 305$ K; $\Delta G = \Delta H - T\Delta S = 0 - (305 \text{ K})(7.62 \text{ J/K}) = -2320$ J

$w = -P\Delta V = -(2.00 \text{ atm})\Delta V$ where $V_f = \dfrac{nRT}{2.00 \text{ atm}}$ and $V_i = \dfrac{nRT}{5.00 \text{ atm}}$

$w = -2.00 \text{ atm} \left(\dfrac{nRT}{2.00} - \dfrac{nRT}{5.00} \right) \text{L} \times (101.3 \text{ J L}^{-1} \text{ atm}^{-1}) = -1520 \text{ J} = -1500$ J

$\Delta E = 0 = q + w, \quad q = +1520 \text{ J} = 1500$ J

b.   Second law, $\Delta S_{univ} > 0$; $\Delta S_{univ} = \Delta S_{sys} + \Delta S_{surr} = \Delta S_{sys} - \dfrac{q_{actual}}{T}$

$\Delta S_{univ} = 7.62 \text{ J/K} - \dfrac{1500 \text{ J}}{305 \text{ K}} = 7.62 - 4.9 = 2.7 \text{ J/K}$;   Thus, the process is spontaneous.

89.   a. $w_{rev} = -nRT \ln (V_2/V_1) = -(1 \text{ mol}) (8.3145 \text{ J mol}^{-1} \text{ K}^{-1}) (298 \text{ K}) \ln \left(\dfrac{20.0}{10.0} \right) = -1720 \text{ J}$

For isothermal expansion: $\Delta E = 0$, so $q = +1720 \text{ J}$

b. $w = -P\Delta V = -1.23 \text{ atm} (20.0 \text{ L} - 10.0 \text{ L}) = -12.3 \text{ L atm}$

$-12.3 \text{ L atm} \times 101.3 \text{ J L}^{-1} \text{ atm}^{-1} = -1250 \text{ J}$

$\Delta E = 0$ for isothermal expansion, so $q = 1250 \text{ J}$.

93.   At equilibrium:

$$P_{H_2} = \dfrac{nRT}{V} = \dfrac{\left(\dfrac{1.10 \times 10^{13} \text{ molecules}}{6.022 \times 10^{23} \text{ molecules/mol}} \right) \left(\dfrac{0.08206 \text{ L atm}}{\text{mol K}} \right) (298 \text{ K})}{1.00 \text{ L}} = 4.47 \times 10^{-10} \text{ atm}$$

Essentially all of the H_2 and Br_2 has reacted. $P_{HBr} = 2.00 \text{ atm}$

Since we began with the same amount of H_2 and Br_2, at equilibrium $P_{H_2} = P_{Br_2} = 4.47 \times 10^{-10} \text{ atm}$.

$K = \dfrac{P_{HBr}^2}{P_{H_2}P_{Br_2}} = \dfrac{(2.00)^2}{(4.47 \times 10^{-10})^2} = 2.00 \times 10^{19}$ Assumptions good.

$\Delta G^\circ = -RT \ln K = -(8.3145 \text{ J mol}^{-1} \text{ K}^{-1})(298 \text{ K}) \ln (2.00 \times 10^{19}) = -1.10 \times 10^5 \text{ J/mol}$

$\Delta S^\circ = \dfrac{\Delta H^\circ - \Delta G^\circ}{T} = \dfrac{-103,800 \text{ J} - (-1.10 \times 10^5 \text{ J})}{298 \text{ K}} = 20 \text{ J/K}$

95. $P_1V_1 = P_2V_2$, $P_2 = \dfrac{P_1V_1}{V_2} = \dfrac{(5.0)(1.0)}{(2.0)} = 2.5 \text{ atm}$

Gas expands isothermally against no pressure, so $\Delta E = 0$, $w = 0$ and $q = 0$.

$\Delta E = 0$, so $q_{rev} = -w_{rev} = nRT \ln (V_2/V_1)$; $T = \dfrac{PV}{nR} = 61 \text{ K}$

$q_{rev} = (1.0 \text{ mol})(8.3145 \text{ J mol}^{-1} \text{ K}^{-1})(61 \text{ K}) \ln (2.0/1.0) = 350 \text{ J}$

99. $K_p = P_{CO_2}$; To keep Ag_2CO_3 from decomposing, P_{CO_2} must be greater than or equal to K_p.

From Exercise 10.47, $\ln K = \dfrac{-\Delta H°}{RT} + \dfrac{\Delta S°}{R}$. For two conditions of K and T, the equation reduces to:

$$\ln(K_2/K_1) = \frac{\Delta H°}{R}\left(\frac{1}{T_1} - \frac{1}{T_2}\right)$$

Let $T_1 = 25°C = 298$ K, $K_1 = 6.23 \times 10^{-3}$ torr; $T_2 = 110.°C = 383$ K, $K_2 = ?$

$$\ln K_2 - \ln(6.23 \times 10^{-3} \text{ torr}) = \frac{79.14 \times 10^3 \text{ J/mol}}{8.3145 \text{ J K}^{-1} \text{ mol}^{-1}}\left(\frac{1}{298 \text{ K}} - \frac{1}{383 \text{ K}}\right)$$

$\ln K_2 = -5.08 + 7.1 = 2.0$, $K_2 = e^{2.0} = 7.4$ torr

To prevent decomposition of Ag_2CO_3, the partial pressure of CO_2 must be equal to or greater than 7.4 torr.

CHAPTER ELEVEN

ELECTROCHEMISTRY

Cell Potential, Standard Reduction Potentials, and Free Energy

5.   The half-reaction for the SCE is:

$$Hg_2Cl_2 + 2\ e^- \rightarrow 2\ Hg + 2\ Cl^- \qquad E_{SCE} = +0.242\ V$$

For a spontaneous reaction to occur, E_{cell} must be positive. Using the standard reduction potentials in Table 11.1 and the given SCE potential, deduce which combination will produce a positive overall cell potential.

a. $Cu^{2+} + 2\ e^- \rightarrow Cu \qquad E° = 0.34\ V$

   $E_{cell} = 0.34 - 0.242 = 0.10\ V$; SCE is the anode.

b. $Fe^{3+} + e^- \rightarrow Fe^{2+} \qquad E° = 0.77\ V$

   $E_{cell} = 0.77 - 0.242 = 0.53\ V$; SCE is the anode.

c. $AgCl + e^- \rightarrow Ag + Cl^- \qquad E° = 0.22\ V$

   $E_{cell} = 0.242 - 0.22 = 0.02\ V$; SCE is the cathode.

d. $Al^{3+} + 3\ e^- \rightarrow Al \qquad E° = -1.66\ V$

   $E_{cell} = 0.242 + 1.66 = 1.90\ V$; SCE is the cathode.

e. $Ni^{2+} + 2\ e^- \rightarrow Ni \qquad E° = -0.23\ V$

   $E_{cell} = 0.242 + 0.23 = 0.47\ V$; SCE is the cathode.

7.   a. $2\ H^+ + 2\ e^- \rightarrow H_2 \qquad E° = 0.00\ V$; $Cu \rightarrow Cu^{2+} + 2\ e^- \qquad -E° = -0.34\ V$

   $E°_{cell} = -0.34\ V$; No, H^+ cannot oxidize Cu to Cu^{2+} at standard conditions ($E°_{cell} < 0$).

b. $2 H^+ + 2 e^- \rightarrow H_2$ $E° = 0.00$ V; $Mg \rightarrow Mg^{2+} + 2 e^-$ $-E° = -(-2.37$ V$)$

$E°_{cell} = 2.37$ V; Yes, H^+ can oxidize Mg to Mg^{2+}.

c. $Fe^{3+} + e^- \rightarrow Fe^{2+}$ $E° = 0.77$ V; $2 I^- \rightarrow I_2 + 2 e^-$ $-E° = -0.54$ V

$E°_{cell} = 0.77 - 0.54 = 0.23$ V; Yes, Fe^{3+} can oxidize I^- to I_2.

d. $Fe^{3+} + e^- \rightarrow Fe^{2+}$ $E° = 0.77$ V; $2 Br^- \rightarrow Br_2 + 2 e^-$ $-E° = -1.09$ V

No, for: $2 Fe^{3+} + 2 Br^- \rightarrow Br_2 + 2 Fe^{2+}$ $E°_{cell} = -0.32$ V; The reaction is not spontaneous.

9.   Good oxidizing agents are easily reduced. Oxidizing agents are on the left side of the reduction half-reactions listed in Table 11.1. We look for the largest, most positive E° values to correspond to the best oxidizing agents.

$$MnO_4^- > Cl_2 > Cr_2O_7^{2-} > Fe^{3+} > Fe^{2+} > Mg^{2+}$$

E°   1.68   1.36   1.33   0.77   -0.44   -2.37

11. $Br_2 + 2 e^- \rightarrow 2 Br^-$ $E° = 1.09$ V $2 H^+ + 2 e^- \rightarrow H_2$ $E° = 0.00$ V
      $Cd^{2+} + 2 e^- \rightarrow Cd$ $E° = -0.40$ V $La^{3+} + 3 e^- \rightarrow La$ $E° = -2.37$ V
      $Ca^{2+} + 2 e^- \rightarrow Ca$ $E° = -2.76$ V

a.   Oxidizing agents are on the left side of the reduction half-reactions. Br_2 is the best oxidizing agent (largest E°).

b.   Reducing agents are on the right side of the reduction half-reactions. Ca is the best reducing agent (most negative E°).

c. $MnO_4^- + 8 H^+ + 5 e^- \rightarrow Mn^{2+} + 4 H_2O$ $E° = 1.51$ V

Permanganate can oxidize Br^-, H_2, Ca and Cd. When MnO_4^- is coupled with these reagents, $E°_{cell}$ is positive.

d. $Zn \rightarrow Zn^{2+} + 2 e^-$ $-E° = 0.76$ V;   Zinc can reduce Br_2 and H^+ since $E°_{cell} > 0$.

13.   a. $E° > 0.80$ V, oxidize Hg; $E° < 0.91$ V, not oxidize Hg_2^{2+}; No half-reaction in this table fits this requirement. However, by changing concentrations, Ag^+ may be able to work.

b. $E° > 1.09$ V, oxidize Br^-; $E° < 1.36$ V, not oxidize Cl^-; $Cr_2O_7^{2-}$, O_2, MnO_2, and IO_3^- are all possible.

c. $Ni^{2+} + 2 e^- \rightarrow Ni$ $E° = -0.23$ V; $Mn^{2+} + 2 e^- \rightarrow Mn$ $E° = -1.18$ V; Any oxidizing agent with -0.23 V $> E° > -1.18$ V will work. $PbSO_4$, Cd^{2+}, Fe^{2+}, Cr^{3+}, Zn^{2+} and H_2O will be able to do this.

15.   Reduce I_2 to I^-, $E° < 0.54$ V; Not reduce Cu^{2+} to Cu, $E° > 0.34$ V; Any reducing agent with a reduction potential between 0.34 V and 0.54 V will work.

17. $H_2O_2 + 2 H^+ + 2 e^- \rightarrow 2 H_2O$ $E° = 1.78$ V; H_2O_2 is the oxidizing agent.
       $O_2 + 2 H^+ + 2 e^- \rightarrow H_2O_2$ $E° = 0.68$ V; H_2O_2 is the reducing agent.

       $H_2O_2 + 2 H^+ + 2 e^- \rightarrow 2 H_2O$ $E° = 1.78$ V
                 $H_2O_2 \rightarrow O_2 + 2 H^+ + 2 e^-$ $-E° = -0.68$ V
       _____

                 $2 H_2O_2 \rightarrow 2 H_2O + O_2$ $E°_{cell} = 1.10$ V

19.   a. $(ClO_2^- \rightarrow ClO_2 + e^-) \times 2$ $-E° = -0.954$ V
                  $Cl_2 + 2 e^- \rightarrow 2 Cl^-$ $E° = 1.36$ V
       _____

       $2 ClO_2^- + Cl_2 \rightarrow 2 ClO_2 + 2 Cl^-$ $E°_{cell} = 0.41$ V $= 0.41$ J/C

       $\Delta G° = -nFE° = -(2$ mol $e^-)(96{,}485$ C/mol $e^-)(0.41$ J/C$) = -7.91 \times 10^4$ J $= -79$ kJ

       $\Delta G° = -RT \ln K$ so $K = \exp(-\Delta G°/RT)$

       $K = \exp[(7.9 \times 10^4$ J$)/(8.3145$ J mol^{-1} K$^{-1})(298$ K$)] = 7.0 \times 10^{13}$

       or $\log K = \dfrac{nE°}{0.0592} = \dfrac{2(0.41)}{0.0592} = 13.85$, $K = 10^{13.85} = 7.1 \times 10^{13}$

       b. $(H_2O + ClO_2 \rightarrow ClO_3^- + 2 H^+ + e^-) \times 5$
               $5 e^- + 4 H^+ + ClO_2 \rightarrow Cl^- + 2 H_2O$
       _____

       $3 H_2O(l) + 6 ClO_2(g) \rightarrow 5 ClO_3^-(aq) + Cl^-(aq) + 6 H^+(aq)$

22.   b. $Cl_2 + 2 I^- \rightarrow I_2 + 2 Cl^-$ $E°_{cell} = +0.82$ V $= 0.82$ J/C

       $\Delta G° = -nFE° = -(2$ mol $e^-)(96{,}485$ C/mol $e^-)(0.82$ J/C$) = -1.6 \times 10^5$ J $= -160$ kJ

       $E° = \dfrac{0.0592}{n} \log K$, $\log K = \dfrac{nE°}{0.0592} = \dfrac{2(0.82)}{0.0592} = 27.70$, $K = 10^{27.70} = 5.0 \times 10^{27}$

       d. $Pb + Cu^{2+} \rightarrow Cu + Pb^{2+}$ $E°_{cell} = 0.47$ V

       $\Delta G° = -nFE° = -(2$ mol $e^-)(96{,}485$ C/mol $e^-)(0.47$ J/C$)$ $(1$ kJ/1000 J$) = -91$ kJ

       $\log K = \dfrac{2(0.47)}{0.0592} = 15.88$, $K = 7.6 \times 10^{15}$

       e. $(Fe^{2+} \rightarrow Fe^{3+} + e^-) \times 4$ $-E° = -0.77$ V
               $4 H^+ + O_2 + 4 e^- \rightarrow 2 H_2O$ $E° = 1.23$ V
       _____

       $4 H^+ + O_2 + 4 Fe^{2+} \rightarrow 4 Fe^{3+} + 2 H_2O$ $E°_{cell} = +0.46$ V

       $\Delta G° = -nFE° = -(4$ mol $e^-)(96{,}485$ C/mol $e^-)(0.46$ J/C$)$ $(1$ kJ/1000 J$) = -180$ kJ

       $\log K = \dfrac{4(0.46)}{0.0592} = 31.08$, $K = 1.2 \times 10^{31}$

24.   a.
$$(Mn \rightarrow Mn^{2+} + 2 \ e^-) \times 3 \qquad -E° = 1.18 \ V$$
$$(4 \ H^+ + NO_3^- + 3 \ e^- \rightarrow NO + 2 \ H_2O) \times 2 \qquad E° = 0.96 \ V$$

$$3 \ Mn + 8 \ H^+ + 2 \ NO_3^- \rightarrow 2 \ NO + 4 \ H_2O + 3 \ Mn^{2+} \qquad E°_{cell} = 2.14 \ V$$

$$5 \times (2 \ e^- + 2 \ H^+ + IO_4^- \rightarrow IO_3^- + H_2O) \qquad E° = 1.60 \ V$$
$$2 \times (Mn^{2+} + 4 \ H_2O \rightarrow MnO_4^- + 8 \ H^+ + 5 \ e^-) \qquad -E° = -1.51 \ V$$

$$5 \ IO_4^- + 2 \ Mn^{2+} + 3 \ H_2O \rightarrow 5 \ IO_3^- + 2 \ MnO_4^- + 6 \ H^+ \qquad E°_{cell} = 0.09 \ V$$

b.   Nitric acid oxidation:

$$\Delta G° = -(6 \ mol \ e^-)(96,485 \ C/mol \ e^-)(2.14 \ J/C) = -1.24 \times 10^6 \ J = -1240 \ kJ$$

$$\log K = \frac{nE°}{0.0592} = \frac{6(2.14)}{0.0592} = 217, \ K \approx 10^{217}$$

Periodate oxidation:

$$\Delta G° = -(10 \ mol \ e^-)(96,485 \ C/mol \ e^-)(0.09 \ J/C) \ (1 \ kJ/1000 \ J) = -90 \ kJ$$

$$\log K = \frac{10(0.09)}{0.0592} = 15.2, \ K = 10^{15.2} = 2 \times 10^{15}$$

26.   a.
$$(2 \ H^+ + 2 \ e^- \rightarrow H_2) \times 2 \qquad E° = 0.00 \ V$$
$$2 \ H_2O \rightarrow O_2 + 4 \ H^+ + 4 \ e^- \qquad -E° = -1.23 \ V$$

$$2 \ H_2O \rightarrow 2 \ H_2 + O_2 \qquad E°_{cell} = -1.23 \ V$$

$$\Delta G° = -nFE° = -(4 \ mol \ e^-)(96,485 \ C/mol \ e^-)(-1.23 \ J/C) \ (1 \ kJ/1000 \ J) = 475 \ kJ$$

b. $\Delta H° = -2 \ \Delta H_f° (H_2O) = -2 \ mol \ (-286 \ kJ/mol) = 572 \ kJ$

$\Delta S° = 2 \ mol \ (131 \ J \ K^{-1} \ mol^{-1}) + 1(205) - 2(70) = 327 \ J/K$

c.   At 90.°C (363 K): $\Delta G° = 572 \ kJ - (363 \ K)(0.327 \ kJ/K) = 453 \ kJ$

$$\Delta G° = -nFE°, \ E° = \frac{-\Delta G°}{nF} = \frac{-4.53 \times 10^5 \ J}{(4 \ mol \ e^-) \ (96,485 \ C/mol \ e^-)} = -1.17 \ J/C = -1.17 \ V$$

At 0°C: $\Delta G° = 572 \ kJ - (273 \ K)(0.327 \ kJ/K) = 483 \ kJ$

$$E° = \frac{-\Delta G°}{nF} = \frac{-4.83 \times 10^5 \ J}{(4 \ mol \ e^-) \ (96,485 \ C/mol \ e^-)} = -1.25 \ J/C = -1.25 \ V$$

28. $CH_3OH(l) + 3/2 \ O_2(g) \rightarrow CO_2(g) + 2 \ H_2O(l) \qquad \Delta G° = 2(-237) + (-394) - [-166] = -702 \ kJ$

The balanced half-reactions are:

$$H_2O + CH_3OH \rightarrow CO_2 + 6 \ H^+ + 6 \ e^- \ \text{and} \ O_2 + 4 \ H^+ + 4 \ e^- \rightarrow 2 \ H_2O$$

For 3/2 mol O_2, 6 moles of electrons will be transferred (n = 6).

$$\Delta G° = -nFE°, \quad E° = \frac{-\Delta G°}{nF} = \frac{702,000 \text{ J}}{(6 \text{ mol e}^-)(96,485 \text{ C/mol e}^-)} = 1.21 \text{ J/C} = 1.21 \text{ V}$$

For this reaction: $\Delta S° = 2(70) + 214 - [127 + 3/2(205)] = -81 \text{ J/K}$

$$E° = \frac{T\Delta S°}{nF} - \frac{\Delta H°}{nF};$$ Since $\Delta S°$ is negative, $E°$ will decrease with an increase in temperature.

29. $\Delta G° = -nFE° = -(1 \text{ mol e}^-)(96,485 \text{ C/mol e}^-)(0.80 \text{ J/C})\ (1 \text{ kJ}/1000 \text{ J}) = -77 \text{ kJ}; \quad \Delta G_f° (e^-) = 0$

   $-77 \text{ kJ} = \Delta G_f° (Ag) - \Delta G_f° (Ag^+), \quad -77 \text{ kJ} = 0 - \Delta G_f° (Ag^+), \quad \Delta G_f° (Ag^+) = 77 \text{ kJ/mol}$

32.   a. $E_{cell}° = 0.52 - 0.16 = 0.36 \text{ V};$ spontaneous

   b. $E_{cell}° = -0.14 \text{ V} - (0.15 \text{ V}) = -0.29 \text{ V};$ not spontaneous

   c. $E_{cell}° = -0.44 \text{ V} - (0.77 \text{ V}) = -1.21 \text{ V};$ not spontaneous

   d. $E_{cell}° = 1.65 - 1.21 = 0.44 \text{ V};$ spontaneous

34.
$$\begin{array}{lll}
Ag^+ + e^- \rightarrow Ag & E° = 0.80 \text{ V} \\
Ag + 2\,S_2O_3^{2-} \rightarrow Ag(S_2O_3)_2^{3-} + e^- & -E° = -0.017 \text{ V} \\
\hline
Ag^+ + 2\,S_2O_3^{2-} \rightarrow Ag(S_2O_3)_2^{3-} & E_{cell}° = 0.78 \text{ V} & K = ?
\end{array}$$

$$\log K = \frac{nE°}{0.0592} = \frac{(1)(0.78)}{0.0592} = 13.18, \quad K = 10^{13.18} = 1.5 \times 10^{13}$$

36.
$$\begin{array}{lll}
Ag \rightarrow Ag^+ + e^- & -E° = -0.80 \text{ V} \\
e^- + AgI \rightarrow Ag + I^- & E_{AgI}° = ? \\
\hline
AgI \rightarrow Ag^+ + I^- & E_{cell}° = -0.80 + E_{AgI}° & K_{sp} = 1.5 \times 10^{-16}
\end{array}$$

For this overall reaction:

$$E_{cell}° = \frac{0.0592}{n} \log K_{sp} = \frac{0.0592}{1} \log (1.5 \times 10^{-16}) = -0.94 \text{ V}$$

$E_{cell}° = -0.94 \text{ V} = -0.80 \text{ V} + E_{AgI}°, \quad E_{AgI}° = -0.94 + 0.80 = -0.14 \text{ V}$

The Nernst Equation

38.   a.   n = 2 for this reaction.

$$E = E° - \frac{0.0592}{2} \log \left(\frac{1}{[H^+]^2[HSO_4^-]^2} \right) = 2.04 \text{ V} + \frac{0.0592}{2} \log ([H^+]^2\,[HSO_4^-]^2)$$

$$E = 2.04 \text{ V} + \frac{0.0592}{2} \log [(4.5)^2(4.5)^2] = 2.04 \text{ V} + 0.077 \text{ V} = 2.12 \text{ V}$$

b. We can calculate $\Delta G°$ from $\Delta G° = \Delta H° - T\Delta S°$ and then $E°$ from $\Delta G° = -nFE°$; or we can use the equation derived in Exercise 11.25.

$$E° = \frac{T\Delta S° - \Delta H°}{nF} = \frac{(253 \text{ K}) (263.5 \text{ J/K}) + 315.9 \times 10^3 \text{ J}}{(2 \text{ mol e}^-) (96{,}485 \text{ C/mol e}^-)} = 1.98 \text{ J/C} = 1.98 \text{ V}$$

c. $E = E° - \dfrac{RT}{nF} \ln Q = E° + \dfrac{RT}{nF} \ln ([H^+]^2 [HSO_4^-]^2)$

$$E = 1.98 \text{ V} + \frac{(8.3145 \text{ J/K mol}) (253 \text{ K})}{(2 \text{ mol e}^-) (96{,}485 \text{ C/mol e}^-)} \ln [(4.5)^2 (4.5)^2]$$

$$E = 1.98 \text{ V} + 0.066 \text{ V} = 2.05 \text{ V}$$

d. As the temperature decreases, the cell potential decreases. Also, since oil becomes more viscous at lower temperatures, it is more difficult to start an engine on a cold day. The combination of these two factors results in batteries failing more often on cold days than on warm days.

40. $5 \text{ e}^- + 8 \text{ H}^+ + MnO_4^- \rightarrow Mn^{2+} + 4 \text{ H}_2O$ 　　　　　　$E° = 1.51 \text{ V}$
　　　　　　　　$(Fe^{2+} \rightarrow Fe^{3+} + e^-) \times 5$ 　　　　　　　　$-E° = -0.77 \text{ V}$

$$\overline{8 \text{ H}^+ + MnO_4^- + 5 \text{ Fe}^{2+} \rightarrow 5 \text{ Fe}^{3+} + Mn^{2+} + 4 \text{ H}_2O \qquad E°_{cell} = 0.74 \text{ V}}$$

$$E = E° - \frac{0.0592}{n} \log Q = 0.74 \text{ V} - \frac{0.0592}{5} \log \frac{[Fe^{3+}]^5 [Mn^{2+}]}{[Fe^{2+}]^5 [MnO_4^-] [H^+]^8}$$

$$E = 0.74 - \frac{0.0592}{5} \log \frac{(1 \times 10^{-6})^5 (1 \times 10^{-6})}{(1 \times 10^{-3})^5 (1 \times 10^{-2}) (1 \times 10^{-4})^8}$$

$$E = 0.74 - \frac{0.0592}{5} \log (1 \times 10^{13}) = 0.74 \text{ V} - 0.15 \text{ V} = 0.59 \text{ V} = 0.6 \text{ V}$$

Yes, $E > 0$ so reaction will occur as written.

43.   a. $E = E° = \dfrac{0.0592}{n} \log \dfrac{[OH^-]^5}{[CrO_4^{2-}]}$; $[OH^-] = 10^{-6.60} = 2.5 \times 10^{-7} \, M$

$$E = -0.13 \text{ V} - \frac{0.0592}{3} \log \frac{(2.5 \times 10^{-7})^5}{1.0 \times 10^{-6}}$$

$$E = -0.13 - \frac{0.0592}{3} \log (9.8 \times 10^{-28}) = -0.13 \text{ V} + 0.53 \text{ V} = +0.40 \text{ V}$$

b. $E = E° - \dfrac{0.0592}{n} \log \dfrac{[Cr^{3+}]^2}{[Cr_2O_7^{2-}][H^+]^{14}} = 1.33\ V - \dfrac{0.0592}{6} \log \dfrac{(1.0 \times 10^{-6})^2}{(1.0 \times 10^{-6})(1.0 \times 10^{-2})^{14}}$

$E = 1.33 - \dfrac{0.0592}{6} \log (1.0 \times 10^{22}) = 1.33\ V - 0.22\ V = 1.11\ V$

45.   Cathode: $O_2 + 2\ H_2O + 4\ e^- \rightarrow 4\ OH^-$ $E° = 0.40\ V$
        Anode: $(Fe \rightarrow Fe^{2+} + 2\ e^-) \times 2$ $-E° = 0.44\ V$
        _____
        $O_2 + 2\ H_2O + 2\ Fe \rightarrow 2\ Fe^{2+} + 4\ OH^-$ $E°_{cell} = 0.84\ V$

$E = 0.84\ V - \dfrac{0.0592}{4} \log \left(\dfrac{[OH^-]^4[Fe^{2+}]^2}{P_{O_2}} \right)$

If $[OH^-]$ is very small, say $10^{-14} = [OH^-]$ ($[H^+] = 1.0\ M$), the log term will become more positive. Thus, as the solution becomes more acidic, E_{cell} becomes more positive, and the corrosion process becomes more spontaneous. Note: This is oversimplified as $Fe(OH)_2(s)$ or $Fe_2O_3(s)$ formation has been ignored.

Electrolysis

47.   a. $Al^{3+} + 3\ e^- \rightarrow Al$; 3 mol e^- are needed to produce 1 mol Al.

$1.0 \times 10^3\ g \times \dfrac{1\ mol\ Al}{27.0\ g} \times \dfrac{3\ mol\ e^-}{mol\ Al} \times \dfrac{96{,}485\ C}{mol\ e^-} \times \dfrac{1\ s}{100.0\ C} = 1.07 \times 10^5\ s = 3.0 \times 10^1\ hours$

b. $1.0\ g\ Ni \times \dfrac{1\ mol}{58.7\ g} \times \dfrac{2\ mol\ e^-}{mol\ Ni} \times \dfrac{96{,}485\ C}{mol\ e^-} \times \dfrac{1\ s}{100.0\ C} = 33\ s$

c. $5.0\ mol\ Ag \times \dfrac{1\ mol\ e^-}{mol\ Ag} \times \dfrac{96{,}485\ C}{mol\ e^-} \times \dfrac{1\ s}{100.0\ C} = 4.8 \times 10^3\ s = 1.3\ hours$

49. $2.30\ min \times \dfrac{60\ s}{min} = 138\ s$; $138\ s \times \dfrac{2.00\ C}{s} \times \dfrac{1\ mol\ e^-}{96{,}485\ C} \times \dfrac{1\ mol\ Ag}{mol\ e^-} = 2.86 \times 10^{-3}\ mol\ Ag$

$[Ag^+] = 2.86 \times 10^{-3}\ mol\ Ag^+/0.250\ L = 1.14 \times 10^{-2}\ M$

51. $Fe^{2+} + 2\ e^- \rightarrow Fe$ $E = E° = -0.44\ V$

$Ag^+ + e^- \rightarrow Ag$ $E = E° - \dfrac{0.0592}{1} \log (1/[Ag^+]) = 0.80 + 0.0592 \log [Ag^+]$

$E_{Ag} = 0.80\ V + 0.0592 \log(0.010) = 0.68\ V$; It is still easier to plate out Ag.

54. $600.\ s \times \dfrac{5.00\ C}{s} \times \dfrac{1\ mol\ e^-}{96{,}485\ C} \times \dfrac{1\ mol\ M}{3\ mol\ e^-} = 1.04 \times 10^{-2}\ mol\ M$

Atomic mass $= \dfrac{1.19 \text{ g M}}{1.04 \times 10^{-2} \text{ mol}} = \dfrac{114 \text{ g}}{\text{mol}}$; The element is indium, In. Indium forms 3+ ions.

57. F_2 is produced at the anode: $2 \text{ F}^- \rightarrow F_2 + 2 \text{ e}^-$

$2.00 \text{ h} \times \dfrac{60 \text{ min}}{\text{h}} \times \dfrac{60 \text{ s}}{\text{min}} \times \dfrac{10.0 \text{ C}}{\text{s}} \times \dfrac{1 \text{ mol e}^-}{96{,}485 \text{ C}} = 0.746 \text{ mol e}^-$

$0.746 \text{ mol e}^- \times \dfrac{1 \text{ mol } F_2}{2 \text{ mol e}^-} = 0.373 \text{ mol } F_2$; $V = \dfrac{nRT}{P} = \dfrac{(0.373)\,(0.08206)\,(298)}{1.00} = 9.12 \text{ L } F_2$

K is produced at the cathode: $K^+ + e^- \rightarrow K$

$0.746 \text{ mol e}^- \times \dfrac{1 \text{ mol K}}{\text{mol e}^-} \times \dfrac{39.10 \text{ g K}}{\text{mol K}} = 29.2 \text{ g K}$

60. $(2 \text{ H}_2\text{O} \rightarrow 4 \text{ H}^+ + \text{O}_2 + 4 \text{ e}^-) \times 1/2$
         $2 \text{ e}^- + 2 \text{ H}_2\text{O} \rightarrow \text{H}_2 + 2 \text{ OH}^-$
         _____

                $\text{H}_2\text{O} \rightarrow \text{H}_2 + 1/2 \text{ O}_2$ $n = 2$ for reaction as it is written.

$15.0 \text{ min} \times \dfrac{60 \text{ s}}{\text{min}} \times \dfrac{2.50 \text{ C}}{\text{s}} \times \dfrac{1 \text{ mol e}^-}{96{,}485 \text{ C}} \times \dfrac{1 \text{ mol } \text{H}_2}{2 \text{ mol e}^-} = 1.17 \times 10^{-2} \text{ mol } \text{H}_2$

At STP, 1 mole of an ideal gas occupies a volume of 22.42 L (see chapter 5).

$1.17 \times 10^{-2} \text{ mol } \text{H}_2 \times \dfrac{22.42 \text{ L}}{\text{mol } \text{H}_2} = 0.262 \text{ L} = 262 \text{ mL } \text{H}_2$

$1.17 \times 10^{-2} \text{ mol } \text{H}_2 \times \dfrac{0.500 \text{ mol } \text{O}_2}{\text{mol } \text{H}_2} \times \dfrac{22.42 \text{ L}}{\text{mol } \text{O}_2} = 0.131 \text{ L} = 131 \text{ mL } \text{O}_2$

Additional Exercises

64. $Zn^{2+} + 2 \text{ e}^- \rightarrow Zn$ $E° = -0.76 \text{ V}$; $Fe^{2+} + 2 \text{ e}^- \rightarrow Fe$ $E° = -0.44 \text{ V}$

It is easier to oxidize Zn than Fe, so the Zn will be oxidized protecting the iron of the *Monitor's* hull.

66. $Al^{3+} + 3 \text{ e}^- \rightarrow Al$ $E° = -1.66 \text{ V}$
        $Al + 6 \text{ F}^- \rightarrow AlF_6^{3-} + 3 \text{ e}^-$ $-E° = -(-2.07 \text{ V})$
        _____

        $Al^{3+} + 6 \text{ F}^- \rightarrow AlF_6^{3-}$ $E°_{cell} = 0.41 \text{ V}$ $K_f = ?$

$\log K_f = \dfrac{nE°}{0.0592} = \dfrac{3(0.41)}{0.0592} = 20.78$, $K_f = 10^{20.78} = 6.0 \times 10^{20}$

69. a. In base, $Co(OH)_2$ will precipitate ($K_{sp} = 2.5 \times 10^{-16}$). We need $E°$ for $Co(OH)_2 + 2\ e^- \rightarrow Co + 2\ OH^-$.

We look at the effect of the solubility on:

$$Co^{2+} + 2\ e^- \rightarrow Co \quad E = -0.28 - \frac{0.0592}{2} \log \frac{1}{[Co^{2+}]}$$

Since $K_{sp} = [Co^{2+}]\ [OH^-]^2$, $E = -0.28 - \frac{0.0592}{2} \log \frac{[OH^-]^2}{K_{sp}}$

If $[OH^-] = 1.0\ M$, then the E we calculate is $E°$ for $Co(OH)_2 + 2\ e^- \rightarrow Co + 2\ OH^-$.

$$E = -0.28 - \frac{0.0592}{2} \log \frac{(1.0)^2}{2.5 \times 10^{-16}} = -0.74$$

$$
\begin{array}{ll}
(2\ OH^- + Co \rightarrow Co(OH)_2 + 2\ e^-) \times 2 & -E° = 0.74\ V \\
O_2 + 2\ H_2O + 4\ e^- \rightarrow 4\ OH^- & E° = 0.40\ V \\
\hline
2\ Co + O_2 + 2\ H_2O \rightarrow 2\ Co(OH)_2 & E° = 1.14\ V
\end{array}
$$

Yes, the corrosion reaction is spontaneous.

b. $O_2 + 4\ H^+ + 4e^- \rightarrow 2\ H_2O \qquad E° = 1.23\ V$

This half-reaction is even more positive than the reduction of O_2 in base. Yes, corrosion will also occur in $1.0\ M\ H^+$.

c. Using the reaction: $2\ Co + O_2 + 4\ H^+ \rightarrow 2\ H_2O + 2\ Co^{2+} \quad E° = 1.23\ V - (-0.28\ V) = 1.51\ V$

$$E = 1.51\ V - \frac{0.0592}{4} \log \frac{[Co^{2+}]^2}{P_{O_2}\ [H^+]^4}, [H^+] = 1.0 \times 10^{-7}\ M$$

$$E = 1.51\ V - \frac{0.0592}{4} \log (1.0 \times 10^{28}) - \frac{0.0592}{4} \log \frac{[Co^{2+}]^2}{P_{O_2}}$$

$$E = 1.51\ V - 0.41\ V - \frac{0.0592}{4} \log \frac{[Co^{2+}]^2}{P_{O_2}}$$

Typically, $[Co^{2+}]$ won't be very large and $P_{O_2} \approx 0.2$ atm. E will still be greater than zero and the corrosion reaction is spontaneous at pH = 7.

71. a. $E_{cell} = E_{ref} + 0.05916$ pH, $0.480\ V = 0.250\ V + 0.05916$ pH

$$pH = \frac{0.480 - 0.250}{0.05916} = 3.888; \text{ Uncertainty} = \pm 1\ mV = \pm 0.001\ V$$

$$pH_{max} = \frac{0.481 - 0.250}{0.05916} = 3.905; \quad pH_{min} = \frac{0.479 - 0.250}{0.05916} = 3.871$$

So if the uncertainty in potential is $\pm$ 0.001 V, the uncertainty in pH is $\pm$ 0.017 or about $\pm$ 0.02 pH units.

For this measurement, $[H^+] = 1.29 \times 10^{-4}$ M. For an error of + 1 mV, $[H^+] = 1.24 \times 10^{-4}$ M. For an error of -1 mV, $[H^+] = 1.35 \times 10^{-4}$ M. So the uncertainty in $[H^+]$ is $\pm$ 0.06 $\times 10^{-4}$ M.

b. From the previous example, we will be within $\pm$ 0.02 pH units if we measure the potential to the nearest $\pm$ 0.001 V (1 mV).

74.   Cathode: $M^{2+} + 2e^- \rightarrow M(s)$ $E° = 0.80$ V
       Anode: $M(s) \rightarrow M^{2+} + 2e^-$ $-E° = -0.80$ V

       _____

                      M^{2+} (cathode) $\rightarrow M^{2+}$ (anode) $E° = 0.00$ V

$$E_{cell} = 0.44 \text{ V} = 0.00 \text{ V} - \frac{0.0592}{2} \log \frac{[M^{2+}]_{anode}}{[M^{2+}]_{cathode}}, \quad 0.44 = -\frac{0.0592}{2} \log \frac{[M^{2+}]_a}{1.0}$$

$$\log [M^{2+}]_a = -\frac{2(0.44)}{0.0592} = -14.86, \quad [M^{2+}]_{anode} = 1.4 \times 10^{-15} \text{ } M$$

Since we started with equal numbers of moles of SO_4^{2-} and M^{2+}, then $[M^{2+}] = [SO_4^{2-}]$ at equilibrium.

$$K_{sp} = [M^{2+}][SO_4^{2-}] = (1.4 \times 10^{-15})^2 = 2.0 \times 10^{-30}$$

76.   a. $3 \times (e^- + 2\text{ H}^+ + NO_3^- \rightarrow NO_2 + H_2O)$ $E° = 0.775$ V
                          $2 H_2O + NO \rightarrow NO_3^- + 4 H^+ + 3 e^-$ $-E° = -0.957$ V

       _____

       $2 H^+(aq) + 2 NO_3^-(aq) + NO(g) \rightarrow 3 NO_2(g) + H_2O(l)$ $E°_{cell} = -0.182$ V   K = ?

$$\log K = \frac{nE°}{0.0592} = \frac{3(-0.182)}{0.0592} = -9.223, \quad K = 10^{-9.223} = 5.98 \times 10^{-10}$$

b. Let C = concentration of $HNO_3 = [H^+] = [NO_3^-]$

$$5.98 \times 10^{-10} = \frac{P_{NO_2}^3}{P_{NO} [H^+]^2 [NO_3^-]^2} = \frac{P_{NO_2}^3}{P_{NO} C^4}$$

If 0.20 mol % NO_2 and $P_{tot} = 1.00$ atm:

$$P_{NO_2} = \frac{0.20 \text{ mol } NO_2}{100. \text{ mol total}} \times 1.00 \text{ atm} = 2.0 \times 10^{-3} \text{ atm}; \quad P_{NO} = 1.00 - 0.0020 = 1.00 \text{ atm}$$

$$5.98 \times 10^{-10} = \frac{(2.0 \times 10^{-3})^3}{(1.00) C^4}, \quad C = 1.9 \text{ } M \text{ } HNO_3$$

79.   a. $3 e^- + 4 H^+ + NO_3^- \rightarrow NO + 2 H_2O$ $E° = 0.96$ V

Nitric acid can oxidize Co to Co^{2+}, but is not strong enough to oxidize Co to Co^{3+}. Co^{2+} is the primary product.

b.   Concentrated nitric acid is about 16 mol/L. $[H^+] = [NO_3^-] = 16$ M; Assume $P_{NO} = 1$ atm

$$E = 0.96 \text{ V} - \frac{0.0592}{3} \log \frac{P_{NO}}{[H^+]^4 [NO_3^-]} = 0.96 - \frac{0.0592}{3} \log \frac{1}{(16)^5} = 0.96 + 0.12 = 1.08 \text{ V}$$

No, concentrated nitric acid will still only be able to oxidize Co to Co^{2+}.

c. $H_2O_2 + 2 H^+ + 2 e^- \rightarrow 2 H_2O$ $E° = 1.78$ V

Hydrogen peroxide should oxidize Co to Co^{3+}. Co^{3+} is the primary product.

CHAPTER TWELVE

QUANTUM MECHANICS AND ATOMIC THEORY

Light and Matter

2. $\nu = \dfrac{c}{\lambda} = \dfrac{2.998 \times 10^8 \text{ m/s}}{780. \times 10^{-9} \text{ m}} = 3.84 \times 10^{14} \text{ s}^{-1}; \ \ E = h\nu = 2.54 \times 10^{-19} \text{ J where } h = 6.626 \times 10^{-34} \text{ J s}$

4. $E_{photon} = h\nu \text{ and } \lambda\nu = c. \ \ \text{So, } \nu = \dfrac{c}{\lambda} \text{ and } E = \dfrac{hc}{\lambda}$

$\lambda = \dfrac{hc}{E_{photon}} = \dfrac{(6.626 \times 10^{-34} \text{ J s}) (2.998 \times 10^8 \text{ m/s})}{7.21 \times 10^{-19} \text{ J}} = 2.76 \times 10^{-7} \text{ m} = 276 \text{ nm}$

7. $\dfrac{890.1 \text{ kJ}}{\text{mol}} \times \dfrac{1 \text{ mol}}{6.022 \times 10^{23} \text{ atoms}} = \dfrac{1.478 \times 10^{-21} \text{ kJ}}{\text{atom}} = \dfrac{1.478 \times 10^{-18} \text{ J}}{\text{atom}}$

$E = \dfrac{hc}{\lambda}, \ \ \lambda = \dfrac{hc}{E} = \dfrac{(6.626 \times 10^{-34} \text{ J s}) (2.9979 \times 10^8 \text{ m/s})}{1.478 \times 10^{-18} \text{ J}} = 1.344 \times 10^{-7} \text{ m} = 134.4 \text{ nm}$

No, it will take light with a wavelength of 134.4 nm or less to ionize gold. A photon of light with a wavelength of 225 nm is longer wavelength and, thus, less energy than 134.4 nm light.

9. The energy to remove a single electron is:

$\dfrac{208.4 \text{ kJ}}{\text{mol}} \times \dfrac{1 \text{ mol}}{6.022 \times 10^{23}} = 3.461 \times 10^{-22} \text{ kJ} = 3.461 \times 10^{-19} \text{ J} = E_w$

Energy of 254 nm light is:

$E = \dfrac{hc}{\lambda} = \dfrac{(6.626 \times 10^{-34} \text{ J s}) (2.998 \times 10^8 \text{ m/s})}{254 \times 10^{-9} \text{ m}} = 7.82 \times 10^{-19} \text{ J}$

$E_{photon} = E_K + E_w, \ \ E_K = 7.82 \times 10^{-19} \text{ J} - 3.461 \times 10^{-19} \text{ J} = 4.36 \times 10^{-19} \text{ J} = \text{maximum KE}$

Hydrogen Atom: The Bohr Model

11.   For the H-atom: $E_n = \dfrac{-R_H}{n^2}$, $R_H = 2.178 \times 10^{-18}$ J; For a spectral transition, $\Delta E = E_f - E_i$:

$$\Delta E = \left(\dfrac{-R_H}{n_f^2} \right) - \left(\dfrac{-R_H}{n_i^2} \right) = -R_H \left(\dfrac{1}{n_f^2} - \dfrac{1}{n_i^2} \right)$$

The quantum numbers n_i and n_f are the initial and final states of the electron, respectively. If we follow this convention a positive value of ΔE will correspond to absorption of light and a negative value of ΔE will correspond to emission of light.

a. $\Delta E = -2.178 \times 10^{-18}$ J $\left(\dfrac{1}{2^2} - \dfrac{1}{3^2} \right) = -2.178 \times 10^{-18}$ J $\left(\dfrac{1}{4} - \dfrac{1}{9} \right)$

$\Delta E = -2.178 \times 10^{-18}$ J $(0.2500 - 0.1111) = -3.025 \times 10^{-19}$ J

The photon of light will have energy equal to 3.025×10^{-19} J.

$$|\Delta E| = E_{photon} = h\nu = \dfrac{hc}{\lambda} \text{ or } \lambda = \dfrac{hc}{|\Delta E|}$$

$$\lambda = \dfrac{(6.626 \times 10^{-34} \text{ J s}) (2.9979 \times 10^8 \text{ m/s})}{3.025 \times 10^{-19} \text{ J}} = 6.567 \times 10^{-7} \text{ m} = 656.7 \text{ nm}$$

b. $\Delta E = -2.178 \times 10^{-18}$ J $\left(\dfrac{1}{2^2} - \dfrac{1}{4^2} \right) = -4.084 \times 10^{-19}$ J

$$\lambda = \dfrac{hc}{|\Delta E|} = \dfrac{(6.626 \times 10^{-34} \text{ J s}) (2.9979 \times 10^8 \text{ m/s})}{4.084 \times 10^{-19} \text{ J}} = 4.864 \times 10^{-7} \text{ m} = 486.4 \text{ nm}$$

c. $\Delta E = -2.178 \times 10^{-18}$ J $\left(\dfrac{1}{1^2} - \dfrac{1}{2^2} \right) = -1.634 \times 10^{-18}$ J

$$\lambda = \dfrac{(6.626 \times 10^{-34} \text{ J s}) (2.9979 \times 10^8 \text{ m/s})}{1.634 \times 10^{-18} \text{ J}} = 1.216 \times 10^{-7} \text{ m} = 121.6 \text{ nm}$$

d. $\Delta E = -2.178 \times 10^{-18}$ J $\left(\dfrac{1}{3^2} - \dfrac{1}{4^2} \right) = -1.059 \times 10^{-19}$ J

$$\lambda = \dfrac{(6.626 \times 10^{-34} \text{ J s}) (2.9979 \times 10^8 \text{ m/s})}{1.059 \times 10^{-19} \text{ J}} = 1.876 \times 10^{-6} \text{ m} = 1876 \text{ nm}$$

12.   Ionization from n = 1 corresponds to the transition n = 1 $\rightarrow$ n = ∞ where $E_\infty = 0$.

$$\Delta E = E_\infty - E_1 = -E_1 = R_H \left(\dfrac{1}{1^2} \right) = R_H, \quad \Delta E = 2.178 \times 10^{-18} \text{ J} = E_{photon}$$

$$\lambda = \frac{hc}{E} = \frac{(6.626 \times 10^{-34} \text{ J s}) (2.9979 \times 10^8 \text{ m/s})}{2.178 \times 10^{-18} \text{ J}} = 9.120 \times 10^{-8} \text{ m} = 91.20 \text{ nm}$$

To ionize from n = 3, $\Delta E = 0 - E_3 = R_H \left(\frac{1}{3^2} \right) = 2.178 \times 10^{-18} \text{ J} \left(\frac{1}{9} \right)$

$\Delta E = 2.420 \times 10^{-19}$ J; $\lambda = 8.208 \times 10^{-7}$ m = 820.8 nm

14.   The longest wavelength light emitted will correspond to the transition with the lowest energy change. This is the transition from n = 6 to n = 5.

$$\Delta E = -2.178 \times 10^{-18} \text{ J} \left(\frac{1}{5^2} - \frac{1}{6^2} \right) = -2.662 \times 10^{-20} \text{ J}$$

$$\lambda = \frac{hc}{|\Delta E|} = \frac{(6.626 \times 10^{-34} \text{ J s}) (2.9979 \times 10^8 \text{ m/s})}{2.662 \times 10^{-20} \text{ J}} = 7.462 \times 10^{-6} \text{ m} = 7462 \text{ nm}$$

The shortest wavelength emitted will correspond to the largest ΔE; this is n = 6 → n = 1.

$$\Delta E = -2.178 \times 10^{-18} \text{ J} \left(\frac{1}{1^2} - \frac{1}{6^2} \right) = -2.118 \times 10^{-18} \text{ J}$$

$$\lambda = \frac{hc}{|\Delta E|} = \frac{(6.626 \times 10^{-34} \text{ J s}) (2.9979 \times 10^8 \text{ m/s})}{2.118 \times 10^{-18} \text{ J}} = 9.379 \times 10^{8} \text{ m} = 93.79 \text{ nm}$$

Wave Mechanics and Particle in a Box

16. $\lambda = \dfrac{h}{mv} = $ wavelength of particle

a.   5.0% of speed of light = $0.050 \times 3.00 \times 10^8$ m/s = 1.5×10^7 m/s

$$\lambda = \frac{6.63 \times 10^{-34} \text{ J s}}{1.67 \times 10^{-27} \text{ kg} \times (1.5 \times 10^7 \text{ m/s})} = 2.6 \times 10^{-14} \text{ m} = 2.6 \times 10^{-5} \text{ nm}$$

Note: For units to come out, the mass must be in kg since $1 \text{ J} = \dfrac{1 \text{ kg m}^2}{\text{s}^2}$.

b. $\lambda = \dfrac{6.63 \times 10^{-34} \text{ J s}}{9.11 \times 10^{-31} \text{ kg} \times (0.15 \times 3.00 \times 10^8 \text{ m/s})} = 1.6 \times 10^{-11} \text{ m} = 1.6 \times 10^{-2} \text{ nm}$

c. $m = 5.2 \text{ oz} \times \dfrac{1 \text{ lb}}{16 \text{ oz}} \times \dfrac{1 \text{ kg}}{2.205 \text{ lb}} = 0.15 \text{ kg}$

$$v = \frac{100.8 \text{ mi}}{\text{hr}} \times \frac{1 \text{ hr}}{3600 \text{ s}} \times \frac{1760 \text{ yd}}{\text{mi}} \times \frac{0.9144 \text{ m}}{\text{yd}} = 45.06 \text{ m/s}$$

$$\lambda = \frac{h}{mv} = \frac{6.63 \times 10^{-34} \text{ J s}}{0.15 \text{ kg} \times 45.06 \text{ m/s}} = 9.8 \times 10^{-35} \text{ m} = 9.8 \times 10^{-26} \text{ nm}$$

This number is so small that it is essentially zero. We cannot detect a wavelength this small. The meaning of this number is that we do not have to consider the wave properties of large objects.

18. $\lambda = \dfrac{h}{mv}$, $v = \dfrac{h}{\lambda m}$; For $\lambda = 1.0 \times 10^2$ nm $= 1.0 \times 10^{-7}$ m:

$$v = \frac{6.63 \times 10^{-34} \text{ J s}}{(9.11 \times 10^{-31} \text{ kg}) (1.0 \times 10^{-7} \text{ m})} = 7.3 \times 10^3 \text{ m/s}$$

For $\lambda = 1.0$ nm $= 1.0 \times 10^{-9}$ m: $v = \dfrac{6.63 \times 10^{-34} \text{ J s}}{(9.11 \times 10^{-31} \text{ kg}) (1.0 \times 10^{-9} \text{ m})} = 7.3 \times 10^5$ m/s

22.   a. $\Delta p = m\Delta v = 9.11 \times 10^{-31}$ kg $\times 0.100$ m/s $= \dfrac{9.11 \times 10^{-32} \text{ kg m}}{\text{s}}$

$$\Delta p \Delta x \geq \frac{h}{4\pi}, \ \Delta x = \frac{h}{4\pi \Delta p} = \frac{6.626 \times 10^{-34} \text{ J s}}{4 \times 3.142 \times (9.11 \times 10^{-32} \text{ kg m/s})} = 5.79 \times 10^{-4} \text{ m}$$

b. $\Delta x = \dfrac{h}{4\pi \Delta p} = \dfrac{6.626 \times 10^{-34} \text{ J s}}{4 \times 3.142 \times 0.145 \text{ kg} \times 0.100 \text{ m/s}} = 3.64 \times 10^{-33}$ m

c.   Diameter of H atom is roughly 1.0×10^{-8} cm. The uncertainty in position is much larger than the size of the atom.

d.   The uncertainty is insignificant compared to the size of a baseball.

23. $E_n = \dfrac{n^2 h^2}{8 \text{ mL}^2}$; $\Delta E = E_5 - E_1 = \dfrac{h^2}{8 \text{ mL}^2} (5^2 - 1^2)$

$$\Delta E = \frac{(6.626 \times 10^{-34} \text{ J s})^2}{8(9.11 \times 10^{-31} \text{ kg}) (40.0 \times 10^{-12} \text{ m})^2} (24) = 9.04 \times 10^{-16} \text{ J}$$

$$\Delta E = \frac{hc}{\lambda}, \ \lambda = \frac{hc}{\Delta E} = \frac{(6.626 \times 10^{-34} \text{ J•s}) (2.998 \times 10^8 \text{ m/s})}{(9.04 \times 10^{-16} \text{ J})} = 2.20 \times 10^{-10} \text{ m} = 0.220 \text{ nm}$$

24. $E_n = \dfrac{n^2 h^2}{8 \text{ mL}^2}$;   As L increases, E_n will decrease and the spacing between energy levels will also decrease.

Orbitals and Quantum Numbers

28.   1p: $n = 1$, $\ell = 1$, not possible; 3f: $n = 3$, $\ell = 3$, not possible; 2d: $n = 2$, $\ell = 2$, not possible; In all three incorrect cases, $n = \ell$. The maximum value ℓ can have is $n - 1$, not n.

31.   5p: three orbitals $3d_{z^2}$: one orbital   4d: five orbitals

        $n = 5$: $\ell = 0$ (1 orbital), $\ell = 1$ (3 orbitals), $\ell = 2$ (5 orbitals), $\ell = 3$ (7 orbitals), $\ell = 4$ (9 orbitals)

        Total for $n = 5$ is 25 orbitals.

        $n = 4$: $\ell = 0$ (1), $\ell = 1$ (3), $\ell = 2$ (5), $\ell = 3$ (7); Total for $n = 4$ is 16 orbitals.

34.   The 2p orbitals differ from each other in the direction in which they point in space.

38.   A node occurs when $\psi = 0$. $\psi_{300} = 0$ when $27 - 18\sigma + 2\sigma^2 = 0$.

        Solving using the quadratic formula: $\sigma = \dfrac{18 \pm \sqrt{(18)^2 - 4(2)\,(27)}}{4} = \dfrac{18 \pm \sqrt{108}}{4}$

        $\sigma = 7.10$ or $\sigma = 1.90$; Since $\sigma = r/a_o$, the nodes occur at $r = 7.10\ a_o = 3.76 \times 10^{-10}$ m and at $r = 1.90\ a_o = 1.01 \times 10^{-10}$ m where r is the distance from the nucleus.

Polyelectronic Atoms

40. $E_n = \dfrac{-R_H Z^2}{n^2}$, $R_H = 2.178 \times 10^{-18}$ J, Z = atomic number (nuclear charge)

        Normal ionization energy is for the transition $n = 1 \rightarrow n = \infty$ ($E = 0$). Thus, the I.E. is given by the energy of state $n = 1$.

        a. $IE = 2.178 \times 10^{-18}\ J\left(\dfrac{1^2}{1^2}\right) = 2.178 \times 10^{-18}$ J/atom

        $IE = \dfrac{2.178 \times 10^{-18}\ J}{atom} \times \dfrac{1\ kJ}{1000\ J} \times \dfrac{6.022 \times 10^{23}\ atoms}{mol} = 1311.6$ kJ/mol ≈ 1312 kJ/mol

        For brevity, the I.E. of heavier one electron species can be given as:

        $IE = \dfrac{1311.6\ kJ}{mol}\left(\dfrac{Z^2}{n^2}\right)$ (We will carry an extra significant figure.)

        We get this by combining $IE = 2.178 \times 10^{-18}\ J\left(\dfrac{Z^2}{n^2}\right)$ and

        $\dfrac{2.178 \times 10^{-18}\ J}{atom} \times \dfrac{6.022 \times 10^{23}\ atoms}{mol} \times \dfrac{1\ kJ}{1000\ J} = \dfrac{1311.6\ kJ}{mol}$.

b. He^+: $Z = 2$; $IE = 1311.6$ kJ/mol $\times 2^2 = 5246$ kJ/mol   (Assume n = 1 for all.)

c. Li^{2+}: $Z = 3$; $IE = 1311.6$ kJ/mol $\times 3^2 = 1.180 \times 10^4$ kJ/mol

d. C^{5+}: $Z = 6$; $IE = 1311.6$ kJ/mol $\times 6^2 = 4.722 \times 10^4$ kJ/mol

e. Fe^{25+}: $Z = 26$; $IE = 1311.6$ kJ/mol $\times (26)^2 = 8.866 \times 10^5$ kJ/mol

41.   The size of the 1s orbitals would be proportional to 1/Z, that is as Z increases, the electrons are more strongly attracted to the nucleus and will be drawn in closer. Thus the relative sizes would be:

$$H : He^+ : Li^{2+} : C^{5+} : Fe^{25+} \quad \rightarrow \quad 1 : \frac{1}{2} : \frac{1}{3} : \frac{1}{6} : \frac{1}{26}$$

44.   a.   n = 4: ℓ can be 0, 1, 2, or 3. Thus we have s(2 e⁻), p(6 e⁻), d(10 e⁻) and f(14 e⁻) orbitals present. Total number of electrons to fill these orbitals is 32.

b.   n = 5, m_ℓ = +1: For n = 5, ℓ = 0, 1, 2, 3, 4. For ℓ = 1, 2, 3, 4, all can have m_ℓ = +1. Four distinct orbitals, thus 8 electrons.

c.   n = 5, m_s = +1/2: For n = 5, ℓ = 0, 1, 2, 3, 4. Number of orbitals = 1, 3, 5, 7, 9 for each value of ℓ, respectively. There are 25 orbitals with n = 5. They can hold 50 electrons and 25 of these electrons can have m_s = +1/2.

d.   n = 3, ℓ = 2: These quantum numbers define a set of 3d orbitals. There are 5 degenerate 3d orbitals which can hold a total of 10 electrons.

e.   n = 2, ℓ = 1; These define a set of 2p orbitals. There are 3 degenerate 2p orbitals which can hold a total of 6 electrons.

f.   It is impossible for n = 0. Thus, no electrons can have this set of quantum numbers.

g.   The 4 quantum number completely specify a single electron.

h.   n = 3: 3s, 3p and 3d orbitals all have n = 3. These orbitals can hold up to 18 electrons.

i.   n = 2, ℓ = 2: This combination is not possible (ℓ ≠ 2 for n = 2). Zero electrons in an atom can have these quantum numbers.

j.   n = 1, ℓ = 0, m_ℓ = 0: These define a 1s orbital which can hold 2 electrons.

48.   K: $1s^2 2s^2 2p^6 3s^2 3p^6 4s^1$; Rb: $1s^2 2s^2 2p^6 3s^2 3p^6 4s^2 3d^{10} 4p^6 5s^1$

Fr: $1s^2 2s^2 2p^6 3s^2 3p^6 4s^2 3d^{10} 4p^6 5s^2 4d^{10} 5p^6 6s^2 4f^{14} 5d^{10} 6p^6 7s^1$ or $[Rn]7s^1$

Pu: $[Rn]7s^2 6d^1 5f^5$ (expected from periodic table)

Sb: $1s^2 2s^2 2p^6 3s^2 3p^6 4s^2 3d^{10} 4p^6 5s^2 4d^{10} 5p^3$; Os: $[Xe]6s^2 4f^{14} 5d^6$

Pd: $1s^2 2s^2 2p^6 3s^2 3p^6 4s^2 3d^{10} 4p^6 5s^2 4d^8$ (expected from periodic table)

Pb: $[Xe]6s^2 4f^{14} 5d^{10} 6p^2$; I: $1s^2 2s^2 2p^6 3s^2 3p^6 4s^2 3d^{10} 4p^6 5s^2 4d^{10} 5p^5$

50.   a.   The smallest halogen is fluorine: $1s^2 2s^2 2p^5$ b.   K: $1s^2 2s^2 2p^6 3s^2 3p^6 4s^1$

c.   Be: $1s^2 2s^2$;   Mg: $1s^2 2s^2 2p^6 3s^2$;   Ca: $1s^2 2s^2 2p^6 3s^2 3p^6 4s^2$

d.   In: $[Kr]5s^2 4d^{10} 5p^1$ e.   C : $1s^2 2s^2 2p^2$; Si : $1s^2 2s^2 2p^6 3s^2 3p^2$

f.   This will be element #118: $[Rn]7s^2 5f^{14} 6d^{10} 7p^6$

53.   O: $1s^2 2s^2 2p_x^2 2p_y^2$ ($\underline{\uparrow\downarrow}$ $\underline{\uparrow\downarrow}$ $\underline{}$); There are no unpaired electrons in this oxygen atom. This
configuration would be an excited state and in going to the ground state ($\underline{\uparrow\downarrow}$ $\underline{\uparrow}$ $\underline{\uparrow}$), energy would
be released.

55.   a.   This atom has 10 electrons. Ne   b.   S

c.   The ground state configuration is $[Kr]5s^2 4d^9$. The element is Ag.

d.   Bi: $[Xe]6s^2 4f^{14} 5d^{10} 6p^3$

The Periodic Table and Periodic Properties

56.   a.   Be < Mg < Ca   b.   Xe < I < Te   c.   Ge < Ga < In

d.   F < N < As   e.   F < Cl < S

60.   Size also decreases going across a period. Sc & Ti and Y & Zr are adjacent elements. There are
14 elements (the lanthanides) between La and Hf, making Hf considerably smaller.

62.   a.   Uus will have 117 electrons. $[Rn]7s^2 5f^{14} 6d^{10} 7p^5$

b.   It will be in the halogen family and most similar to astatine, At.

c.   NaUus, $Mg(Uus)_2$, $C(Uus)_4$, $O(Uus)_2$

d.   Assuming Uus is like the other halogens: $UusO^-$, $UusO_2^-$, $UusO_3^-$, $UusO_4^-$

63.   a.   O < S, S most exothermic   b.   I < Br < F < Cl, Cl most exothermic

c.   N < O < F, F most exothermic

67.   a.   Li   b.   P   c. O^+

68.   a.   Cs   b.   Ga   c.   Tl

71.   a. The electron affinity of Mg^{2+} is ΔH for: $Mg^{2+}(g) + e^- \rightarrow Mg^+(g)$; This is just the reverse of the second ionization energy, or: $EA(Mg^{2+}) = -IE_2(Mg) = -1445$ kJ/mol

       b. EA of Al^+ is ΔH for: $Al^+(g) + e^- \rightarrow Al(g)$; $EA(Al^+) = -IE_1(Al) = -580$ kJ/mol

       c. IE of Cl^- is ΔH for: $Cl^-(g) \rightarrow Cl(g) + e^-$; $IE(Cl^-) = -EA(Cl) = +348.7$ kJ/mol

       d. $Cl(g) \rightarrow Cl^+(g) + e^-$ $IE = 1255$ kJ/mol (Table 12.6)

       e. $Cl^+(g) + e^- \rightarrow Cl(g)$ $\Delta H = -IE_1 = -1255$ kJ/mol $= EA (Cl^+)$

74.   As electrons are removed, the effective nuclear charge exerted on the remaining electrons increases. Since the remaining electrons are 'held' more strongly by the nucleus, the energy required to remove these electrons increases.

76.   a. More favorable EA: Li, S, B, Cl   b. Higher IE: Li, S, N, F

       c. Larger radius: K, Sc, B, Cl

The Alkaline Metals

78.   It should be potassium peroxide, K_2O_2. K^{2+} ions are not stable; the second ionization energy of K is very large compared to the first.

80. $\nu = \dfrac{c}{\lambda} = \dfrac{2.9979 \times 10^8 \text{ m/s}}{455.5 \times 10^{-9} \text{ m}} = 6.582 \times 10^{14} \text{ s}^{-1}$

       $E = h\nu = (6.626 \times 10^{-34} \text{ J s})(6.582 \times 10^{14} \text{ s}^{-1}) = 4.361 \times 10^{-19} \text{ J}$

81.   a. Carbonate ion is CO_3^{2-}. Lithium form Li^+ ions. Thus, lithium carbonate is Li_2CO_3.

       b. $\dfrac{1 \times 10^{-3} \text{ mol Li}}{L} \times \dfrac{6.9 \text{ g Li}}{\text{mol Li}} = \dfrac{7 \times 10^{-3} \text{ g Li}}{L}$

82.   a. Li_3N;   lithium nitride   b. NaBr;   sodium bromide

       c. K_2S;   potassium sulfide

83.   It should be element #119 with ground state electron configuration: $[Rn] 7s^2 5f^{14} 6d^{10} 7p^6 8s^1$

Additional Exercises

86.   We get a number of unpaired electrons by looking at the incompletely filled subshells.

       O: $[He]2s^2 2p^4$: 2 unpaired e^-: $2p^4$:   ↑↓ ↑ ↑

O^+: $[He]2s^22p^3$: 3 unpaired e⁻: $2p^3$:   ↿ ↿ ↿

O^-: $[He]2s^22p^5$: 1 unpaired e⁻: $2p^5$:   ⇅ ⇅ ↿

Fe: $[Ar]4s^23d^6$: 4 unpaired e⁻: $3d^6$:   ⇅ ↿ ↿ ↿ ↿

Mn: $[Ar]4s^23d^5$: 5 unpaired e⁻: $3d^5$:   ↿ ↿ ↿ ↿ ↿

S: $[Ne]3s^23p^4$: 2 unpaired e⁻: $3p^4$:   ⇅ ↿ ↿

F: $[He]2s^22p^5$: 1 unpaired e⁻: $2p^5$:   ⇅ ⇅ ↿

Ar: $[Ne]3s^23p^6$: no unpaired e⁻: $3p^6$:   ⇅ ⇅ ⇅

88.   For $r = a_o$ and $\theta = 0°$ ($Z = 1$ for H):

$$\psi_{2p_z} = \frac{1}{4(2\pi)^{1/2}}\left(\frac{1}{5.29 \times 10^{-11}}\right)^{3/2}(1)\, e^{-1/2}\cos 0 = 1.57 \times 10^{14};\ \psi^2 = 2.46 \times 10^{28}$$

For $r = a_o$ and $\theta = 90°$: $\psi_{2p_z} = 0$ since $\cos 90° = 0$; $\psi^2 = 0$

90.   a. $P(g) \rightarrow P^+(g) + e^-$ b. $P(g) + e^- \rightarrow P^-(g)$

It is important to remember that these terms are defined for the gaseous state.

92.   The electron is no longer part of that atom. The proton and electron are completely separated.

93.   a. excited state of boron   b. ground state of neon

   B ground state: $1s^22s^22p^1$

96. $E_{photon} = \dfrac{hc}{\lambda} = \dfrac{6.626 \times 10^{-34}\ J\ s \times (2.998 \times 10^8\ m/s)}{589 \times 10^{-9}\ m} = 3.37 \times 10^{-19}\ J$

$E = 3.37 \times 10^{-19}\ J \times \dfrac{1\ kJ}{1000\ J} \times \dfrac{6.022 \times 10^{23}}{mol} = 203\ kJ/mol$

No, since $E_{photon} < IE$, this light cannot ionize sodium.

99. $E = \dfrac{310.\ kJ}{mol} \times \dfrac{1\ mol}{6.022 \times 10^{23}} = 5.15 \times 10^{-22}\ kJ = 5.15 \times 10^{-19}\ J$

$\lambda = \dfrac{hc}{E} = \dfrac{6.626 \times 10^{-34}\ J\ s \times (2.998 \times 10^8\ m/s)}{5.15 \times 10^{-19}\ J} = 3.86 \times 10^{-7}\ m = 386\ nm$

100.   a. $n = 3$: We can have 3s, 3p, and 3d orbitals. Nine orbitals can hold 18 electrons.

     b. $n = 2$, $\ell = 0$: Specifies a 2s orbital. 2 electrons

     c. $n = 2$, $\ell = 2$: Not possible; No electrons can have this combination of quantum numbers.

     d. These four quantum numbers completely specify a single electron.

103.   a. $Cu^+(g) + e^- \rightarrow Cu(g)$ $-I_1 = -746$ kJ
                $Cu^+(g) \rightarrow Cu^{2+}(g) + e^-$ $I_2 = 1958$ kJ

          —————————————————————————————

          $2\ Cu^+(g) \rightarrow Cu(g) + Cu^{2+}(g)$ $\Delta H = 1212$ kJ

     b. $Na^-(g) \rightarrow Na(g) + e^-$ $-EA = 52$ kJ
          $Na^+(g) + e^- \rightarrow Na(g)$ $-I_1 = -495$ kJ

          —————————————————————————————

          $Na^-(g) + Na^+(g) \rightarrow 2\ Na(g)$ $\Delta H = -443$ kJ

     c. $Mg^{2+}(g) + e^- \rightarrow Mg^+(g)$ $-I_2 = -1445$ kJ
                $K(g) \rightarrow K^+(g) + e^-$ $I_1 = 419$ kJ

          —————————————————————————————

          $Mg^{2+}(g) + K(g) \rightarrow Mg^+(g) + K^+(g)$ $\Delta H = -1026$ kJ

105.   a. As: $1s^2 2s^2 2p^6 3s^2 3p^6 4s^2 3d^{10} 4p^3$

     b. Element 116 will be below Po in the periodic table: $[Rn]\ 7s^2 5f^{14} 6d^{10} 7p^4$

     c. Ta: $[Xe]6s^2 4f^{14} 5d^3$ or Ir: $[Xe]6s^2 4f^{14} 5d^7$

     d. Ti: $[Ar]4s^2 3d^2$; Ni: $[Ar]4s^2 3d^8$; Os: $[Xe]6s^2 4f^{14} 5d^6$

107.   a. The 4+ ion contains 20 electrons. Thus, the electrically neutral atom will contain 24 electrons. The atomic number is 24.

     b. The ground state electron configuration of the ion must be: $1s^2 2s^2 2p^6 3s^2 3p^6 4s^0 3d^2$; There are 6 electrons in s orbitals.

     c. 12   d. 2

     e. This is an isotope of $^{50}_{24}Cr$. There are 26 neutrons in the nucleus.

     f. 3.01×10^{23} atoms $\times \dfrac{49.9\ \text{amu}}{\text{atom}} \times \dfrac{1\ \text{g}}{6.022 \times 10^{23}\ \text{amu}} = 24.94$ g ≈ 24.9 g

     g. $1s^2 2s^2 2p^6 3s^2 3p^6 4s^1 3d^5$ is the ground state electron configuration for Cr.

110. a. Each orbital could hold 4 electrons.

b. First period: 4; Second period: 16   c. 20   d. 28

113. $\psi_{1s} = \dfrac{1}{\sqrt{\pi}}\left(\dfrac{Z}{a_0}\right)^{3/2} e^{-\sigma}$; $Z = 1$ for H, $\sigma = \dfrac{Zr}{a_0} = \dfrac{r}{a_0}$, $a_0 = 5.29 \times 10^{-11}$ m

$\psi_{1s} = \dfrac{1}{\sqrt{\pi}}\left(\dfrac{1}{a_0}\right)^{3/2} \exp\left(\dfrac{-r}{a_0}\right)$

Probability is proportional to ψ^2: $\psi_{1s}^2 = \dfrac{1}{\pi}\left(\dfrac{1}{a_0}\right)^3 \exp\left(\dfrac{-2r}{a_0}\right)$ (units of $\psi^2 = $ m^{-3})

a. ψ_{1s}^2 (at nucleus) $= \dfrac{1}{\pi}\left(\dfrac{1}{a_0}\right)^3 \exp\left[\dfrac{-2\,(0)}{a_0}\right] = 2.15 \times 10^{30}$ m^{-3}

If we assume this probability is constant throughout the 1.0×10^{-3} pm^3 volume then the total probability, p, is $\psi_{1s}^2 \times $ V.

1.0×10^{-3} pm$^3 = (1.0 \times 10^{-3}$ pm$) \times (10^{-12}$ m/pm$)^3 = 1.0 \times 10^{-39}$ m^3

total probability $= p = (2.15 \times 10^{30}$ m$^{-3}) \times (1.0 \times 10^{-39}$ m$^3) = 2.2 \times 10^{-9}$

b. For an electron that is 1.0×10^{-11} m from the nucleus:

$\psi_{1s}^2 = \dfrac{1}{\pi}\left(\dfrac{1}{5.29 \times 10^{-11}}\right)^3 \exp\left[\dfrac{-2(1.0 \times 10^{-11})}{(5.29 \times 10^{-11})}\right] = 1.5 \times 10^{30}$ m^{-3}

$V = 1.0 \times 10^{-39}$ m^3; $p = \psi_{1s}^2 \times V = 1.5 \times 10^{-9}$

c. $\psi_{1s}^2 = 2.15 \times 10^{30}$ m^{-3} $\exp\left[\dfrac{-2(53 \times 10^{-12})}{(5.29 \times 10^{-11})}\right] = 2.9 \times 10^{29}$; $V = 1.0 \times 10^{-39}$ m^3

$p = \psi_{1s}^2 \times V = 2.9 \times 10^{-10}$

d. $V = \dfrac{4}{3}\pi\,[(10.05 \times 10^{-12}$ m$)^3 - (9.95 \times 10^{-12}$ m$)^3] = 1.3 \times 10^{-34}$ m^3

We shall evaluate ψ_{1s}^2 at the middle of the shell, r = 10.00 pm, and assume ψ_{1s}^2 is constant from r = 9.95 to 10.05 pm. The concentric spheres are assumed centered about the nucleus.

$\psi_{1s}^2 = 2.15 \times 10^{30}$ m^{-3} $\exp\left[\dfrac{-2(10.0 \times 10^{-12}$ m$)}{(5.29 \times 10^{-11}$ m$)}\right] = 1.47 \times 10^{30}$ m^{-3}

$$p = (1.47 \times 10^{30} \text{ m}^{-3})(1.3 \times 10^{-34} \text{ m}^3) = 1.9 \times 10^{-4}$$

e. $V = \dfrac{4}{3}\pi\,[(52.95 \times 10^{-12} \text{ m})^3 - (52.85 \times 10^{-12} \text{ m})^3] = 4 \times 10^{-33} \text{ m}^3$

Evaluate ψ_{1s}^2 at r = 52.90 pm: $\psi_{1s}^2 = 2.15 \times 10^{30} \text{ m}^{-3}\,(e^{-2}) = 2.91 \times 10^{29} \text{ m}^{-3}; \quad p = 1 \times 10^{-3}$

114.

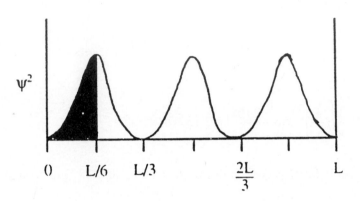

Total Area = 1; Area of one hump = 1/3

Shaded area = 1/6 = probability of finding the electron between x = 0 and x = L/6
in a one dimensional box with n = 3.

117. $E = \dfrac{h^2(n_x^2 + n_y^2 + n_z^2)}{8\,mL^2}; \quad E_{111} = \dfrac{3\,h^2}{8\,mL^2}; \quad E_{112} = \dfrac{6\,h^2}{8\,mL^2}; \quad \Delta E = \dfrac{3\,h^2}{8\,mL^2} = E_{112} - E_{111}$

$\Delta E = \dfrac{hc}{\lambda} = \dfrac{(6.626 \times 10^{-34} \text{ J·sec})(2.998 \times 10^8 \text{ m/s})}{9.50 \times 10^{-9} \text{ m}} = 2.09 \times 10^{-17} \text{ J}$

$L^2 = \dfrac{3\,h^2}{8\,m\Delta E}, \quad L = \left(\dfrac{3\,h^2}{8\,m\Delta E}\right)^{1/2} = \left[\dfrac{3(6.626 \times 10^{-34} \text{ J sec})^2}{8(9.11 \times 10^{-31} \text{ kg})(2.09 \times 10^{-17} \text{ J})}\right]^{1/2}$

$L = 9.30 \times 10^{-11} \text{ m} = 93.0 \text{ pm}$

The sphere that fits in this cube will touch the cube at the center of each face. The diameter of the sphere will equal the length of the cube. So:

2 r = L and r = 46.5 pm

CHAPTER THIRTEEN

BONDING: GENERAL CONCEPTS

Chemical Bonds and Electronegativity

1. a. Electronegativity: The ability of an atom <u>in a molecule</u> to attract electrons to itself.

    Electron affinity: The energy change for $M(g) + e^- \rightarrow M^-(g)$. EA deals with isolated atoms in the gas phase.

    b. Covalent bond: Sharing of electron pair(s); Polar covalent bond: Unequal sharing of electron pair(s).

    c. Ionic bond: Electrons are no longer shared, i.e., complete transfer of electron(s) from one atom to another.

3. Using the periodic table we expect the general trend for electronegativity to be:
    1) increase as we go from left to right across a period
    2) decrease as we go down a group

    a. $C < N < O$ b. $Se < S < Cl$ c. $Sn < Ge < Si$ d. $Tl < Ge < S$

4. The most polar bond will have the greatest difference in electronegativity between the two atoms. From positions in the periodic table, we would predict:

    a. Ge-F   b. P-Cl   c. S-F   d. Ti-Cl

5. The general trends in electronegativity used on Exercises 13.3 and 13.4 are only rules of thumb. In this exercise we use experimental values of electronegativities and can begin to see several exceptions. The order of EN from Figure 13.3 is:

    a. $C\ (2.5) < N\ (3.0) < O\ (3.5)$ same as predicted

    b. $Se\ (2.4) < S\ (2.5) < Cl\ (3.0)$ same

    c. $Si = Ge = Sn\ (1.8)$ different   d. $Tl\ (1.8) = Ge\ (1.8) < S\ (2.5)$ different

Most polar bonds using actual EN values:

    a.   Si-F and Ge-F equal polarity (Ge-F predicted)

    b.   P-Cl (same as predicted)

    c.   S-F (same as predicted)   d.   Ti-Cl (same as predicted)

Ionic Compounds

7.   a. $Cu > Cu^+ > Cu^{2+}$ b. $Pt^{2+} > Pd^{2+} > Ni^{2+}$ c. $Se^{2-} > S^{2-} > O^{2-}$

For answer a, as electrons are removed from an atom, the size decreases. Answers b - c follow the radii trend.

8.   a. Mg^{2+}: $1s^2 2s^2 2p^6$ Sn^{2+}: $[Kr]5s^2 4d^{10}$

            K^+: $1s^2 2s^2 2p^6 3s^2 3p^6$ Al^{3+}: $1s^2 2s^2 2p^6$

            Tl^+: $[Xe]6s^2 4f^{14} 5d^{10}$ As^{3+}: $[Ar]4s^2 3d^{10}$

     b. N^{3-}, O^{2-} and F^-: $1s^2 2s^2 2p^6$ Te^{2-}: $[Kr]5s^2 4d^{10} 5p^6$

9.   a. Sc^{3+} b. Te^{2-}

10.   Isoelectronic: Same number of electrons.

There are two variables, number of protons and number of electrons, that will determine the size of an ion. Keeping the number of electrons constant we only have to consider the number of protons to predict trends in size. The smallest ion has the most protons.

12.   Lattice energy is proportional to $\dfrac{Q_1 Q_2}{r}$.

In general, charge effects are much greater than size effects.

     a.   NaCl, Na^+ smaller than K^+ b.   LiF, F^- smaller than Cl^-

     c.   MgO, O^{2-} greater charge than OH^-

14.

$Na(s) \rightarrow Na(g)$	$\Delta H = 109$ kJ (sublimation)
$Na(g) \rightarrow Na^+(g) + e^-$	$\Delta H = 495$ kJ (ionization energy)
$1/2\ Cl_2(g) \rightarrow Cl(g)$	$\Delta H = 239/2$ kJ (bond energy)
$Cl(g) + e^- \rightarrow Cl^-(g)$	$\Delta H = -349$ kJ (electron affinity)
$Na^+(g) + Cl^-(g) \rightarrow NaCl(s)$	$\Delta H = -786$ kJ (lattice energy)

$$Na(s) + 1/2\ Cl_2(g) \rightarrow NaCl(s) \qquad \Delta H_f^{\cdot} = -412 \text{ kJ/mol}$$

16. a. From the data given, it costs less energy to produce $Mg^+(g) + O^-(g)$ than to produce $Mg^{2+}(g) + O^{2-}(g)$. However, the lattice energy for $Mg^{2+}O^{2-}$ will be much larger than for Mg^+O^-. The favorable lattice energy term will dominate and $Mg^{2+}O^{2-}$ forms.

b. Mg^+ and O^- both have unpaired electrons. In Mg^{2+} and O^{2-}, there are no unpaired electrons. Hence, Mg^+O^- would be paramagnetic; $Mg^{2+}O^{2-}$ would be diamagnetic. Paramagnetism can be detected by measuring the mass of a sample in the presence and absence of a magnetic field. The apparent mass of a paramagnetic substance will be larger in a magnetic field because of the force between the unpaired electrons and the field.

18.

$O(g) + e^- \rightarrow O^-(g)$	$\Delta H = -141$ kJ/mol
$O^-(g) + e^- \rightarrow O^{2-}(g)$	$\Delta H = 878$ kJ/mol

$$O(g) + 2\ e^- \rightarrow O^{2-}(g) \qquad \Delta H = 737 \text{ kJ/mol}$$

19. The extra electron-electron repulsions are much greater than the attraction of the electron for the nucleus.

21. The compounds are FeO, Fe_2O_3, $FeCl_2$ and $FeCl_3$. Lattice energy is proportional to the charge of the cation times the charge of the anion, Q_1Q_2.

Compound	Q_1Q_2	Lattice Energy
$FeCl_2$	$(+2)(-1)$	-2631 kJ/mol
$FeCl_3$	$(+3)(-1)$	-3865 kJ/mol
FeO	$(+2)(-2)$	-5359 kJ/mol
Fe_2O_3	$(+3)(-2)$	-14,744 kJ/mol

22. a. Li^+ and N^{3-} are the expected ions. The formula of the compound would be Li_3N (lithium nitride).

b. Ga^{3+} and O^{2-}; Ga_2O_3 [gallium(III) oxide]

c. Rb^+ and Cl^-; $RbCl$ (rubidium chloride)

d. Ba^{2+} and S^{2-}; BaS (barium sulfide)

Bond Energies

23.

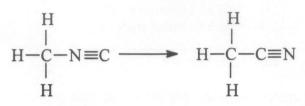

Bonds broken: 1 C – N (305 kJ/mol)   Bonds formed: 1 C – C (347 kJ/mol)

$\Delta H = \Sigma D_{broken} - \Sigma D_{formed}$, $\Delta H = 305 - 347 = -42$ kJ

Note: Many bonds usually remain the same between reactants and products. Only break and form bonds that are involved in the reaction.

24.   a.   H – H + Cl – Cl → 2 H – Cl

Bonds broken: Bonds formed:

    1 H – H (432 kJ/mol)   2 H – Cl (427 kJ/mol)
    1 Cl – Cl (239 kJ/mol)

$\Delta H = \Sigma D_{broken} - \Sigma D_{formed}$, $\Delta H = 432$ kJ $+ 239$ kJ $- 2(427)$ kJ $= -183$ kJ

    b.

$$N \equiv N + 3\,H - H \longrightarrow 2\;H - \underset{\underset{\textstyle H}{|}}{N} - H$$

Bonds broken: Bonds formed:

    1 N ≡ N (941 kJ/mol)   6 N – H (391 kJ/mol)
    3 H – H (432 kJ/mol)

$\Delta H = 941$ kJ $+ 3(432)$ kJ $- 6(391)$ kJ $= -109$ kJ

25.   a. $\Delta H = 2\;\Delta H_f^{\bullet}$ (HCl) $= 2$ mol(-92 kJ/mol) $= -184$ kJ (-183 kJ from bond energies)

    b. $\Delta H = 2\;\Delta H_f^{\bullet}$ (NH$_3$) $= 2$ mol(-46 kJ/mol) $= -92$ kJ (-109 kJ from bond energies)

Comparing the values for each reaction, bond energies seem to give a reasonably good estimate for the enthalpy change of a reaction. The estimate is especially good for gas phase reactions.

28.   a.   I.

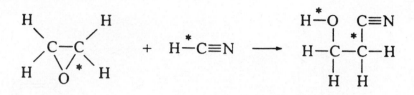

Bonds broken (*):   Bonds formed (*):

   1 C – O (358 kJ)   1 O – H (467 kJ)
   1 H – C (413 kJ)   1 C – C (347 kJ)

ΔH_I = 358 kJ + 413 kJ - [467 kJ + 347 kJ] = -43 kJ

II.

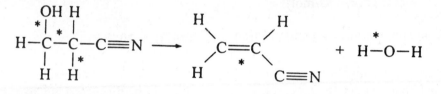

Bonds broken (*):   Bonds formed (*):

   1 C – O (358 kJ/mol)   1 H – O (467 kJ/mol)
   1 C – H (413 kJ/mol)   1 C = C (614 kJ/mol)
   1 C – C (347 kJ/mol)

ΔH_{II} = 358 kJ + 413 kJ + 347 kJ - [467 kJ + 614 kJ] = +37 kJ

$\Delta H = \Delta H_I + \Delta H_{II}$ = -43 kJ + 37 kJ = -6 kJ

b.

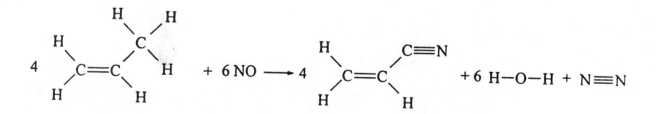

Bonds broken: Bonds formed:

   4 × 3 C – H (413 kJ/mol)   4 C ≡ N (891 kJ/mol)
   6 N = O (630. kJ/mol   6 × 2 H – O (467 kJ/mol)
                                         1 N ≡ N (941 kJ/mol)

$$\Delta H = 12(413) + 6(630.) - [4(891) + 12(467) + 941] = -1373 \text{ kJ}$$

c.

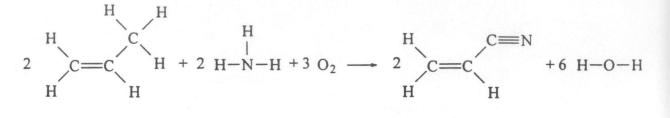

Bonds broken: Bonds formed:

$2 \times 3 \text{ C} - \text{H}$ (413 kJ/mol) $2 \text{ C} \equiv \text{N}$ (891 kJ/mol)
$2 \times 3 \text{ N} - \text{H}$ (391 kJ/mol) $6 \times 2 \text{ O} - \text{H}$ (467 kJ/mol)
$3 \text{ O} = \text{O}$ (495 kJ/mol)

$$\Delta H = 6(413) + 6(391) + 3(495) - [2(891) + 12(467)] = -1077 \text{ kJ}$$

29.   Since both reactions are highly exothermic, the high temperature is not needed to provide
       energy. It must be necessary for some other reason. This will be discussed in Chapter 15 on
       kinetics.

31.   a. $\text{HF(g)} \rightarrow \text{H(g)} + \text{F(g)}$ $\Delta H = 565$ kJ
              $\text{H(g)} \rightarrow \text{H}^+\text{(g)} + \text{e}^-$ $\Delta H = 1312$ kJ
              $\text{F(g)} + \text{e}^- \rightarrow \text{F}^-\text{(g)}$ $\Delta H = -327.8$ kJ

       _____

              $\text{HF(g)} \rightarrow \text{H}^+\text{(g)} + \text{F}^-\text{(g)}$ $\Delta H = 1549$ kJ

       b. $\text{HCl(g)} \rightarrow \text{H(g)} + \text{Cl(g)}$ $\Delta H = 427$ kJ
              $\text{H(g)} \rightarrow \text{H}^+\text{(g)} + \text{e}^-$ $\Delta H = 1312$ kJ
              $\text{Cl(g)} + \text{e}^- \rightarrow \text{Cl}^-\text{(g)}$ $\Delta H = -348.7$ kJ

       _____

              $\text{HCl(g)} \rightarrow \text{H}^+\text{(g)} + \text{Cl}^-\text{(g)}$ $\Delta H = 1390.$ kJ

32.   a.   Using SF_4 data: $SF_4\text{(g)} \rightarrow \text{S(g)} + 4 \text{ F(g)}$

              $\Delta H° = 4 \text{ D}_{SF} = 278.8 \text{ kJ} + 4(79.0 \text{ kJ}) - (-775 \text{ kJ}) = 1370. \text{ kJ}$

              $$\text{D}_{SF} = \frac{1370. \text{ kJ}}{4 \text{ mol SF bonds}} = 342.5 \text{ kJ/mol}$$

              Using SF_6 data: $SF_6\text{(g)} \rightarrow \text{S(g)} + 6 \text{ F(g)}$

              $\Delta H° = 6 \text{ D}_{SF} = 278.8 \text{ kJ} + 6(79.0 \text{ kJ}) - (-1209 \text{ kJ}) = 1962 \text{ kJ}$

              $$\text{D}_{SF} = \frac{1962 \text{ kJ}}{6} = 327.0 \text{ kJ/mol}$$

b. The S – F bond energy in the table is 327 kJ/mol. The value in the table was based on the S – F bond in SF_6.

c. S(g) and F(g) are not the most stable form of the element at 25°C and 1 atm. The most stable forms are $S_8(s)$ and $F_2(g)$; $\Delta H_f^{\bullet} = 0$ for these two species.

33. $NH_3(g) \rightarrow N(g) + 3\ H(g)$

$\Delta H° = 3\ D_{NH} = 472.7\ kJ + 3(216.0\ kJ) - (-46.1\ kJ) = 1166.8\ kJ$

$D_{NH} = \dfrac{1166.8\ kJ}{3\ mol\ NH\ bonds} = 388.93\ kJ/mol$

$D_{calc} = 389$ kJ/mol as compared to 391 kJ/mol in the table. There is good agreement.

34. $N_2 + 3\ H_2 \rightarrow 2\ NH_3$; $\Delta H = D_{N_2} + 3\ D_{H_2} - 6\ D_{NH}$; $\Delta H° = 2(-46\ kJ) = -92\ kJ$

-92 kJ = 941 kJ + 3(432 kJ) - (6 D_{N-H}), 6 D_{N-H} = 2329 kJ, D_{N-H} = 388.2 kJ/mol

Exercise 33: 389 kJ/mol; Table in text: 391 kJ/mol

There is good agreement between all three values.

Lewis Structures and Resonance

37.   a. HCN has 1 + 4 + 5 = 10 valence electrons.

b. PH_3 has 5 + 3(1) = 8 valence electrons.

skeletal	complete

uses 4 e⁻: (6 e⁻ left, 3 pairs)

skeletal	complete

uses 6 e⁻: (2 e⁻ left, 1 pair)

c. $CHCl_3$ has $4 + 1 + 3(7) = 26$ valence electrons.

d. NH_4^+ has $5 + 4(1) - 1 = 8$ valence electrons.

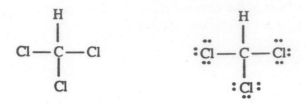

skeletal   complete

uses 8 e⁻: (18 e⁻ left, 9 pairs)

e. BF_4^- has $3 + 4(7) + 1 = 32$ valence electrons.

f. SeF_2 has $6 + 2(7) = 20$ valence electrons.

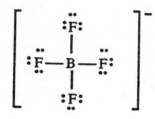

38.   a. $POCl_3$ has $5 + 6 + 3(7) = 32$ valence electrons.

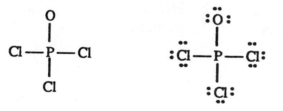

skeletal structure   complete octets

This structure uses all 32 e⁻ while satisfying the octet rule for all atoms. This is a valid Lewis structure.

SO_4^{2-} has $6 + 4(6) + 2 = 32$ valence electrons.

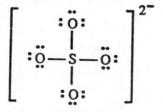

Note: A negatively charged ion will have additional electrons to those that come from the valence shells of the atoms.

XeO$_4$, 8 + 4(6) = 32 e$^-$ PO$_4^{3-}$, 5 + 4(6) + 3 = 32 e$^-$

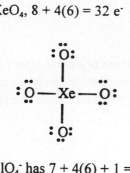   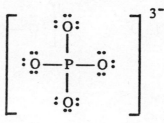

ClO$_4^-$ has 7 + 4(6) + 1 = 32 valence electrons.

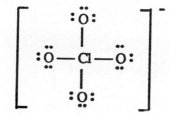

Note: All of these species have the
same number of atoms and the same
number of valence electrons. They also
have the same Lewis structure.

b.   NF$_3$ has 5 + 3(7) = 26 valence electrons.

F—N—F   :F̈—N—F̈:
   | |
   F   :F̈:

skeletal   complete
structure   octets

SO$_3^{2-}$, 6 + 3(6) + 2 = 26 e$^-$ PO$_3^{3-}$, 5 + 3(6) + 3 = 26 e$^-$

ClO$_3^-$, 7 + 3(6) + 1 = 26 e$^-$

Note: Species with the same number of
atoms and valence electrons have similar
Lewis structures.

c. ClO_2^- has $7 + 2(6) + 1 = 20$ valence electrons.

O – Cl – O   [:Ö—Cl̈—Ö:]⁻   All atoms obey the octet rule and we
                                            have used all the valence electrons.
                                            This is a valid Lewis structure.

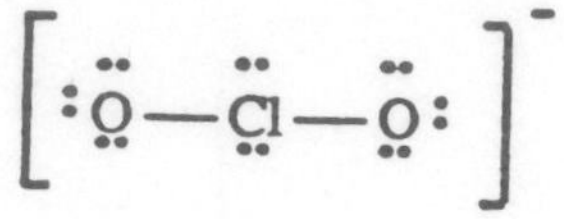

skeletal   complete
structure   octets

SCl_2, $6 + 2(7) = 20$ e⁻ PCl_2^-, $5 + 2(7) + 1 = 20$ e⁻

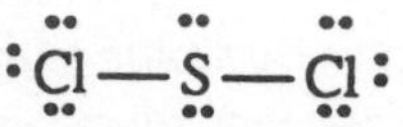

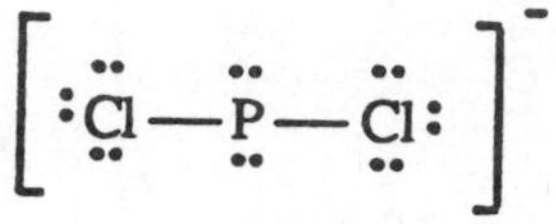

:Cl̈—S̈—Cl̈:   [:Cl̈—P̈—Cl̈:]⁻

Note: Species with the same number of atoms and valence electrons have similar Lewis
structures.

39.   Molecules/ions that have the same number of valence electrons and the same number of atoms
        will have similar Lewis structures.

40.   a. NO_2^- has $5 + 2(6) + 1 = 18$ valence electrons.

O—N—O   :Ö—N—Ö:

skeletal structure   complete octet of more
                                   electronegative oxygen
                                   (16 e⁻ used)

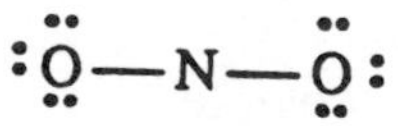

We have 1 more pair of e⁻. Putting this pair on the nitrogen we get:

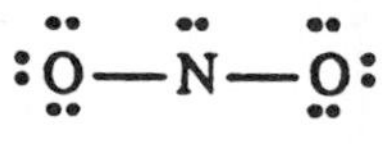

:Ö—N̈—Ö: This accounts for all 18 electrons, but N does not obey the octet rule.

To get an octet about the nitrogen and not use any more electrons, one of the unshared pairs
on an oxygen must be shared between N and O instead.

[:O̤=N̈—Ö:]⁻   ←→   [:Ö—N̈=O̤:]⁻
    0   0   -1   -1   0   0

Since there is no reason to have the double bond to either oxygen atom, we can draw two
resonance structures. Formal charges are shown.

HNO₂ has 1 + 5 + 2(6) = 18 valence electrons.

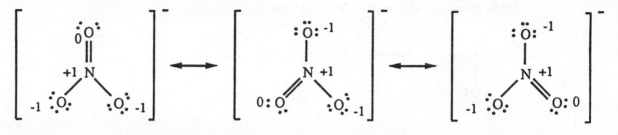

NO₃⁻ has 5 + 3(6) + 1 = 24 valence electrons.

HNO₃ has 1 + 5 + 3(6) = 24 valence electrons.

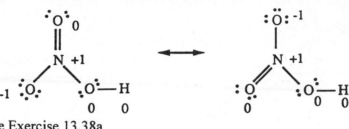

b.   SO₄²⁻, See Exercise 13.38a.

HSO₄⁻ has 1 + 6 + 4(6) + 1 = 32
valence electrons

H₂SO₄ has 2 + 6 + 4(6) = 32
valence electrons

c.   CN⁻, 4 + 5 + 1 = 10 e⁻

$$\left[:C\equiv N:\right]^{-}$$
$$\quad -1 \quad\quad 0$$

HCN, 1 + 4 + 5 = 10 e⁻

H—C≡N:
0   0   0

41.   Ozone: O₃ has 3(6) = 18 valence electrons.

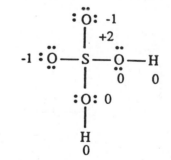

Sulfur dioxide: SO$_2$ has 6 + 2(6) = 18 valence electrons.

$$\ddot{\underset{..}{O}}\!=\!\overset{..}{S}\!-\!\ddot{\underset{..}{O}}\!: \quad\longleftrightarrow\quad :\ddot{\underset{..}{O}}\!-\!\overset{..}{S}\!=\!\ddot{\underset{..}{O}}$$

Sulfur trioxide: SO$_3$ has 6 + 3(6) = 24 valence electrons.

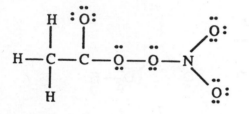

42.   PAN (H$_3$C$_2$NO$_5$)) has 3 + 2(4) + 5 + 5(6) = 46 valence electrons.

Skeletal structure with complete octets about oxygen atoms (46 electrons used).

This structure has used all 46 electrons, but there are only six electrons around one of the carbon atoms and the nitrogen atom. Two unshared pairs must become shared, that is we form two double bonds.

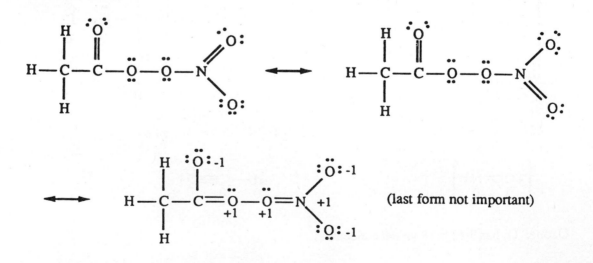

(last form not important)

45.

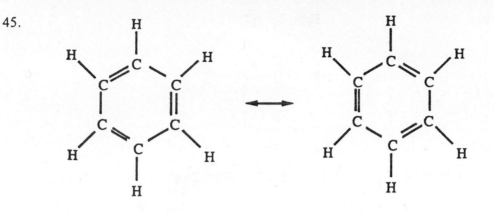

Benzene has 6(4) + 6(1) = 30 valence electrons.

46.   If no resonance:

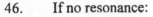

4
different
molecules

With resonance:

3
different
molecules

If resonance is present, we can't distinguish between a single and double bond between adjacent carbons. All carbon-carbon bonds are equivalent (represented by the circle in the structures). Since only 3 isomers are observed provides evidence for the existence of resonance.

47.   Borazine ($B_3N_3H_6$) has 3(3) + 3(5) + 6(1) = 30 valence electrons.

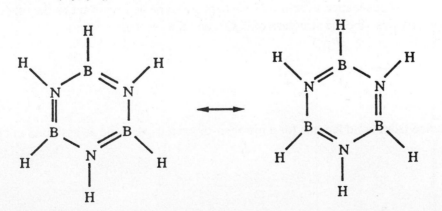

49. PF_5, $5 + 5(7) = 40$ e⁻ BrF_3, $7 + 3(7) = 28$ e⁻

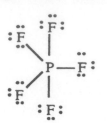   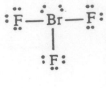

$Be(CH_3)_2$, $2 + 2[4 + 3(1)] = 16$ e⁻ BCl_3, $3 + 3(7) = 24$ e⁻

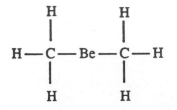   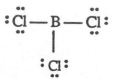

$XeOF_4$, $8 + 6 + 4(7) = 42$ e⁻ XeF_6, $8 + 6(7) = 50$ e⁻

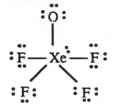   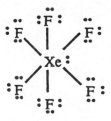

SeF_4 has $6 + 4(7) = 34$ valence electrons.

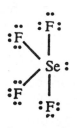

52.   The nitrogen-nitrogen bond length of 112 pm is between a double (120 pm) and a triple (110 pm)
        bond. The nitrogen-oxygen bond length of 119 pm is between a single (147 pm) and a double
        bond (115 pm). The last resonance structure doesn't appear to be as important as the other two
        and we can adequately describe the structure of N_2O using the resonance forms:

        :N══N══O: ⟷ :N≡N—O:

        There is no evidence from bond lengths for a nitrogen-oxygen triple bond as assigned in the third
        resonance form.

54.   CO: :C≡O: Triple bond between C and O.

       CO₂: :O=C=O: Double bond between C and O.

CO₃²⁻:

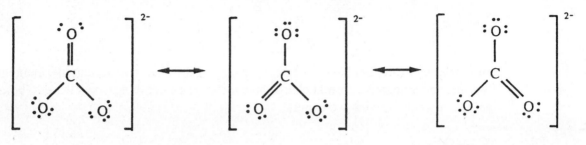

              Average of 1 1/3 bond between C and O.

CH₃OH:

   Single bond between C and O.

       Longest → shortest: $CH_3OH > CO_3^{2-} > CO_2 > CO$

       Weakest → strongest: $CH_3OH < CO_3^{2-} < CO_2 < CO$

Formal Charge

56.   :N̈=N=Ö: ⟷ :N≡N—Ö: ⟷ :N̈—N≡O:

       -1   +1   0   0   +1   -1   -2   +1   +1

       For: (:N̈=) $FC = 5 - 4 - 1/2(4) = -1$

             (=N=) $FC = 5 - 1/2(8) = +1$ Same for ≡N— and —N≡

             (:N̈—) $FC = 5 - 6 - 1/2(2) = -2$

             (:N≡) $FC = 5 - 2 - 1/2(6) = 0$

             (=O̤:) $FC = 6 - 4 - 1/2(4) = 0$

             (—Ö:) $FC = 6 - 6 - 1/2(2) = -1$

             (≡O:) $FC = 6 - 2 - 1/2(6) = +1$

We should eliminate N – N = O since it has a formal charge of +1 on the most electronegative element present (O). This is consistent with the observation that the N - N bond is between a double and triple bond and that the N – O bond is between a single and double bond.

57.   The Lewis structure

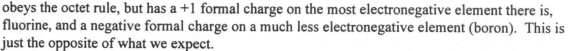

obeys the octet rule, but has a +1 formal charge on the most electronegative element there is, fluorine, and a negative formal charge on a much less electronegative element (boron). This is just the opposite of what we expect.

58. $:C \equiv O:$

Carbon: FC = 4 - 2 - 1/2(6) = -1; Oxygen: FC = 6 - 2 - 1/2(6) = +1

Electronegativity predicts the opposite polarization. The two opposing effects seem to cancel to give a much less polar molecule than expected.

59.   See Exercise 8.38a for Lewis structures of a, b, c and d.

a. $POCl_3$: P, FC = 5 - 1/2(8) = +1   b. SO_4^{2-}: S, FC = 6 - 1/2(8) = +2

c. ClO_4^-: Cl, FC = 7 - 1/2(8) = +3   d. PO_4^{3-}: P, FC = 5 - 1/2(8) = +1

60.   a.   b.

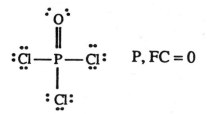

P, FC = 0

S, FC = 0

c.   d.

Cl, FC = 0

P, FC = 0

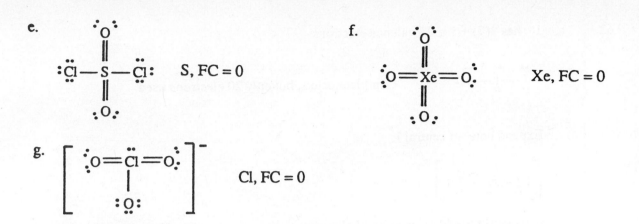

e.   S, FC = 0   f.   Xe, FC = 0

g.   Cl, FC = 0

h. We can't. To minimze the formal charge on N would require N to expand its octet. Nitrogen will never have more than eight electrons around itself.

Molecular Geometry and Polarity

61.   13.37 a.   linear, 180°   b.   trigonal pyramid, < 109.5°

c.   tetrahedral, ≈ 109.5°   d.   tetrahedral, 109.5°

e.   tetrahedral, 109.5°   f.   V-shaped or bent, < 109.5°

13.38 a.   all are tetrahedral, ≈ 109.5°

b.   all are trigonal pyramid, < 109.5°

c.   all are bent (V-shaped), < 109.5°

13.40 a. NO_2^-:   bent, < 120°

HNO_2: bent about N, < 120°; bent about N – O – H, < 109.5°

NO_3^-:   trigonal planar, 120°

HNO_3: trigonal planar about N, 120°; bent about N – O – H, < 109.5°

b.   tetrahedral about S in all three, ≈ 109.5°; bent about S - O - H, < 109.5°

c.   HCN: linear, 180°; CN⁻ has no bond angle.

d.   all are linear; 180°

e.   linear about both carbons, 180°

62.   a. I_3^- has $3(7) + 1 = 22$ valence electrons.

:Ï—Ï—Ï: Complete octets, but only 20 electrons used.

Expand octet of central I:

$$\left[:\ddot{I}-\overset{..}{\underset{..}{I}}-\ddot{I}: \right]^-$$

In general we add extra pairs of electrons to the central atom. We can see a more specific reason when we look at how I_3^- forms in solution:

$$I_2(aq) + I^-(aq) \rightarrow I_3^-(aq)$$

:Ï—Ï: + $\left[:\ddot{I}: \right]^-$ → $\left[:\ddot{I}-\overset{..}{I}-\ddot{I}: \right]^-$

There are 5 pairs of electrons about the central ion. The structure will be based on a trigonal bipyramid. The lone pair requires more room and will occupy the equatorial positions. The bonding pairs will occupy the axial position.

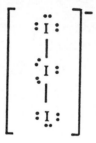

axial: apex of the trigonal pyramid

equatorial: around the middle of the pyramid, the corners of the trigonal plane.

Thus, I_3^- is linear with a 180° bond angle.

   b. ClF_3 has $7 + 3(7) = 28$ valence electrons.

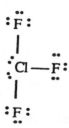

T-shaped, FClF angles are ≈ 90°C. Since the lone pairs will take up more space, the FClF bond angles will probably be slightly less than 90°.

   c. IF_4^+ has $7 + 4(7) - 1 = 34$ valence electrons.

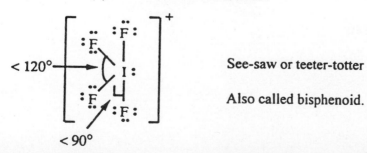

See-saw or teeter-totter

Also called bisphenoid.

d. SF_5^+ has $6 + 5(7) - 1 = 40$ valence electrons.

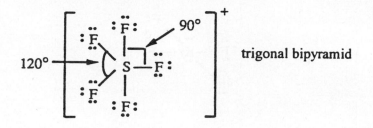

trigonal bipyramid

Note: All of the species in this exercise have 5 pairs of electrons around the central atom. All of the structures are based on a trigonal bipyramid, but only in SF_5^+ are all of the pairs bonding pairs. Thus, SF_5^+ is the only one we describe the molecular structure as trigonal bipyramidal. Still, we had to begin with the trigonal bipyramid to get to the structures of the others.

63.   a. SeO_3^{2-}, $6 + 3(6) + 2 = 26$ e⁻   b. SeH_2, $6 + 2(1) = 8$ e⁻

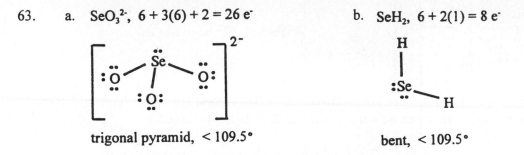

trigonal pyramid, $< 109.5°$ bent, $< 109.5°$

c. SeO_4^{2-} has $6 + 4(6) + 2 = 32$ valence electrons.

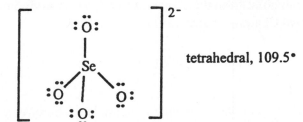

tetrahedral, $109.5°$

Note: There are 4 pairs of electrons about the Se atom in each case in this exercise. All of the structures are based on a tetrahedral geometry, but only SeO_4^{2-} has a tetrahedral structure. We consider only the positions of the atoms when describing the molecular structure.

64.   a. BrF_5, $7 + 5(7) = 42$ e⁻

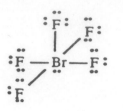

b. KrF_4, $8 + 4(7) = 36$ e⁻

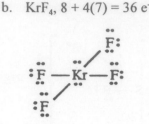

square pyramid, ≈ 90°

square planar, 90°

c. IF_6^+ has $7 + 6(7) - 1 = 48$ valence electrons.

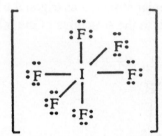

octahedral, 90° bond angles

Note: All these species have 6 pairs of electrons around the central atom. All three structures are based on the octahedron, but only IF_6^+ has octahedral molecular structure.

66.   a.

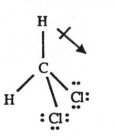

The C–H bonds are assumed nonpolar since the electronegativities of C and H are about equal.

δ+   δ-
C – Cl is the charge distribution for each C–Cl bond. The two individual C–Cl bond dipoles add toghether to give an overall dipole moment for the molecule. The overall dipole will point from the C (positive end) to the midpoint of the two Cl atoms (negative end).

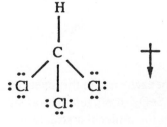

The C–H bond is essentially nonpolar. The three C–Cl bond dipoles add together to give an overall dipole moment for the molecule. The overall dipole will have the negative end at the midpoint of the three chlorines and the positive end at the carbon.

CCl_4 is nonpolar. CCl_4 is a tetrahedral molecule. All four C–Cl bond dipoles cancel when added together. Let's consider just the C and two of the Cl atoms. There will be a net dipole pointing in the direction of the middle of the two Cl atoms.

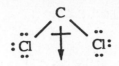

There will be an equal and opposite dipole arising from the other two Cl atoms. Combining:

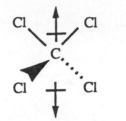

The two dipoles will cancel and CCl_4 is nonpolar.

b. CO_2 is nonpolar. CO_2 is a linear molecule with two equivalent bond dipoles that cancel. N_2O is polar since the bond dipoles do not cancel.

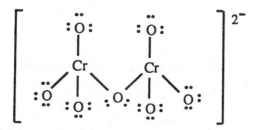

67.   a. CrO_4^{2-} has $6 + 4(6) + 2 = 32$ valence electrons.

$$\begin{bmatrix} \ \ \ \ \ \ :\ddot{O}: \ \ \ \ \ \ \\ \ \ \ \ \ \ \ | \ \ \ \ \ \ \\ :\ddot{O} - Cr - \ddot{O}: \\ \ \ \ \ \ \ \ | \ \ \ \ \ \ \\ \ \ \ \ \ \ :\ddot{O}: \ \ \ \ \ \ \end{bmatrix}^{2-}$$

tetrahedral

Cr has an electron configuration of $[Ar]4s^23d^4$. We count all six electrons beyond the argon core.

b.   Dichromate ion ($Cr_2O_7^{2-}$) has $2(6) + 7(6) + 2 = 56$ valence electrons.

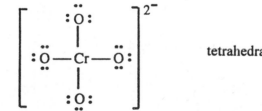

There is no simple way to describe the structure. We would expect there to be a roughly tetrahedral arrangement of O atoms about each Cr and the $Cr - O - Cr$ bond to be bent with an angle $< 109.5°$.

68.   The two requirements for a polar molecule are:

1. polar bonds

2. a structure such that the polar bonds do not cancel.

In addition, some molecules that have no polar bonds, but contain unsymmetrical lone pairs are polar. For example, PH_3 and AsH_3 are slightly polar.

69.   a. OCl_2, $6 + 2(7) = 20$ e⁻ Br_3^-, $3(7) + 1 = 22$ e⁻

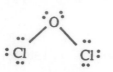

bent, polar   linear, nonpolar

BeH_2, $2 + 2(1) = 4$ e⁻ BH_2^-, $3 + 2(1) + 1 = 6$ e⁻

H—Be—H

linear, nonpolar   bent, polar

Note: All four species contain three atoms. They have different structures because the number of lone pairs of electrons around the central atom are different in each case.

b. BCl_3, $3 + 3(7) = 24$ e⁻ NF_3, $5 + 3(7) = 26$ e⁻

trigonal planar, nonpolar   Trigonal pyramid, polar

IF_3 has $7 + 3(7) = 28$ valence electrons.

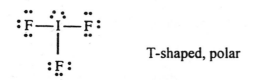

                                                           T-shaped, polar

Note: Each molecule has the same number of atoms, but the structures are different because of differing numbers of lone pairs around each central atom.

c. CF_4, $4 + 4(7) = 32$ e⁻ SeF_4, $6 + 4(7) = 34$ e⁻

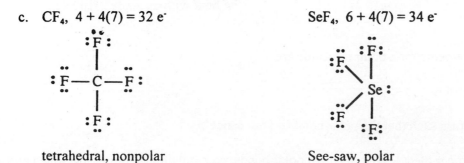

tetrahedral, nonpolar   See-saw, polar

XeF_4, $8 + 4(7) = 36$ valence electrons

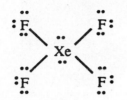

square planar, nonpolar

Again, each molecule has the same number of atoms, but a different structure because of differing numbers of lone pairs around the central atom.

d. IF_5, $7 + 5(7) = 42$ e⁻ AsF_5, $5 + 5(7) = 40$ e⁻

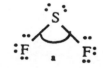

square pyramid, polar   trigonal bipyramid, nonpolar

Yet again, the molecules have the same number of atoms, but different structures because of the presence of differing numbers of lone pairs.

70. SF_2, $6 + 2(7) = 20$ e⁻ SF_4, $6 + 4(7) = 34$ e⁻

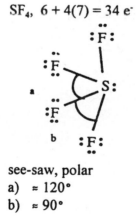

bent, polar   see-saw, polar
a)   109.5°   a)   ≈ 120°
                                                    b)   ≈ 90°

SF_6, $6 + 6(7) = 48$ e⁻

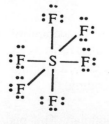

octahedral, nonpolar, 90°

S_2F_4, $2(6) + 4(7) = 40$ e$^-$

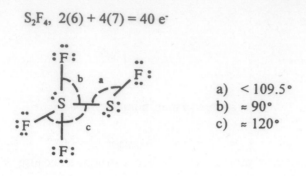

a) $< 109.5°$
b) $\approx 90°$
c) $\approx 120°$

There is no easy description of the S_2F_4 structure. There is a trigonal bipyramidal arrangement (3 F, 1 S, 1 lone pair) about one sulfur and a tetrahedral (1 F, 1 S, 2 lone pairs) arrangement of e$^-$ pairs about the other sulfur. With this picture we can predict values for all bond angles. The molecule will be polar.

73.   a.   b.

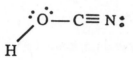

polar

b.

$:\ddot{F} - Be - \ddot{F}:$

nonpolar

c.   d.

(Kr with 4 F)

nonpolar

d.

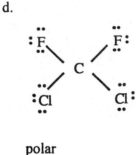

polar

Additional Exercises

74.   The general structure of the trihalide ions is:

$:\ddot{X} - \ddot{X} - \ddot{X}:$

Bromine and iodine are large enough and have low energy, empty d-orbitals to accommodate the expanded octet. Fluorine is small and its valence shell contains only 2s and 2p orbitals (4 orbitals) and cannot expand its octet. The lowest energy d orbitals in F are the 3d orbitals. They are too high in energy, compared to the 2s and 2p orbitals, to be used in bonding.

76.   C ≡ O (1072 kJ/mol) and N ≡ N (941 kJ/mol); CO is polar while N_2 is nonpolar. This may lead to a greater reactivity.

77.   The stable species are:

a. SO_4^{2-}:   We can't draw a Lewis structure that obeys the octet rule for SO_4. The two extra electrons (from the -2 charge) complete octets.

b. PF_5:   N is too small and doesn't have low energy d-orbitals to expand its octet.

c. SF_6:   O is too small and doesn't have low energy d-orbitals to expand its octet.

d. BH_4^-: BH_3 doesn't obey octet rule.

79.   No, we would expect the more highly charged ions to have a greater attraction for an electron. Thus, the electronegativity of an element does depend on its oxidation state.

81.   a. BF_3, $3 + 3(7) = 24$ e⁻   b. PF_3, $5 + 3(7) = 26$ e⁻

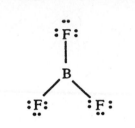

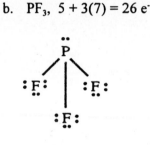

trigonal planar, nonpolar   trigonal pyramid, polar

c. BrF_3 has $7 + 3(7) = 28$ valence electrons.

T-shape, polar

Again we see a series of molecules with the same number of atoms, but different numbers of lone pairs. They all have different structures.

83.

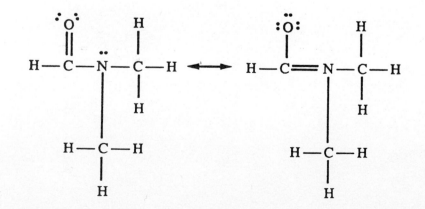

85.   a. $Na^+(g) + Cl^-(g) \rightarrow NaCl(s)$ b. $NH_4^+(g) + Br^-(g) \rightarrow NH_4Br(s)$

       c. $Mg^{2+}(g) + S^{2-}(g) \rightarrow MgS(s)$ d. $1/2\ O_2(g) \rightarrow O(g)$

       e. $O_2(g) \rightarrow 2\ O(g)$

87.   Yes, each structure has the same number of effective pairs around the central atom giving the same molecular structure. (A multiple bond is counted as a single group of electrons.)

CHAPTER FOURTEEN

COVALENT BONDING: ORBITALS

Localized Electron Model and Hybrid Orbitals

1.   a.

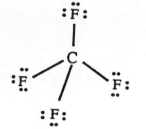

tetradedral   sp³
109.5°   nonpolar

b.

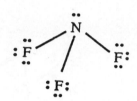

trigonal pyramid   sp³
< 109.5°   polar

The angle should be slightly less than
109.5° because the lone pair requires more
room than the bonding pairs.

c.

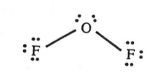

bent   sp³
< 109.5°   polar

d.

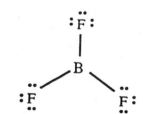

trigonal planar   sp²
120°   nonpolar

e.

f.

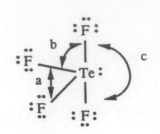

H—Be—H

linear   sp
180°   nonpolar

see-saw
a. ≈ 120°, b. ≈ 90°, c. ≈ 180°
dsp³   polar

g.

h.

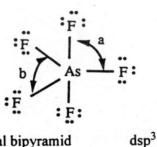

trigonal bipyramid   dsp³
a. 90°, b. 120°   nonpolar

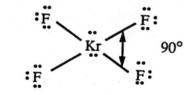

linear   dsp³
180°   nonpolar

i.

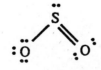

square planar   d²sp³
90°   nonpolar

2.   a.

bent
sp²

Only one resonance form is shown. Resonance does not change the position of the atoms.
We can predict the geometry from only one of the resonance structures.

b.

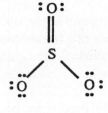

trigonal planar
sp^2

Only one resonance form is shown.

c.

tetradedral
sp^3

d.

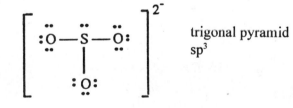

Tetrahedral geometry about each S, sp^3
hybrids; bent arrangement about peroxide
O's, sp^3 hybrids

e.

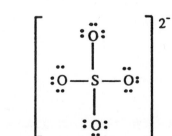

trigonal pyramid
sp^3

f.

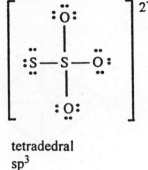

tetrahedral
sp^3

3.   a. P_4, 4(5) = 20 valence electrons

Each P - sp^3 hybridization.

P – P – P bond angle, 60° (Each P is at the corner of a tetrahedron. The faces of a tetrahedron are equilateral triangles.)

Note: We predict sp^3 orbitals because there are 4 pairs of e⁻ about each P. There is considerable strain in this molecule.

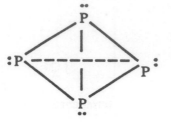

b. P_4O_6, 4(5) + 6(6) = 56 valence electrons

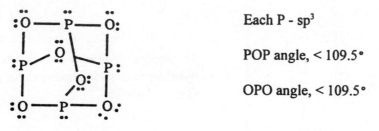

Each P - sp^3

POP angle, < 109.5°

OPO angle, < 109.5°

c. P_4O_{10}, 4(5) + 10(6) = 80 valence electrons

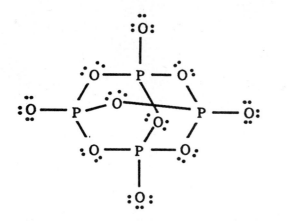

Each P - sp^3

POP angle, < 109.5°

OPO angle, 109.5°

5.   No, the CH_2 planes are mutually perpendicular. The center C-atom is involved in two π-bonds. The p-orbitals used in each bond must be perpendicular to the other. This forces the two CH_2 planes to be perpendicular since different p orbitals are used to form the hybrid orbitals.

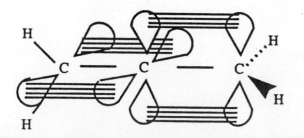

6.   Biacetyl ($C_4H_6O_2$) has $4(4) + 6(1) + 2(6) = 34$ valence electrons.

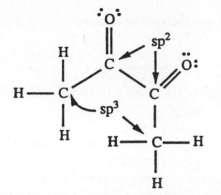

All CCO angles are 120° The six atoms are not in the same plane because of free rotation about the carbon-carbon single bonds.

Acetoin ($C_4H_8O_2$) has $4(4) + 8(1) + 2(6) = 36$ valence electrons.

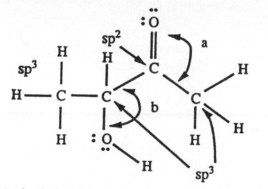

The carbon with the doubly bonded O is sp^2 hybridized. The other 3-C atoms are sp^3 hybridized.

a.   120°, b. 109.5°

7.   A single bond is a σ bond. Double and triple bonds are composed of a σ bond and 1 or 2 π bonds. In biacetyl there are 11 σ and 2 π bonds. In acetoin there are 13 σ and 1 π bonds. Note: CH_3 is shorthand for a carbon singly bonded to three hydrogen atoms.

10.

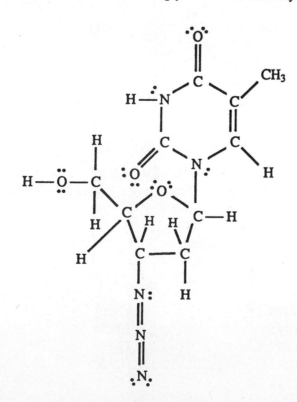

a. 6   b. 4   c. The center N in $-N=N=N$ group

d. 33 σ e. 5 π bonds   f. The six membered ring is planar.

g. 180°   h. < 109.5°   i. sp³ (sp^3)

Note: For f, the six membered ring is planar due to other resonance structures that can be drawn for this ring.

12.   a. Piperine and capsaicin are molecules classified as organic compounds, i.e., compounds based on carbon. The majority of Lewis structures for organic compounds have all atoms with zero formal charge. Therefore, carbon atoms in organic compounds will usually form four bonds, nitrogen atoms will form three bonds and complete the octet with one lone pair of electrons, and oxygen atoms will form two bonds and complete the octet with two lone pairs of electrons. Using these guidelines, the Lewis structures are:

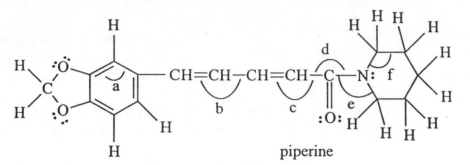

piperine

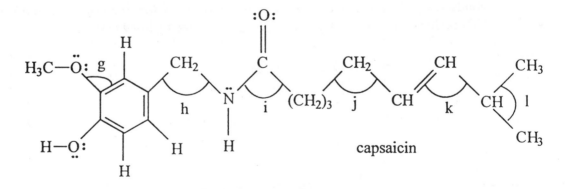

capsaicin

Note: The ring structures are all shorthand notation for rings of carbon atoms. In piperine, the first ring contains 6 carbon atoms and the second ring contains 5 carbon atoms (plus nitrogen).

b. piperine: 0 sp, 11 sp², and 6 sp³ carbons; capsaicin: 0 sp, 9 sp², and 9 sp³ carbons

c. The nitrogens are sp³ hybridized in each molecule.

d. a. 120°   e. ≈ 109.5°   i. 120°
      b. 120°   f. 109.5°   j. 109.5°
      c. 120°   g. 120°   k. 120°
      d. 120°   h. 109.5°   l. 109.5°

The Molecular Orbital Model

14.   If we calculate a non-zero bond order for a molecule, we predict that it can exist (is stable).

    a: H_2^+: $(\sigma_{1s})^1$ B.O. = (1-0)/2 = 1/2, stable

       H_2: $(\sigma_{1s})^2$ B.O. = (2-0)/2 = 1, stable

       H_2^-: $(\sigma_{1s})^2(\sigma_{1s}{}^*)^1$ B.O. = (2-1)/2 = 1/2, stable

       H_2^{2-}: $(\sigma_{1s})^2(\sigma_{1s}{}^*)^2$ B.O. = (2-2)/2 = 0, not stable

    b. He_2^{2+}: $(\sigma_{1s})^2$ B.O. = (2-0)/2 = 1, stable

       He_2^+ $(\sigma_{1s})^2(\sigma_{1s}{}^*)^1$ B.O. = (2-1)/2 = 1/2, stable

       He_2: $(\sigma_{1s})^2(\sigma_{1s}{}^*)^2$ B.O. = (2-2)/2 = 0, not stable

    c. Be_2: $(\sigma_{2s})^2(\sigma_{2s}{}^*)^2$ B.O. = (2-2)/2 = 0, not stable

       B_2: $(\sigma_{2s})^2(\sigma_{2s}{}^*)^2(\pi_{2p})^2$ B.O. = (4-2)/2 = 1, stable

       Li_2: $(\sigma_{2s})^2$ B.O. = (2-0)/2 = 1, stable

16.   For NO: $(\sigma_{2s})^2(\sigma_{2s}{}^*)^2(\pi_{2p})^4(\sigma_{2p})^2(\pi_{2p}{}^*)^1$ B.O. = $\dfrac{8-3}{2}$ = 2.5, 1 unpaired e$^-$

MO model does a better job. It predicts a bond order of 2.5. Measured bond energies and bond lengths are consistent with the bond in NO being stronger than a double bond.

	Bond Length	Bond Energy
N – O	147 pm	201 kJ/mol
N = O	115 pm	607 kJ/mol
NO (nitric oxide)	112 pm	678 kJ/mol

NO has 11 valence electrons. It is impossible to draw a Lewis structure satisfying the octet rule for odd electron species. The most reasonable attempt is to draw:

$$:\!N\!=\!\!=\!O\!: \quad \longleftrightarrow \quad :\!N\!=\!\!=\!O\!: \quad \longleftrightarrow \quad :\!N\!=\!\!=\!O\!:$$

none of which makes the correct prediction for the bond strength and the number of unpaired electrons.

17.   Bond energy is directly proportional to bond order. Bond length is inversely proportional to bond order. Bond energy and length can be measured.

18.

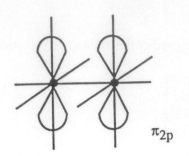

19.

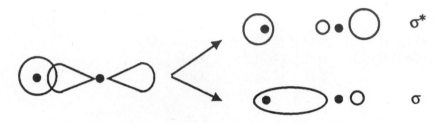

These molecular orbitals are sigma MOs since electron density is cylindrically symmetric about the internuclear axis.

20.   a. H_2: $(\sigma_{1s})^2$ B.O. = (2-0)/2 = 1, diamagetic

b. B_2: $(\sigma_{2s})^2(\sigma_{2s}*)^2(\pi_{2p})^2$ B.O. = (4-2)/2 = 1, paramagnetic

c. F_2: $(\sigma_{2s})^2(\sigma_{2s}*)^2(\pi_{2p})^4(\sigma_{2p})^2(\pi_{2p}*)^4$ B.O. = (8-6)/2 = 1, diamagnetic

d. CN^+: $(\sigma_{2s})^2(\sigma_{2s}*)^2(\pi_{2p})^4$ B.O. = (6-2)/2 = 2, diamagnetic

e. CN: $(\sigma_{2s})^2(\sigma_{2s}*)^2(\pi_{2p})^4(\sigma_{2p})^1$ B.O. = (7-2)/2 = 2.5, paramagnetic

f. CN^-: $(\sigma_{2s})^2(\sigma_{2s}*)^2(\pi_{2p})^4(\sigma_{2p})^2$ B.O. = 3, diamagnetic

25.

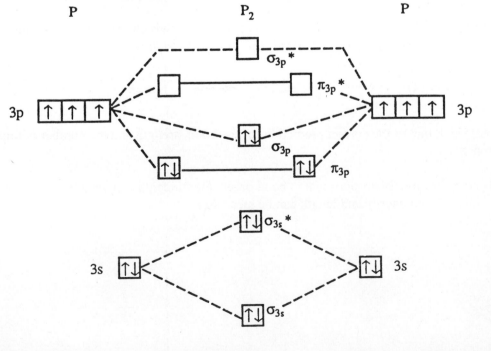

26. C_2^{2-} has 10 valence electrons. The Lewis structure predicts sp hybridization.

$$[:C\equiv C:]^{2-}$$

MO: $(\sigma_{2s})^2(\sigma_{2s}{}^*)^2(\pi_{2p})^4(\sigma_{2p})^2$, B.O. = 3

Both give the same picture, a triple bond composed of a σ and two π-bonds. Both predict the ion to be diamagnetic. Lewis structures deal well with diamagnetic (all electrons paired) species. The Lewis model cannot really predict magnetic properties. C_2^{2-} is isoelectronic with the CO molecule.

27.   a.   The electrons would be closer to F on the average. The F atom is more electronegative than the H atom and the 2p orbital of F is lower in energy than the 1s orbital of H.

       b.   The bonding MO would have more fluorine 2p character since it is closer in energy to the fluorine 2p orbital.

       c.   The antibonding MO would place more electron density closer to H and would have a greater contribution from the higher energy hydrogen 1s atomic orbital.

28.   a.   The electron removed from N_2 is in the σ_{2p} molecular orbital which is lower in energy than the 2p atomic orbital from which the electron in atomic nitrogen is removed. Since the electron removed from N_2 is lower in energy than the electron in N, the ionization energy of N_2 should be greater than for N.

       b. F_2 should have a lower first ionization energy than F. The electron removed from F_2 is in a $\pi_{2p}{}^*$ antibonding molecular orbital which is higher in energy than the 2p atomic orbitals. Thus, it is easier to remove an electron from F_2 than from F.

Additional Exercises

30.   a.   FClO, 7 + 7 + 6 = 20 e⁻   b. $FClO_2$, 7 + 7 + 2(6) = 26 e⁻

       :F̈—C̈l—Ö: :F̈—C̈l—Ö:
                                                       |
                                                      :Ö:

       bent, sp³ hybridization   trigonal pyramid, sp³

       c. $FClO_3$, 7 + 7 + 3(6) = 32 e⁻   d. F_3ClO, 3(7) + 7 + 6 = 34 e⁻

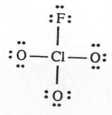

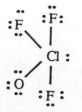

       tetrahedral, sp³   see-saw, dsp³

e. F_3ClO_2, $3(7) + 7 + 2(6) = 40$ valence e$^-$

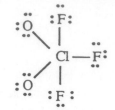

trigonal bipyramid, dsp^3

Note: Two additional Lewis structures are possible, depending on the positions of the oxygen atoms.

31. $FClO_2 + F^- \rightarrow F_2ClO_2^-$ $F_3ClO + F^- \rightarrow F_4ClO^-$

$F_2ClO_2^-$, $2(7) + 7 + 2(6) + 1 = 34$ e$^-$ F_4ClO^-, $4(7) + 7 + 6 + 1 = 42$ e$^-$

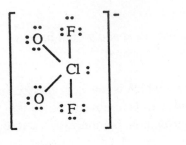   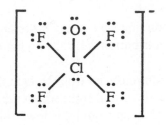

see-saw, dsp^3 square pyramid, d^{2}sp^3

$F_3ClO \rightarrow F^- + F_2ClO^+$ $F_3ClO_2 \rightarrow F^- + F_2ClO_2^+$

F_2ClO^+, $2(7) + 7 + 6 - 1 = 26$ e$^-$ $F_2ClO_2^+$, $2(7) + 7 + 2(6) - 1 = 32$ e$^-$

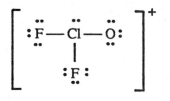   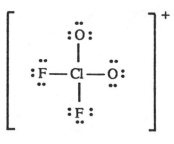

trigonal pyramid, sp^3 tetrahedral, sp^3

35.

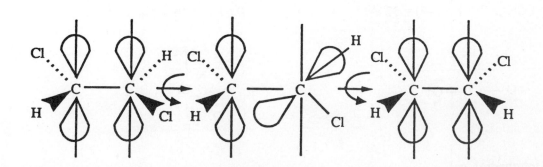

In order to rotate about the double bond, the molecule must go through an intermediate stage where the π bond is broken while the sigma bond remains intact. Bond energies are 347 kJ/mol for C – C and 614 kJ/mol for C = C. If we take the single bond as the strength of the σ bond, then the strength of the π bond is (614 - 347) = 267 kJ/mol. Thus, 267 kJ/mol must be supplied to rotate about a carbon-carbon double bond.

39. NO^+ has 5 + 6 - 1 = 10 valence electrons. The Lewis structure shows a triple bond.

$$\left[:N \equiv O: \right]^+$$

NO has 5 + 6 = 11 valence electrons. The Lewis structures can't predict a stable species.

$$:N = O: \longleftrightarrow :N = O: \longleftrightarrow :N = O:$$

NO⁻ has 12 valence electrons. The Lewis structure predicts a double bond.

$$\left[:N = O: \right]^-$$

M.O. model:

   NO^+ $(\sigma_{2s})^2(\sigma_{2s}{}^*)^2(\pi_{2p})^4(\sigma_{2p})^2$, B.O. = 3, 0 unpaired e⁻ (diamagnetic)

   NO $(\sigma_{2s})^2(\sigma_{2s}{}^*)^2(\pi_{2p})^4(\sigma_{2p})^2(\pi_{2p}{}^*)^1$, B.O. = 2.5, 1 unpaired e⁻ (paramagnetic)

   NO⁻ $(\sigma_{2s})^2(\sigma_{2s}{}^*)^2(\pi_{2p})^4(\sigma_{2p})^2(\pi_{2p}{}^*)^2$, B.O. = 2, 2 unpaired e⁻ (paramagnetic)

Bond Energies: NO⁻ < NO < NO^+; Bond Lengths: NO^+ < NO < NO⁻

The two models only give the same results for NO^+. The M.O. view is the correct one for NO and NO⁻. Lewis structures are inadequate for odd electron species and for predicting magnetic properties. NO⁻ is paramagnetic but the Lewis structure shows all electrons paired.

40. N_2 (ground state): $(\sigma_{2s})^2(\sigma_{2s}{}^*)^2(\pi_{2p})^4(\sigma_{2p})^2$, B.O. = 3, diamagnetic

N_2 (1st excited state): $(\sigma_{2s})^2(\sigma_{2s}{}^*)^2(\pi_{2p})^4(\sigma_{2p})^1(\pi_{2p}{}^*)^1$

B.O. = (7-3)/2 = 2, paramagnetic (2 unpaired e⁻)

The bond strengths are different as well as the magnetic properties.

41.   Be: $1s^2 2s^2$; Each Be has 2 valence electrons. We can draw a Lewis structure:

   Be = Be

This doesn't obey the octet rule, but is consistent with structures we've drawn earlier for Be compounds. There are two pairs of electrons around each Be atom just as in earlier drawings, e.g., BeH_2. From this Lewis structure we would predict Be_2 to be stable.

The MO model (see Exercise 14.14c) predicts a bond order of zero; Be_2 shoudn't exist. Be_2 has not yet been observed. Be is very small; electron-electron repulsions would be extremely large in the Lewis structure drawn.

42.   Paramagnetic: Unpaired electrons are present. Measure the mass of a substance in the presence and absence of a magnetic field. A substance with unpaired electrons will be attracted by the magnetic field, giving an apparent increase in mass in the presence of the field. Greater number of unpaired electrons will give greater attraction and greater observed mass increase.

43.   Considering only the twelve valence electrons in O_2, the MO models would be:

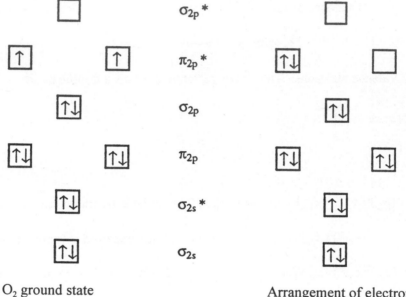

O₂ ground state   Arrangement of electrons consistent
                                             with the Lewis structure (double bond
                                             and no unpaired electrons).

It takes energy to pair electrons in the same orbital. Thus, the structure with no unpaired electrons is at a higher energy; it is an excited state.

47.   a.   Yes, both have 4 sets of electrons about the P. We would predict a tetrahedral structure for both. See below for Lewis structures.

       b.   The hybridization is sp^3 for each P since both structures are tetrahedral.

       c.   P has to use one of its d orbitals to form the π bond.

       d.

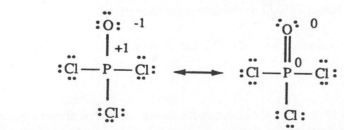

The structure with the P = O bond is favored on the basis of formal charge.

CHAPTER FIFTEEN

CHEMICAL KINETICS

Reaction Rates

1. $\text{Rate} = \dfrac{-\Delta[S_2O_3^{2-}]}{\Delta t} = \dfrac{0.0080 \text{ mol}}{\text{L s}}$; I_2 is consumed at half this rate. $\dfrac{-\Delta[I_2]}{\Delta t} = 0.0040 \text{ mol L}^{-1}\text{ s}^{-1}$

   $\dfrac{\Delta[S_4O_6^{2-}]}{\Delta t} = 0.0040 \text{ mol L}^{-1}\text{ s}^{-1}$; $\dfrac{\Delta[I^-]}{\Delta t} = 0.0080 \text{ mol L}^{-1}\text{ s}^{-1}$

3. a. $\text{mol L}^{-1}\text{ s}^{-1}$

   b. $\text{Rate} = k$; k has units of $\text{mol L}^{-1}\text{ s}^{-1}$

   c. $\text{Rate} = k[A]$, $\dfrac{\text{mol}}{\text{L s}} = k\left(\dfrac{\text{mol}}{\text{L}}\right)$

   k must have units of s^{-1}.

   d. $\text{Rate} = k[A]^2$, $\dfrac{\text{mol}}{\text{L s}} = k\left(\dfrac{\text{mol}}{\text{L}}\right)^2$

   k must have units $\text{L mol}^{-1}\text{ s}^{-1}$.

   e. $\text{L}^2\text{ mol}^{-2}\text{ s}^{-1}$

5. a. $\text{molecules cm}^{-3}\text{ s}^{-1}$

   b. $\text{molecules cm}^{-3}\text{ s}^{-1}$

   c. s^{-1}

   d. $\text{cm}^3\text{ molecules}^{-1}\text{ s}^{-1}$

   e. $\text{cm}^6\text{ molecules}^{-2}\text{ s}^{-1}$

6. $\dfrac{1.24 \times 10^{-12}\text{ cm}^3}{\text{molecules s}} \times \dfrac{1 \text{ L}}{1000 \text{ cm}^3} \times \dfrac{6.022 \times 10^{23}\text{ molecules}}{\text{mol}} = 7.47 \times 10^8 \text{ L mol}^{-1}\text{ s}^{-1}$

7. a. $25 \text{ min} \times \dfrac{60 \text{ s}}{\text{min}} \times \dfrac{1.20 \times 10^{-4}\text{ mol}}{\text{L s}} = \dfrac{0.18 \text{ mol}}{\text{L}}$, 0.18 mol/L HI has been consumed.

   $[HI] = 0.25 - 0.18 = 0.07 \text{ mol/L}$

   b. $t \times \dfrac{1.20 \times 10^{-4}\text{ mol}}{\text{L s}} = \dfrac{0.250 \text{ mol}}{\text{L}}$, $t = 2.08 \times 10^3 \text{ s}$

c. $\dfrac{1.20 \times 10^{-4} \text{ mol HI}}{\text{L s}} \times \dfrac{1 \text{ mol H}_2}{2 \text{ mol HI}} = 6.00 \times 10^{-5} \text{ mol L}^{-1} \text{ s}^{-1} = \dfrac{d[\text{H}_2]}{dt}$

Both H_2 and I_2 are formed at the rate of 6.00×10^{-5} mol L^{-1} s^{-1}.

Rate Laws from Experimental Data: Initial Rates Method

8.   a. In the first two experiments, [NO] is held constant and $[Cl_2]$ is doubled. The rate also
          doubled. Thus, the reaction is first order with respect to Cl_2. Mathematically: Rate =
          $k[NO]^x[Cl_2]^y$

$\dfrac{0.35}{0.18} = \dfrac{k(0.10)^x(0.20)^y}{k(0.10)^x(0.10)^y} = \dfrac{(0.20)^y}{(0.10)^y},\ 1.9 = 2.0^y,\ y \approx 1$

We get the dependence on NO from the second and third experiments.

$\dfrac{1.45}{0.35} = \dfrac{k(0.20)^x(0.20)}{k(0.10)^x(0.20)} = \dfrac{(0.20)^x}{(0.10)^x},\ 4.1 = 2.0^x,\ \log 4.1 = x \log 2.0$

$0.61 = x(0.30),\ x \approx 2;$ So, Rate $= k[NO]^2[Cl_2]$

b. The rate constant k can be determined from the experiments. From experiment 1:

$\dfrac{0.18 \text{ mol}}{\text{L min}} = k \left(\dfrac{0.10 \text{ mol}}{\text{L}} \right)^2 \left(\dfrac{0.10 \text{ mol}}{\text{L}} \right),\ k = 180 \text{ L}^2 \text{ mol}^{-2} \text{ min}^{-1}$

From the other experiments:

$k = 175 \text{ L}^2 \text{ mol}^{-2} \text{ min}^{-1}$ (2nd exp.); $k = 181 \text{ L}^2 \text{ mol}^{-2} \text{ min}^{-1}$ (3rd exp.)

To two significant figures, $k_{mean} = 1.8 \times 10^2$ L^2 mol^{-2} min^{-1}.

9.   a. Rate $= k[I^-]^x[S_2O_8^{2-}]^y;\ \dfrac{12.50 \times 10^{-6}}{6.250 \times 10^{-6}} = \dfrac{k(0.080)^x(0.040)^y}{k(0.040)^x(0.040)^y},\ 2.000 = 2.0^x,\ x = 1$

$\dfrac{12.50 \times 10^{-6}}{5.560 \times 10^{-6}} = \dfrac{k(0.080)^x(0.040)^y}{k(0.080)^x(0.020)^y},\ 2.248 = 2.0^y$

$\log 2.248 = y \log 2.0,\ 0.3518 = 0.30\,y,\ y = 1.2 \approx 1$

Rate $= k[I^-][S_2O_8^{2-}]$

b. For the first experiment:

$\dfrac{12.50 \times 10^{-6} \text{ mol}}{\text{L s}} = k \left(\dfrac{0.080 \text{ mol}}{\text{L}} \right) \left(\dfrac{0.040 \text{ mol}}{\text{L}} \right),\ k = 3.9 \times 10^{-3} \text{ L mol}^{-1} \text{ s}^{-1}$

The other values are:

Initial Rate (mol L^{-1} s^{-1})	k (L mol^{-1} s^{-1})
12.5 × 10^{-6}	3.9 × 10^{-3}
6.25 × 10^{-6}	3.9 × 10^{-3}
5.56 × 10^{-6}	3.5 × 10^{-3}
4.35 × 10^{-6}	3.4 × 10^{-3}
6.41 × 10^{-6}	3.6 × 10^{-3}

$k_{mean} = 3.7 \times 10^{-3}$ L mol^{-1} s^{-1} ± 0.3 × 10^{-3} L mol^{-1} s^{-1}

11. a. Rate = $k[Hb]^x[CO]^y$

Comparing the first two experiments, [CO] is unchanged, [Hb] doubles, and the rate doubles. Therefore, $x = 1$ and the reaction is first order in Hb. Comparing the second and third experiments, [Hb] is unchanged, [CO] triples and the rate triples. Therefore, $y = 1$ and the reaction is first order in CO.

b. Rate = k[Hb][CO]

c. From the first experiment:

0.619 μmol L^{-1} s^{-1} = k (2.21 μmol/L)(1.00 μmol/L), k = 0.280 L μmol^{-1} s^{-1}

The second and third experiments give similar k values, so $k_{mean} = 0.280$ L μmol^{-1} s^{-1}.

d. Rate = k[Hb][CO] = $\dfrac{0.280 \text{ L}}{\mu\text{mol s}} \times \dfrac{3.36 \ \mu\text{mol}}{\text{L}} \times \dfrac{2.40 \ \mu\text{mol}}{\text{L}}$ = 2.26 μmol L^{-1} s^{-1}

Integrated Rate Laws from Experimental Data

13. The first guess to make is that the reaction is first order. For a first order reaction a graph of ln [C$_4$H$_6$] vs. t should yield a straight line. If this isn't linear, then try the second order plot of 1/[C$_4$H$_6$] vs. t. The data for these two plots follow and the actual plots are on the next page.

Time	195	604	1246	2180	6210 s
[C$_4$H$_6$]	1.6 × 10^{-2}	1.5 × 10^{-2}	1.3 × 10^{-2}	1.1 × 10^{-2}	0.68 × 10^{-2} M
ln [C$_4$H$_6$]	-4.14	-4.20	-4.34	-4.51	-4.99
1/[C$_4$H$_6$]	62.5	66.7	76.9	90.9	147 M^{-1}

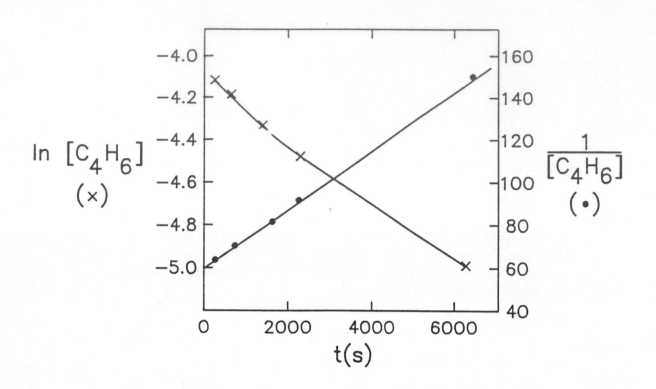

The natural log plot is not linear, so the reaction is not first order. The next guess is that the reaction is second order. For a second order reaction, a plot of $1/[C_4H_6]$ vs. t should yield a straight line. Since we get a straight line for this graph, we conclude the reaction is second order in butadiene. The differential rate law is:

$$\text{Rate} = \frac{-d[C_4H_6]}{dt} = k[C_4H_6]^2$$

For a second order reaction, the integrated rate law is: $\dfrac{1}{[C_4H_6]_t} = \dfrac{1}{[C_4H_6]_o} + kt$

The slope of the straight line equals the value of the rate constant. Using the points on the line at 1000. and 6000. s:

$$k = \text{slope} = \frac{144 \text{ L/mol} - 73 \text{ L/mol}}{6000. \text{ s} - 1000. \text{ s}} = 1.4 \times 10^{-2} \text{ L mol}^{-1} \text{ s}^{-1}$$

This value was obtained from reading the graph and "eyeballing" a straight line with a ruler.

14.   This problem differs in two ways from the previous problem:
        1. a product is measured instead of a reactant and
        2. only the volume of a gas is given and not the concentration.
    We can find the initial concentration of $C_6H_5N_2Cl$ from the amount of N_2 evolved after infinite time when all the $C_6H_5N_2Cl$ has decomposed (assuming the reaction goes to completion).

$$n = \frac{PV}{RT} = \frac{1.00 \text{ atm} \times (58.3 \times 10^{-3} \text{ L})}{\dfrac{0.08206 \text{ L atm}}{\text{mol K}} \times 323 \text{ K}} = 2.20 \times 10^{-3} \text{ mol N}_2$$

Since each mole of $C_6H_5N_2Cl$ that decomposes produces one mole of N_2, then the initial concentration (t = 0) of $C_6H_5N_2Cl$ was:

$$\frac{2.20 \times 10^{-3} \text{ mol}}{40.0 \times 10^{-3} \text{ L}} = 0.0550 \text{ } M$$

We can similarly calculate the moles of N_2 evolved at each point of the experiment, subtract that from 2.20×10^{-3} mol to get the moles of $C_6H_5N_2Cl$ remaining, and calculate $[C_6H_5N_2Cl]$ at each time. We would then use these results to make the appropriate graph to check the order of the reaction. Since the rate constant is the slope of a straight line, we would favor this approach to get a value for the rate constant.

There is a simpler way to check for the order of the reaction and saves doing a lot of math. The quantity $(V_\infty - V_t)$ where V_∞ = 58.3 mL N_2 evolved and V_t = mL of N_2 evolved at time t will be proportional to the moles of $C_6H_5N_2Cl$ remaining; $(V_\infty - V_t)$ will also be proportional to the concentration of $C_6H_5N_2Cl$. Thus, we can get the same information by using $(V_\infty - V_t)$ as our measure of $[C_6H_5N_2Cl]$. If the reaction is first order a graph of ln $(V_\infty - V_t)$ vs. t would be linear. The data for such a graph are:

t (s)	V_t (mL)	$(V_\infty - V_t)$	ln $(V_\infty - V_t)$
0	0	58.3	4.066
6	19.3	39.0	3.664
9	26.0	32.3	3.475
14	36.0	22.3	3.105
22	45.0	13.3	2.588
30	50.4	7.9	2.07

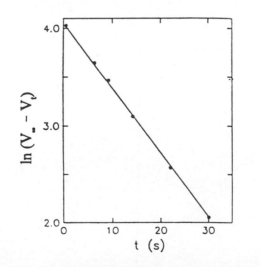

We can see from the graph that this plot is linear, so the reaction is first order. The differential rate law is: $-d[C_6H_5N_2Cl]/dt = k[C_6H_5N_2Cl]$ and the integrated rate law is: $\ln[C_6H_5N_2Cl] = -kt + \ln[C_6H_5N_2Cl]_0$. From separate data, k was determined to be $6.9 \times 10^{-2} \text{ s}^{-1}$.

15.

Time (s)	[H₂O₂] (mol/L)	ln[H₂O₂]
0	1.0	0
120.	0.91	-0.094
300.	0.78	-0.25
600.	0.59	-0.53
1200.	0.37	-0.99
1800.	0.22	-1.51
2400.	0.13	-2.04
3000.	0.082	-2.50
3600.	0.050	-3.00

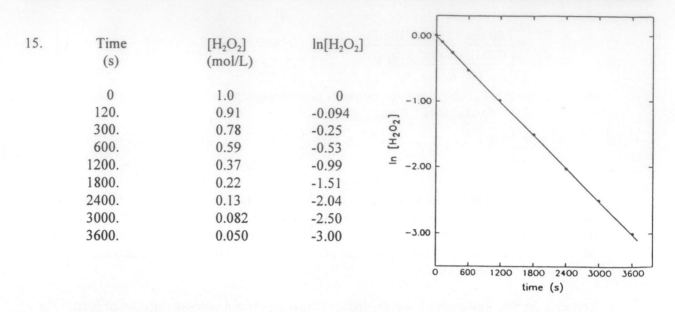

The plot of $\ln[H_2O_2]$ vs. t is linear. Thus, the reaction is first order. The integrated and differential rate laws are:

$$\ln[H_2O_2] = -kt + \ln[H_2O_2]_0 \text{ and Rate} = -d[H_2O_2]/dt = k[H_2O_2]$$

$$\text{Slope} = -k = \frac{0 - (3.00)}{0 - 3600.} = -8.3 \times 10^{-4} \text{ s}^{-1}, \ k = 8.3 \times 10^{-4} \text{ s}^{-1}$$

17.   a.   First, we guess the reaction to be first order with respect to O. Hence, a graph of ln [O] vs. t should be linear if the reaction is first order.

t (s)	[O] (atoms/cm³)	ln [O]
0	5.0×10^9	22.33
$10. \times 10^{-3}$	1.9×10^9	21.37
$20. \times 10^{-3}$	6.8×10^8	20.34
$30. \times 10^{-3}$	2.5×10^8	19.34

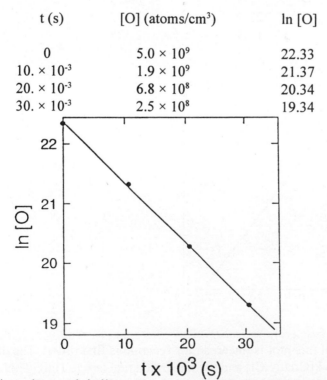

Since the graph is linear, we can conclude the reaction is first order with respect to O.

b. The overall rate law is: Rate = k[NO$_2$][O]; With an excess of NO$_2$, the rate law becomes:
Rate = k'[O] where k' = k[NO$_2$].

For a first order reaction: ln [A]$_t$ = -kt + ln [A]$_o$; We can get k' from the slope of the graph:

$$k' = \text{-slope} = -\frac{19.34 - 22.33}{(30. \times 10^{-3} - 0) \text{ s}}, \quad k' = 1.0 \times 10^2 \text{ s}^{-1}$$

k' = k[NO$_2$], 1.0×10^2 s^{-1} = k(1.0 × 10^{13} molecules/cm^3), k = 1.0 × 10^{-11} cm^3 molecules^{-1} s^{-1}

Half-Life

19.   a. $k = \dfrac{\ln 2}{t_{1/2}} = \dfrac{0.69315}{t_{1/2}}$; For ^{239}Pu, $k = \dfrac{0.69315}{24{,}360 \text{ yr}} = 2.845 \times 10^{-5}$ yr^{-1}

$$\frac{2.845 \times 10^{-5}}{\text{yr}} \times \frac{1 \text{ yr}}{365 \text{ d}} \times \frac{1 \text{ d}}{24 \text{ hr}} \times \frac{1 \text{ hr}}{60 \text{ min}} \times \frac{1 \text{ min}}{60 \text{ s}} = 9.021 \times 10^{-13} \text{ s}^{-1}$$

For ^{241}Pu, $k = \dfrac{0.693}{13 \text{ yr}} = 0.0533$ yr^{-1} = 1.7 × 10^{-9} s^{-1}

b.   The rate constant is larger for the decay of ^{241}Pu, hence, ^{241}Pu decays more rapidly.

c.   For radioactive decay, Rate = kN where N is the number of radioactive nuclei.

$$\text{Rate} = 1.7 \times 10^{-9} \text{ s}^{-1} \times \left(5.0 \text{ g} \times \frac{1 \text{ mol}}{241 \text{ g}} \times \frac{6.02 \times 10^{23} \text{ atoms}}{\text{mol}} \right) = 2.1 \times 10^{13} \text{ disintegrations/s}$$

$$\ln \frac{[A]_t}{[A]_o} = \text{-kt}; \quad \ln \left(\frac{N}{5.0} \right) = \text{-0.0533 yr}^{-1}(1.0 \text{ yr}), \quad \ln N = \text{-0.0533} + \ln 5.0$$

Note: We will carry an extra significant figure for the quantity kt.

ln N = -0.0533 + ln 5.0 = -0.0533 + 1.609 = 1.556, N = e$^{1.556}$ = 4.7 g left after 1.0 yr

ln N = -0.0533 yr^{-1}(10. yr) + ln 5.0 = -0.533 + 1.609 = 1.076, N = e$^{1.076}$ = 2.9 g ^{241}Pu left after
10. years

ln N = -0.0533 yr^{-1}(100. yr) + ln 5.0 = -5.33 + 1.609 = -3.72, N = e$^{-3.72}$ = 0.024 g left after
100. yr

20.   If [A]$_o$ = 100.0, then after 65 s, 45.0% of A has reacted or [A]$_{65}$ = 55.0.

$$\ln \left(\frac{[A]_t}{[A]_o} \right) = \text{-kt}, \quad \ln \left(\frac{55.0}{100.0} \right) = \text{-k(65 s)}, \quad k = 9.2 \times 10^{-3} \text{ s}^{-1}; \quad t_{1/2} = \frac{0.693}{k} = 75 \text{ s}$$

21. $\ln\left(\dfrac{[A]_t}{[A]_o}\right) = -kt; \quad k = \dfrac{0.6931}{t_{1/2}} = \dfrac{0.6931}{14.3\ d} = 4.85 \times 10^{-2}\ d^{-1}$

If $[A]_o = 100.0$, then after 95.0% completion, $[A]_t = 5.0$.

$\ln(0.050) = -4.85 \times 10^{-2}\ d^{-1} \times t, \quad t = 62\ days$

22.   For a second order reaction: $t_{1/2} = \dfrac{1}{k[A]_o}$ or $k = \dfrac{1}{t_{1/2}[A]_o}$

$k = \dfrac{1}{143\ s(0.060\ mol/L)} = 0.12\ L\ mol^{-1}\ s^{-1}$

Reaction Mechanisms

25.   a.   An elementary step (reaction) is one in which the rate law can be written from the molecularity, i.e., from the coefficients in the balanced equation.

       b.   The mechanism of a reaction is the series of elementary reactions that occur to give the overall reaction. The sum of all the steps in the mechanism gives the balanced chemical reaction.

       c.   The rate determining step is the slowest elementary reaction in any given mechanism.

26.   a.   Rate = $k[CH_3NC]$ b.   Rate = $k[O_3][NO]$

27.   The rate law is: Rate = $k[NO]^2[Cl_2]$. If we assume the first step is rate determining, we would expect the rate law to be: Rate = $k_1[NO][Cl_2]$. This isn't correct. However, if we assume the second step to be rate determining: Rate = $k_2[NOCl_2][NO]$. To see if this agrees with experiment, we must substitute for the intermediate $NOCl_2$ concentration. Assuming a fast equilibrium first step (rate reverse = rate forward):

$k_{-1}[NOCl_2] = k_1[NO][Cl_2], \quad [NOCl_2] = \dfrac{k_1}{k_{-1}}[NO][Cl_2];$ Substituting into the rate equation:

$Rate = \dfrac{k_2 k_1}{k_{-1}}[NO]^2[Cl_2] = k[NO]^2[Cl_2]$

This is a possible mechanism with the second step the rate determining step since the derived rate law agrees with experiment.

29.   Let's determine the rate law for each mechanism. If this rate law is the same as the experimental rate law, then the mechanism is possible. When deriving rate laws from a mechanism, we must substitute for all intermediate concentrations.

       a.   Rate = $k[NO][O_2]$ <u>not possible</u>

b.   Rate = k[NO$_3$][NO] and $\dfrac{[NO_3]}{[NO][O_2]}$ = K$_{eq}$ = k$_1$/k$_{-1}$ or [NO$_3$] = K$_{eq}$[NO][O$_2$]

      Rate = kK$_{eq}$[NO]^2[O$_2$]   <u>possible</u>

c.   Rate = k[NO]^2 <u>not possible</u>

d.   Rate = k[N$_2$O$_2$] and [N$_2$O$_2$] = K$_{eq}$[NO]^2; Rate = kK$_{eq}$[NO]^2 <u>not possible</u>

30.   If the first step is slow, Rate = k$_1$[NO$_2$Cl] which has the same form as the experimental rate law. Thus, the first step is rate determining.

Temperature Dependence of Rate Constants and the Collision Model

33.   a.   The greater the frequency of collisions, the greater the opportunities for molecules to react, and, hence, the greater the rate.

    b.   Chemical reactions involve the making and breaking of chemical bonds. The kinetic energy of the collision can be used to break bonds.

    c.   For a reaction to occur, it is the reactive portion of each molecule that must be involved in a collision. Thus, only some collisions have the correct orientation.

34.   In a unimolecular reaction, a single reactant molecule decomposes to products. In a bimolecular reaction, two molecules collide to give products.

35.   The probability of the simultaneous collision of three molecules with the correct energy and orientation is exceedingly small.

36.   H$_3$O$^+$(aq) + OH$^-$(aq) → 2 H$_2$O(l) should have the faster rate. H$_3$O$^+$ and OH$^-$ will be electrostatically attracted to each other; Ce^{4+} and Hg$_2^{2+}$ will repel each other.

37.   k = A exp(-E$_a$/RT) or ln k = $\dfrac{-E_a}{RT}$ + ln A

For two conditions: $\ln\left(\dfrac{k_2}{k_1}\right) = \dfrac{E_a}{R}\left(\dfrac{1}{T_1} - \dfrac{1}{T_2}\right)$ (Assuming A is temperature independent.)

Let k$_1$ = 2.0 × 10^3 s^{-1}, T$_1$ = 298 K; k$_2$ = ?, T$_2$ = 348 K; E$_a$ = 15.0 × 10^3 J/mol

$\ln\left(\dfrac{k_2}{2.0 \times 10^3 \text{ s}^{-1}}\right) = \dfrac{15.0 \times 10^3 \text{ J/mol}}{8.3145 \text{ J mol}^{-1} \text{K}^{-1}}\left(\dfrac{1}{298 \text{ K}} - \dfrac{1}{348 \text{ K}}\right) = 0.87$

$\ln\left(\dfrac{k_2}{2.0 \times 10^3}\right) = 0.87, \quad \dfrac{k_2}{2.0 \times 10^3} = e^{0.87} = 2.4, \quad k_2 = 2.4(2.0 \times 10^3) = 4.8 \times 10^3 \text{ s}^{-1}$

40.   From the Arrhenius equation, $k = A \exp(-E_a/RT)$ or in logarithmic form, $\ln k = -E_a/RT + \ln A$.
       Hence, a graph of $\ln k$ vs. $1/T$ should yield a straight line with a slope equal to $-E_a/R$.

T (K)	1/T (K⁻¹)	k (L mol⁻¹ s⁻¹)	ln k
195	5.13×10^{-3}	1.08×10^{9}	20.80
230	4.35×10^{-3}	2.95×10^{9}	21.81
260	3.85×10^{-3}	5.42×10^{9}	22.41
298	3.36×10^{-3}	12.0×10^{9}	23.21
369	2.71×10^{-3}	35.5×10^{9}	24.29

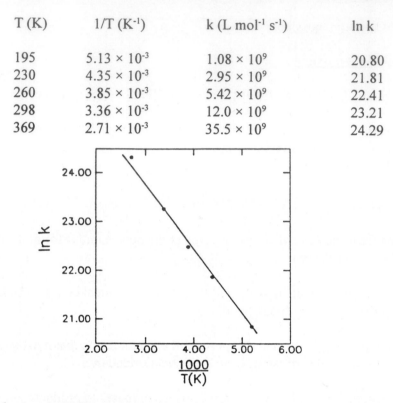

From the "eyeball" line on the graph:

$$\text{slope} = \frac{20.95 - 23.65}{5.00 \times 10^{-3} - 3.00 \times 10^{-3}} = \frac{-2.70}{2.00 \times 10^{-3}} = -1.35 \times 10^{3} \text{ K} = \frac{-E_a}{R}$$

$$E_a = 1.35 \times 10^{3} \text{ K} \times \frac{8.3145 \text{ J}}{\text{K mol}} = 1.12 \times 10^{4} \text{ J/mol} = 11.2 \text{ kJ/mol}$$

From the best straight line (by computer): slope = -1.43×10^{3} K and $E_a = 11.9$ kJ/mol

41.   If we double the rate, k doubles and $\dfrac{k_{35}}{k_{25}} = 2.00 = \dfrac{A \exp[-E_a/R(308)]}{A \exp[-E_a/R(298)]}$

$$\ln 2.00 = \frac{-E_a}{308\,R} + \frac{E_a}{298\,R} = E_a \left(\frac{1}{298\,R} - \frac{1}{308\,R} \right), \quad 0.693 = E_a (4.04 \times 10^{-4} - 3.91 \times 10^{-4})$$

$$\frac{0.693}{0.13 \times 10^{-4}} = E_a = 5.3 \times 10^{4} \text{ J/mol} = 53 \text{ kJ/mol}$$

43.

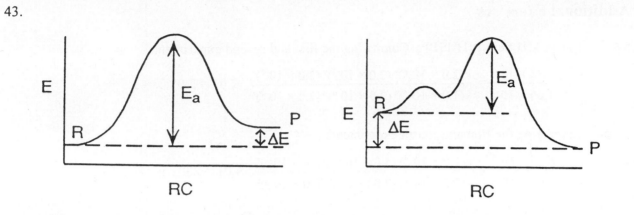

Catalysis

46.   a.   A homogeneous catalyst is in the same phase as the reactants.

   b.   A heterogeneous catalyst is in a different phase than the reactants. The catalyst is usually a solid, although a catalyst in a liquid phase can act as a heterogeneous catalyst for some gas phase reactions.

47.   A catalyst increases the rate of a reaction by providing an alternate pathway (mechanism) with a lower activation energy.

48.   Yes, the catalyst takes part in the mechanism and will appear in the rate law.

49.   No, the catalyzed reaction has a different mechanism and hence, a different rate law.

50.   a.   NO is the catalyst.

   b. NO_2 is an intermediate

   c. $k = A \exp(-E_a/RT)$

$$\frac{k_{cat}}{k_{un}} = \frac{A \exp[-E_a(cat)/RT]}{A \exp[-E_a(un)/RT]} = \exp\left(\frac{E_a(un) - E_a(cat)}{RT}\right)$$

$$\frac{k_{cat}}{k_{un}} = \exp\left(\frac{2100 \text{ J/mol}}{8.3145 \text{ J mol}^{-1} \text{ K}^{-1} \times 298 \text{ K}}\right) = e^{0.85} = 2.3$$

The catalyzed reaction is 2.3 times faster than the uncatalyzed reaction at 25°C.

53.   At high [S], the enzyme is completely saturated with substrate. Once the enzyme is completely saturated, the rate of decomposition of ES can no longer increase and the overall rate remains constant.

Additional Exercises

54.   Rate = $k[H_2SeO_3]^x[H^+]^y[I^-]^z$; Comparing the first and second experiments:

$$\frac{3.33 \times 10^{-7}}{1.66 \times 10^{-7}} = \frac{k(2.0 \times 10^{-4})^x \, (2.0 \times 10^{-2})^y \, (2.0 \times 10^{-2})^z}{k(1.0 \times 10^{-4})^x \, (2.0 \times 10^{-2})^y \, (2.0 \times 10^{-2})^z}, \;\; 2.01 = 2.0^x, \;\; x = 1$$

Comparing the first and fourth experiments:

$$\frac{6.66 \times 10^{-7}}{1.66 \times 10^{-7}} = \frac{k(1.0 \times 10^{-4}) \, (4.0 \times 10^{-2})^y \, (2.0 \times 10^{-2})^z}{k(1.0 \times 10^{-4}) \, (2.0 \times 10^{-2})^y \, (2.0 \times 10^{-2})^z}, \;\; 4.01 = 2.0^y, \;\; y = 2$$

Comparing the first and sixth experiments:

$$\frac{13.2 \times 10^{-7}}{1.66 \times 10^{-7}} = \frac{k(1.0 \times 10^{-4}) \, (2.0 \times 10^{-2})^2 \, (4.0 \times 10^{-2})^z}{k(1.0 \times 10^{-4}) \, (2.0 \times 10^{-2})^2 \, (2.0 \times 10^{-2})^z}$$

$$7.95 = 2.0^z, \;\; z = \frac{\log 7.95}{\log 2.0} = 2.99 \approx 3$$

Rate = $k[H_2SeO_3][H^+]^2[I^-]^3$

Experiment #1:

$$\frac{1.66 \times 10^{-7} \, \text{mol}}{L \, s} = k \left(\frac{1.0 \times 10^{-4} \, \text{mol}}{L} \right) \left(\frac{2.0 \times 10^{-2} \, \text{mol}}{L} \right)^2 \left(\frac{2.0 \times 10^{-2} \, \text{mol}}{L} \right)^3$$

$k = 5.19 \times 10^5 \, L^5 \, mol^{-5} \, s^{-1} = 5.2 \times 10^5 \, L^5 \, mol^{-5} \, s^{-1}$

For all experiments:

Exp #	k ($L^5 \, mol^{-5} \, s^{-1}$)	
1	5.19×10^5	
2	5.20×10^5	
3	5.20×10^5	
4	5.20×10^5	$k_{mean} = 5.2 \times 10^5 \, L^5 \, mol^{-5} \, s^{-1}$
5	5.25×10^5	
6	5.16×10^5	
7	5.25×10^5	

57.

Heating Time	Untreated		Deacidifying		Antioxidant	
(days)	s	ln s	s	ln s	s	ln s
0.00	100.0	4.605	100.1	4.606	114.6	4.741
1.00	67.9	4.218	60.8	4.108	65.2	4.177
2.00	38.9	3.661	26.8	3.288	28.1	3.336
3.00	16.1	2.779	-	-	11.3	2.425
6.00	6.8	1.92	-	-	-	-

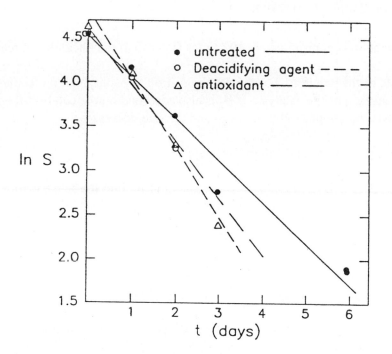

a. We used a calculator to fit the data by least squares. The results follow.

Untreated: ln s = -0.465 t + 4.55, k = -0.465 day^{-1}

Deacidifying agent: ln s = -0.659 t + 4.66, k = 0.659 day^{-1}

Antioxidant: ln s = -0.779 t + 4.84, k = 0.779 day^{-1}

b. No, the silk degrades more rapidly with the additives.

58. $t_{1/2} = (\ln 2)/k$

Untreated: $t_{1/2}$ = 1.49 day; Deacidifying agent: $t_{1/2}$ = 1.05 day; Antioxidant: $t_{1/2}$ = 0.890 day

61.   a.   W since it has a lower activation energy than the Os catalyst.

        b. $k_w = A_w \exp[-E_a(W)/RT]$; $k_{uncat} = A_{uncat} \exp[-E_a(uncat)/RT]$;   Assume $A_w = A_{uncat}$

$$\frac{k_w}{k_{uncat}} = \exp\left(\frac{-E_a(W)}{RT} + \frac{E_a(uncat)}{RT} \right)$$

$$\frac{k_w}{k_{uncat}} = \exp\left(\frac{-163,000 \text{ J/mol} + 335,000 \text{ J/mol}}{(8.3145 \text{ J mol}^{-1} \text{ K}^{-1})(298 \text{ K})} \right) = 1.41 \times 10^{30}$$

The W catalyzed reaction is approximately 10^{30} times faster than the uncatalyzed reaction.

        c. H_2 decreases the rate of the reaction. For the decomposition to occur, NH_3 molecules must be adsorbed on the surface of the catalyst. If H_2 is also adsorbed on the catalyst, then there are fewer sites for NH_3 molecules to be adsorbed and the rate decreases.

62.   Rate $= k_2[I^-][HOCl]$; From the fast equilibrium first step:

$$k_1[OCl^-] = k_{-1}[HOCl][OH^-], \quad [HOCl] = \frac{k_1[OCl^-]}{k_{-1}[OH^-]}; \quad \text{Substituting into the rate equation:}$$

$$\text{Rate} = \frac{k_2 k_1[I^-][OCl^-]}{k_{-1}[OH^-]} = \frac{k[I^-][OCl^-]}{[OH^-]}$$

63.   Rate $= k[BrO_3^-][SO_3^{2-}][H^+]$; First step: $SO_3^{2-} + H^+ \rightleftharpoons HSO_3^-$ (fast)

From the rate law we can say that the rate determining step contains one of each ion. Thus, a possible second step could be:

$$BrO_3^- + HSO_3^- \rightarrow \text{Products}   \text{(slow)}$$

A likely choice is: $BrO_3^- + HSO_3^- \rightarrow SO_4^{2-} + HBrO_2$ (slow)

Followed by: $HBrO_2 + SO_3^{2-} \rightarrow HBrO + SO_4^{2-}$ (fast);
                  $HBrO + SO_3^{2-} \rightarrow SO_4^{2-} + H^+ + Br^-$ (fast)

All species in this mechanism (HSO_3^-, $HBrO_2$, $HBrO$) are known substances. This mechanism also gives the correct experimentally determined rate law.

Rate $= k_2[BrO_3^-][HSO_3^-]$; Assuming reaction one is a fast equilibrium step:

$$k_1[SO_3^{2-}][H^+] = k_{-1}[HSO_3^-], \quad [HSO_3^-] = \frac{k_1}{k_{-1}}[SO_2^{2-}][H^+]$$

$$\text{Rate} = \frac{k_2 k_1}{k_{-1}}[BrO_3^-][SO_3^{2-}][H^+] = k[BrO_3^-][SO_3^{2-}][H^+]$$

65.   The integrated rate law for each reaction is:

$$\ln[A] = -4.50 \times 10^{-4} \text{ s}^{-1}(t) + \ln[A]_o \text{ and } \ln[B] = -3.70 \times 10^{-3} \text{ s}^{-1}(t) + \ln[B]_o$$

Subtracting the second equation from the first equation ($\ln[A]_o = \ln[B]_o$):

$$\ln[A] - \ln[B] = -4.50 \times 10^{-4} (t) + 3.70 \times 10^{-3} (t), \ \ln\left(\frac{[A]}{[B]}\right) = 3.25 \times 10^{-3} \text{ s}^{-1} (t)$$

When $[A] = 4.00[B]$, $\ln 4.00 = 3.25 \times 10^{-3} (t)$, $t = 427$ s

67. $\ln\left(\dfrac{k_2}{k_1}\right) = \dfrac{E_a}{R}\left(\dfrac{1}{T_1} - \dfrac{1}{T_2}\right)$; $\dfrac{k_2}{k_1} = 7.00$; $T_1 = 275$ K; $T_2 = 300.$ K

$$\ln 7.00 = \frac{E_a}{8.3145 \text{ J mol}^{-1}\text{K}^{-1}}\left(\frac{1}{275 \text{ K}} - \frac{1}{300. \text{ K}}\right)$$

$$E_a = \frac{(8.3145 \text{ J mol}^{-1}\text{K}^{-1})(\ln 7.00)}{3.0 \times 10^{-4}\text{K}^{-1}} = 5.4 \times 10^4 \text{ J/mol} = 54 \text{ kJ/mol}$$

69.   a.   Let P_o = initial partial pressure of $C_2H_5OH = 250.$ torr. If x torr of C_2H_5OH reacts, then at any time:

$$P_{C_2H_5OH} = 250. - x, \ P_{CH_3CHO} = P_{H_2} = x; \ P_{tot} = 250. - x + x + x = 250. + x$$

Therefore, $P_{C_2H_5OH}$ at any time can be calculated from the data by determining x ($= P_{tot} - 250.$) and then subtracting from 250. torr. Using the $P_{C_2H_5OH}$ data, a plot of $P_{C_2H_5OH}$ vs. t is linear. The reaction is zero order in $P_{C_2H_5OH}$. One could also use the P_{tot} vs. t data since P_{tot} increases at the same rate that $P_{C_2H_5OH}$ decreases. Note: The ln P vs. t plot is also linear. The reaction hasn't been followed for enough time for curvature to be seen. However, since $P_{C_2H_5OH}$ decreases at steady increments, we can conclude that the reaction is zero order in C_2H_5OH.

From the data, the integrated rate law involving P_{tot} is:

$$P_{tot} = \frac{13}{100.}t + 250.; \ \text{At } t = 900. \text{ s, } P_{tot} = \frac{13}{100.}(900.) + 250. = 370 \text{ torr}$$

b.   From the $P_{C_2H_5OH}$ vs. t plot:

$$\text{slope} = -k = \frac{-13 \text{ torr}}{100. \text{ s}} \times \frac{1 \text{ atm}}{760 \text{ torr}}, \ k = 1.7 \times 10^{-4} \text{ atm/s}$$

Note: P_{tot} increases at the same rate that $P_{C_2H_5OH}$ decreases. Therefore, the rate constant k could have been determined from a P_{tot} vs. t plot.

c.   Zero order in C_2H_5OH since $P_{C_2H_5OH}$ vs. t is linear.

71.   a.

t (s)	$[C_4H_6]$ (M)	$\ln[C_4H_6]$	$1/[C_4H_6]$ (M^{-1})
0	0.01000	-4.6052	1.000×10^2
1000.	0.00629	-5.069	1.59×10^2
2000.	0.00459	-5.384	2.18×10^2
3000.	0.00361	-5.624	2.77×10^2

The plot of $1/[C_4H_6]$ vs. t is linear, thus the reaction is second order in butadiene. From the plot, the integrated rate law is:

$$\frac{1}{[C_4H_6]} = 5.90 \times 10^{-2}\, t + 100.0$$

b.   When dimerization is 1.0% complete, 99.0% of C_4H_6 is left.

$$[C_4H_6] = 0.990(0.01000) = 0.00990\ M;\quad \frac{1}{0.00990} = 5.90 \times 10^{-2}\, t + 100.0,\ \ t = 17.1\ s \approx 20\ s$$

c.   2.0% complete, $[C_4H_6] = 0.00980\ M;\quad \dfrac{1}{0.00980} = 5.90 \times 10^{-2}\, t + 100.0,\ \ t = 34.6\ s \approx 30\ s$

d. $\dfrac{1}{[C_4H_6]} = kt + \dfrac{1}{[C_4H_6]_o};\ \ [C_4H_6]_o = 0.020\ M;\ \ \text{At}\ t = t_{1/2},\ [C_4H_6] = 0.010\ M$

$$\frac{1}{0.010} = (5.90 \times 10^{-2})t_{1/2} + \frac{1}{0.020};\ \ t = 847\ s = 850\ s \approx 800\ s$$

$$\text{Or, } t_{1/2} = \frac{1}{k[A]_o} = \frac{1}{(5.90 \times 10^{-2})\,(2.0 \times 10^{-2})} = 850\ s$$

e.   From Exercise 15.13, $k = 1.4 \times 10^{-2}$ L mol^{-1} s^{-1} at 500. K. From this problem, $k = 5.90 \times 10^{-2}$ L mol^{-1} s^{-1} at 620. K.

$$\ln\left(\frac{k_2}{k_1}\right) = \frac{E_a}{R}\left(\frac{1}{T_1} - \frac{1}{T_2}\right);\ \ \ln\left(\frac{5.90 \times 10^{-2}}{1.4 \times 10^{-2}}\right) = \frac{E_a}{8.3145\ \text{J mol}^{-1}\,\text{K}^{-1}}\left(\frac{1}{500.\ \text{K}} - \frac{1}{620.\ \text{K}}\right)$$

$$12 = E_a\,(3.9 \times 10^{-4}),\ E_a = 3.1 \times 10^4\ \text{J/mol} = 31\ \text{kJ/mol}$$

74.   Sucessive half-lives increase in time for a second order reaction. Therefore, assume reaction is second order in A.

$$t_{1/2} = \frac{1}{k[A]_o},\ k = \frac{1}{t_{1/2}[A]_o} = \frac{1}{(10.0\ \text{min})\,(0.10\ M)} = 1.0\ \text{L mol}^{-1}\ \text{min}^{-1}$$

a. $\dfrac{1}{[A]} = 1.0(80.0\ \text{min}) + \dfrac{1}{0.10\ M} = 90.\ M^{-1},\ \ [A] = 1.1 \times 10^{-2}\ M$

b.   30.0 min = 2 half-lives, so 25% of original A is remaining.

$[A] = 0.25(0.10 \ M) = 0.025 \ M$

75.   Rate $= k[A]^x[B]^y[C]^z$; During the course of experiment 1, [A] and [C] are essentially constant, and Rate $= k'[B]^y$ where $k' = k[A]_o^x [C]_o^z$.

[B] (M)	time (s)	ln[B]	1/[B] (M^{-1})
1.0×10^{-3}	0	-6.91	1.0×10^3
2.7×10^{-4}	1.0×10^5	-8.22	3.7×10^3
1.6×10^{-4}	2.0×10^5	-8.74	6.3×10^3
1.1×10^{-4}	3.0×10^5	-9.12	9.1×10^3
8.5×10^{-5}	4.0×10^5	-9.37	12×10^3
6.9×10^{-5}	5.0×10^5	-9.58	14×10^3
5.8×10^{-5}	6.0×10^5	-9.76	17×10^3

The plot of 1/[B] vs. t is linear. The reaction is second order in B and the integrated rate equation is:

$1/[B] = (2.7 \times 10^{-2} \ M^{-1} \ s^{-1}) \ t + 1.0 \times 10^3$; $k' = 2.7 \times 10^{-2} \ M^{-1} \ s^{-1}$

For experiment 2, [B] and [C] are essentially constant and Rate $= k''[A]^x$ where $k'' = k[B]_o^y [C]_o^z = k[B]_o^2 [C]_o^z$.

[A] (M)	time (s)	ln[A]	1/[A] (M^{-1})
1.0×10^{-2}	0	-4.61	1.0×10^2
8.9×10^{-3}	1.0	-4.72	110
7.1×10^{-3}	3.0	-4.95	140
5.5×10^{-3}	5.0	-5.20	180
3.8×10^{-3}	8.0	-5.57	260
2.9×10^{-3}	10.0	-5.84	340
2.0×10^{-3}	13.0	-6.21	5.0×10^2

The plot of ln[A] vs. t is linear. The reaction is first order in A and the integrated raw law is:

$\ln[A] = -(0.123 \ s^{-1}) \ t - 4.61$; $k'' = 0.123 \ s^{-1}$

Note: We will carry an extra significant figure in k''.

Experiment 3:   [A] and [B] are constant; Rate $= k'''[C]^z$

The plot of [C] vs. t is linear. Thus, $z = 0$.

The overall rate law is: Rate $= k[A][B]^2$

From Experiment 1 (to determine k):

$k' = 2.7 \times 10^{-2}\ M^{-1}\ s^{-1} = k[A]_o^x\ [C]_o^z = k[A]_o = k(2.0\ M),\ \ k = 1.4 \times 10^{-2}\ L^2\ mol^{-2}\ s^{-1}$

From Experiment 2: $k'' = 0.123\ s^{-1} = k[B]_o^2,\ \ k = \dfrac{0.123\ s^{-1}}{(3.0\ M)^2} = 1.4 \times 10^{-2}\ L^2\ mol^{-2}\ s^{-1}$

Thus, rate $= k[A][B]^2$ and $k = 1.4 \times 10^{-2}\ L^2\ mol^{-2}\ s^{-1}$.

77.   a.   Rate $= k[CH_3X]^x[Y]^y$; For experiment 1, [Y] is constant so Rate $= k'[CH_3X]^x$ where $k' = k(3.0\ M)^y$.

A plot of $\ln[CH_3X]$ vs t is linear (x = 1). The integrated rate law is:

$\ln[CH_3X] = -0.93\ t - 3.99;\ \ k' = 0.93\ h^{-1}$

For Exeriment 2, [Y] is again constant with Rate $= k''[CH_3X]^x$ where $k'' = k(4.5\ M)^y$. The ln plot is linear again with an integrated rate law:

$\ln[CH_3X] = -0.93\ t - 5.40;\ \ k'' = 0.93\ h^{-1}$

Dividing the rate constant values: $\dfrac{k'}{k''} = \dfrac{0.93}{0.93} = \dfrac{k(3.0)^y}{k(4.5)^y},\ \ 1.0 = (0.67)^y,\ \ y = 0$

Reaction is first order in CH_3X and zero order in Y. The overall rate law is:

Rate $= k[CH_3X]$ where $k = 0.93\ h^{-1}$ at 25 °C.

b. $t_{1/2} = (\ln 2)/k = 0.6931/(7.88 \times 10^8\ h^{-1}) = 8.80 \times 10^{-10}$ hour

c. $\ln(k_2/k_1) = (E_a/R)(1/T_1 - 1/T_2) = \ln\left(\dfrac{7.88 \times 10^8}{0.93}\right) = \dfrac{E_a}{8.3145\ J\ K^{-1}\ mol^{-1}}\left(\dfrac{1}{298\ K} - \dfrac{1}{358\ K}\right)$

$E_a = 3.0 \times 10^5$ J/mol $= 3.0 \times 10^2$ kJ/mol

d.   The activation energy is close to the C-X bond energy. A plausible mechanism is:

$CH_3X \rightarrow CH_3 + X$ (slow)

$CH_3 + Y \rightarrow CH_3Y$ (fast)

79.   a.   If the interval between flashes is 16.3 sec, then the rate is:

1 flash/16.3 s $= 6.13 \times 10^{-2}\ s^{-1} = k$

Interval	k	T
16.3 s	$6.13 \times 10^{-2} \text{ s}^{-1}$	21.0°C (294.2 K)
13.0 s	$7.69 \times 10^{-2} \text{ s}^{-1}$	27.8°C (301.0 K)

$$\ln\left(\frac{k_2}{k_1}\right) = \frac{E_a}{R}\left(\frac{1}{T_1} - \frac{1}{T_2}\right); \text{ Solving: } E_a = 2.5 \times 10^4 \text{ J/mol} = 25 \text{ kJ/mol}$$

b. $$\ln\left(\frac{k}{6.13 \times 10^{-2}}\right) = \frac{2.4 \times 10^4 \text{ J/mol}}{8.3145 \text{ J K}^{-1}\text{mol}^{-1}}\left(\frac{1}{294.2 \text{ K}} - \frac{1}{303.2 \text{ K}}\right)$$

$$\ln k = 0.29 + \ln(6.13 \times 10^{-2}) = -2.50$$

$$k = e^{-2.50} = 8.2 \times 10^{-2} \text{ s}^{-1}; \text{ Interval} = 1/k = 12 \text{ seconds}$$

c.

T	Interval	54-2(Intervals)
21.0 °C	16.3 s	21 °C
27.8 °C	13.0 s	28 °C
30.0 °C	12 s	30. °C

This rule of thumb gives excellent agreement to two significant figures.

80.   a. $MoCl_5^-$

b. Rate = $\dfrac{d[NO_2^-]}{dt} = k_2[NO_3^-][MoCl_5^-]$; Apply the steady-state approximation to $MoCl_5^-$.

$$\frac{d[MoCl_5^-]}{dt} = 0, \text{ so } k_1[MoCl_6^{2-}] = k_{-1}[MoCl_5^-][Cl^-] + k_2[NO_3^-][MoCl_5^-]$$

$$[MoCl_5^-] = \frac{k_1[MoCl_6^{2-}]}{k_{-1}[Cl^-] + k_2[NO_3^-]}; \text{ Rate} = \frac{d[NO_2^-]}{dt} = \frac{k_1k_2[NO_3^-][MoCl_6^{2-}]}{k_{-1}[Cl^-] + k_2[NO_3^-]}$$

82.   Rate = $\dfrac{-d[N_2O_5]}{dt} = k_1[M][N_2O_5] - k_{-1}[NO_3][NO_2][M]$

Assume $d[NO_3]/dt = 0$, so $k_1[N_2O_5][M] = k_{-1}[NO_3][NO_2][M] + k_2[NO_3][NO_2] + k_3[NO_3][NO]$

$$[NO_3] = \frac{k_1[N_2O_5][M]}{k_{-1}[NO_2][M] + k_2[NO_2] + k_3[NO]}$$

Assume $\dfrac{d[NO]}{dt} = 0$, so $k_2[NO_3][NO_2] = k_3[NO_3][NO]$, $[NO] = \dfrac{k_2}{k_3}[NO_2]$

Substituting: $[NO_3] = \dfrac{k_1[N_2O_5][M]}{k_{-1}[NO_2][M] + k_2[NO_2] + \dfrac{k_3k_2}{k_3}[NO_2]} = \dfrac{k_1[N_2O_5][M]}{[NO_2](k_{-1}[M] + 2k_2)}$

Solving for the rate law:

$$\text{Rate} = \dfrac{-d[N_2O_5]}{dt} = k_1[N_2O_5][M] - \dfrac{k_{-1}k_1[NO_2][N_2O_5][M]^2}{[NO_2](k_{-1}[M] + 2k_2)} = k_1[N_2O_5][M] - \dfrac{k_{-1}k_1[M]^2[N_2O_5]}{k_{-1}[M] + 2k_2}$$

$$\text{Rate} = \dfrac{-d[N_2O_5]}{dt} = \left(k_1 - \dfrac{k_{-1}k_1[M]}{k_{-1}[M] + 2k_2} \right)[N_2O_5][M]; \ \text{Simplifying:}$$

$$\text{Rate} = \dfrac{-d[N_2O_5]}{dt} = \dfrac{2 k_1k_2[M][N_2O_5]}{k_{-1}[M] + 2k_2}$$

86.   a.   Experiments 1 and 2: $[H_2O_2]$ doubles, $[I^-]$ is constant, and the rate doubles; First order in $[H_2O_2]$

Experiments 1 and 3: $[I^-]$ doubles, $[H_2O_2]$ is constant, and the rate doubles; First order in $[I^-]$

Rate = $k[H_2O_2][I^-]$

   b. 7.0×10^{-4} mol L^{-1} min^{-1} = k(0.10 mol/L) (0.10 mol/L), k = 7.0×10^{-2} L mol^{-1} min^{-1} = k_{mean}

   c.   Rate = $\dfrac{7.0 \times 10^{-2} \text{ L}}{\text{mol min}} \times \dfrac{0.50 \text{ mol}}{\text{L}} \times \dfrac{0.25 \text{ mol}}{\text{L}} = 8.8 \times 10^{-3}$ mol L^{-1} min^{-1} = $\dfrac{d[I_3^-]}{dt}$

$0.50 \text{ L} \times \dfrac{8.8 \times 10^{-3} \text{ mol}}{\text{L min}} = \dfrac{4.4 \times 10^{-3} \text{ mol } I_3^-}{\text{min}}$

CHAPTER SIXTEEN

LIQUIDS AND SOLIDS

Intermolecular Forces and Physical Properties

1. There is an electrostatic attraction between the permanent dipoles of the polar molecules. The greater the polarity, the greater the attraction among molecules.

2. London dispersion (LDF) < dipole-dipole < H-bonding < metallic bonding, covalent network, ionic.

    Yes, there is considerable overlap. Consider some of the examples in Exercise 16.12. Benzene (only LDF) has a higher boiling point than acetone (dipole-dipole). Also, there is even more overlap of the stronger forces (metallic, covalent, and ionic).

3. As the size of the molecule increases, the strength of the London dispersion forces also increases. As the electron cloud gets larger it is easier for the electrons to be drawn away from the nucleus (more polarizable).

4. Yes, there are some substances in which only dispersion forces are present such as naphthalene, $C_{10}H_{18}$, and polyethylene that are solids at room temperature. Since these substances are solids at room temperature, then their interparticle forces are stronger than those that are liquids at room temperature, such as water in which there are hydrogen bonds.

5. As the strengths of interparticle forces increase: surface tension, viscosity, melting point, and boiling point increase, while the vapor pressure decreases.

6. The nature of the forces stays the same. As the temperature increases and the phase changes, solid → liquid → gas, occur, a greater fraction of the forces are overcome by the increased thermal (kinetic) energy of the particles.

7. a. ionic   b. LDF, dipole   c. LDF only

    d. LDF mostly; For all practical purposes, we consider a C – H bond to be nonpolar even though there is a small difference in electronegativity.

e. metallic   f. metallic   g. LDF only

h. H-bonding, LDF   i. ionic   j. metallic

k. LDF mostly; C – F bonds are polar, but polymers like teflon are so large the LDF are the predominant interparticle forces.

8.   a. OCS: OCS is polar and has dipole-dipole forces in addition to LDF. All polar molecules have dipole forces. CO_2 is nonpolar and only has LD forces. In all of the following (b-d), only one molecule is polar and, in turn, has dipole-dipole forces. To predict polarity, draw the Lewis structure and deduce if the individual bond dipoles cancel.

        b. PF_3 is polar (PF_5 is nonpolar).

9.   Dipole forces are generally weaker than hydrogen bonding. They are similar in that they arise from an unequal sharing of electrons. We can look at hydrogen bonding as a particularly strong dipole force.

10.   a. $H_2NCH_2CH_2NH_2$; More extensive hydrogen bonding is possible.

        b. $B(OH)_3$; No hydrogen bonding in BH_3. For hydrogen bonding to occur, an H-atom must be covalently bonded to O, N, or F.

11.   a. Neopentane is more compact than n-pentane. There is less surface area contact between neopentane molecules. This leads to weaker LD forces and a lower boiling point.

        b. Ethanol is capable of H-bonding, dimethylether is not.

        c. HF is capable of H-bonding.

        d. LiCl is ionic. Ionic forces are much stronger than the intermolecular forces present in molecular solids. $TiCl_4$ is a nonpolar molecular substance with relatively weak London dispersion forces.

12.

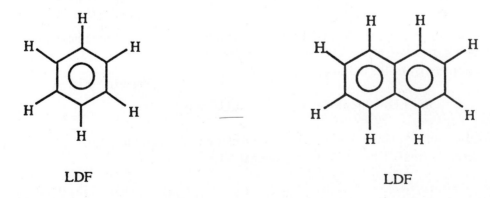

        LDF   LDF

Note: LDF in molecules like benzene and naphthalene are fairly large. The molecules are flat and there is efficient surface area contact between molecules. Large surface area contact leads to stronger London dispersion forces.

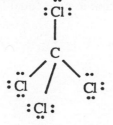

In terms of size and shape: $CCl_4 < C_6H_6 < C_{10}H_8$

The strengths of the LDF are proportional to size and are related to shape. Although the size of CCl_4 is fairly large, the overall spherical shape gives rise to relatively weak LD forces as compared to flat molecules like benzene and and naphthalene. The physical properties are consistent with the order listed above. Each of the physical properties will increase with an increase in interparticle forces.

LDF, dipole

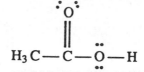

LDF, dipole, H-bonding

LDF, dipole, H-bonding

We would predict the strength of interparticle forces of the last three molecules to be:

acetone   <   acetic acid   <   benzoic acid

polar   H-bonding   H-bonding, but large LDF because of greater size and shape.

This ordering is consistent with the values given for bp, mp, and ΔH_{vap}.

The order of the strengths of interparticle forces based on physical properties are:

acetone $< CCl_4 < C_6H_6 <$ acetic acid $<$ naphthalene $<$ benzoic acid

The order seems reasonable except for acetone and napthalene. Since acetone is polar, we would not expect it to boil at the lowest temperature. However, in terms of size and shape, acetone is the smallest molecule and the LDF in acetone must be very small compared to the other molecules. Napthalene must have very strong LDF because of its size and flat shape.

14.   FHF⁻ can be thought of as forming from a HF molecule and a F⁻ ion to give equal F – H
       distances. The structure will be linear as predicted by VSEPR.

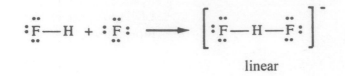

                                              linear

15.   Only a fraction of the hydrogen bonds are broken in going from the solid phase to the liquid
       phase. Most of the hydrogen bonds are still present in the liquid phase and must be broken
       during the liquid to gas phase transition.

17.   Both molecules are capable of H-bonding. However, in oil of wintergreen the hydrogen bonding
       is intramolecular.

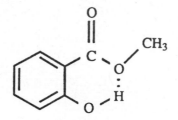

       In methyl-4-hydroxybenzoate, the H-bonding is intermolecular, resulting in stronger
       intermolecular forces and a higher melting point.

19.   a.   NaCl; strong ionic bonding in lattice

       b. H_2; nonpolar like CH_4, smaller than CH_4, weaker LDF

       c. SiO_2; covalent network solid vs. a gas and a liquid

       d. $HOCH_2CH_2OH$ (ethylene glycol); Greatest amount of H-bonding since two –OH groups are
            present.

20. $C_{25}H_{52}$ has the stronger intermolecular forces because it has the higher boiling point. Even
       though $C_{25}H_{52}$ is nonpolar, it is so large that its London dispersion forces are much stronger than
       the sum of the London dispersion and hydrogen bonding interactions found in H_2O.

22.   a.   Polarizability of an atom refers to the ease of distorting the electron cloud. It can also refer
            to distorting the electron clouds in molecules or ions. Polarity refers to the presence of a
            permanent dipole moment in a molecule.

       b.   London dispersion forces are present in all substances. LDF can be referred to as accidental
            dipole - induced dipole forces. Dipole - dipole forces involve the attraction of molecules
            with permanent dipoles for each other.

       c.   inter: between; intra: within

For example, in H_2 the covalent bond is an intramolecular force, holding the two H-atoms together in the molecule. The much weaker London dispersion forces are the intermolecular forces of attraction.

Properties of Liquids

24.   Liquids and solids both have characteristic volume and are not very compressible. Liquids and gases flow and assume the shape of their container.

25.   Critical temperature: The temperature above which a liquid cannot exist, i.e., the gas cannot be liquified by increased pressure.

Critical pressure: The pressure that must be applied to a substance at its critical temperature to produce a liquid.

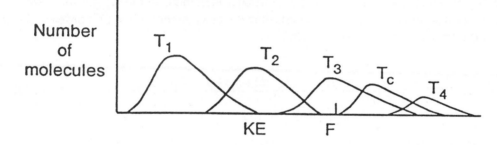

The kinetic energy distribution changes as one raises the temperature ($T_4 > T_c > T_3 > T_2 > T_1$). At the critical temperature, T_c, all molecules have kinetic energies greater than the interparticle forces, F, and a liquid can't form.

26.   As the interparticle forces increase the critical temperature increases.

28.   The attraction of H_2O for glass is stronger than the $H_2O – H_2O$ attraction. The miniscus is concave to increase the area of contact between glass and H_2O. The Hg – Hg attraction is greater than the Hg – glass attraction. The miniscus is convex to minimize the Hg – glass contact. Polyethylene is a nonpolar substance. The $H_2O – H_2O$ attraction is stronger than the $H_2O –$ polyethylene attraction. Thus, the miniscus will have a convex shape.

31.   The structure of H_2O_2 is H – O – O – H, which produces greater hydrogen bonding than water. Long chains of hydrogen bonded H_2O_2 molecules then get tangled together.

Structures and Properties of Solids

33.   a.   Crystalline solid: Regular, repeating structure

             Amorphous solid: Irregular arrangement of atoms or molecules

b. Ionic solid: Made up of ions held together by ionic bonding.

    Molecular solid: Made up of discrete covalently bonded molecules held together in the solid by weaker forces (LDF, dipole, or hydrogen bonds).

c. Molecular solid: Discrete molecules

    Covalent network solid: No discrete molecules; A covalent network solid is one large molecule. The interparticle forces are the covalent bonds between atoms.

34. A crystalline solid because a regular, repeating arrangement is necessary to produce planes of atoms that will diffract the x-rays.

35. No, an example is common glass which is primarily amorphous SiO_2 (a covalent network solid) as compared to ice (a crystalline solid held together by weaker H-bonds). The interparticle forces in the amorphous solid in this case are stronger than those in the crystalline solid. Whether or not a solid is amorphous or crystalline depends on the long range order in the solid and not on the strengths of the interparticle forces.

37. $n\lambda = 2d \sin \theta, \quad \lambda = \dfrac{2d \sin \theta}{n} = \dfrac{2 \times (201 \times 10^{-12} \text{ m}) \sin 34.68°}{1}, \quad \lambda = 2.29 \times 10^{-10} \text{ m} = 229 \text{ pm}$

39. $n\lambda = 2d \sin \theta; \quad 1.54 \text{ Å} = 1.54 \times 10^{-10} \text{ m} = 154 \text{ pm}$

$d = \dfrac{n\lambda}{2 \sin \theta} = \dfrac{1 \times 154 \text{ pm}}{2 \times \sin 14.22°} = 313 \text{ pm} = 3.13 \times 10^{-10} \text{ m} = 3.13 \text{ Å}$

40.

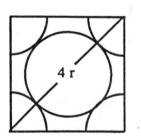

3.92 × 10⁻⁸ cm = length of cube edge = l

4r = length of diagonal

From the Pythagorean theorem:

$(4r)^2 = l^2 + l^2 = (3.92 \times 10^{-8})^2 + (3.92 \times 10^{-8})^2, \quad r = 1.39 \times 10^{-8} \text{ cm} = 139 \text{ pm} = 1.39 \text{ Å}$

Note: For all face-centered unit cells, the radius and the cube edge length are related by $4r = \sqrt{2}\, l$

In a face centered cubic unit cell: 8 corners × $\dfrac{1/8 \text{ atom}}{\text{corner}}$ + 6 faces × $\dfrac{1/2 \text{ atom}}{\text{face}}$ = 4 atoms

density = $\dfrac{\text{mass}}{\text{volume}}$; For a unit cell where AM = atomic mass:

$$\text{mass} = 4 \text{ atoms} \times \frac{1 \text{ mol}}{6.022 \times 10^{23} \text{ atoms}} \times \frac{\text{AM g}}{\text{mol}}; \quad \text{volume} = (\text{edge})^3 = (3.92 \times 10^{-8} \text{ cm})^3$$

$$\text{density} = 21.45 \text{ g/cm}^3 = \frac{4 \times \text{AM} \times \dfrac{1}{6.022 \times 10^{23}}}{(3.92 \times 10^{-8} \text{ cm})^3}; \quad \text{Solving:}$$

AM = 194.5 g/mol ≈ 195 g/mol; The metal is platinum.

41.   A cubic closest packed structure has a face centered cubic unit cell. A face centered cubic unit cell will contain 4 Co atoms. The length of the face diagonal is related to the radius of Co by $\sqrt{2}\, l = 4r$, where l is the cube edge length. See solution to Exercise 16.40 for details.

$$l = 4r/\sqrt{2} = 4(1.25 \times 10^{-8} \text{ cm})/\sqrt{2} = 3.54 \times 10^{-8} \text{ cm}$$

For a unit cell of the β form:

$$d = \frac{\text{mass}}{\text{volume}} = \frac{4 \text{ atoms} \times \dfrac{1 \text{ mol}}{6.022 \times 10^{23} \text{ atoms}} \times \dfrac{58.93 \text{ g}}{\text{mol}}}{(3.54 \times 10^{-8} \text{ cm})^3} = \frac{3.91 \times 10^{-22} \text{ g}}{4.44 \times 10^{-23} \text{ cm}^3} = 8.81 \text{ g/cm}^3$$

There appears to be a slight difference in density between the two forms.

42.   There are 4 Ir atoms in the unit cell. (See Exercise 16.40.)

$$22.61 \text{ g/cm}^3 = \frac{4 \text{ atoms} \times \dfrac{1 \text{ mol}}{N_o \text{ atoms}} \times \dfrac{192.2 \text{ g}}{\text{mol}}}{(3.833 \times 10^{-8} \text{ cm})^3}, \quad N_o = \frac{4 \times 192.2}{22.61 \times (3.833 \times 10^{-8})^3} = 6.038 \times 10^{23}$$

43.   Body centered unit cell: $8 \text{ corners} \times \dfrac{1/8 \text{ Ti}}{\text{corner}} + \text{Ti at body center} = 2 \text{ Ti atoms}$

All body centered unit cells have 2 atoms per unit cell. For a unit cell:

$$d = 4.50 \text{ g/cm}^3 = \frac{2 \text{ atoms} \times \dfrac{1 \text{ mol}}{6.022 \times 10^{23} \text{ atoms}} \times \dfrac{47.88 \text{ g}}{\text{mol}}}{l^3}, \quad l = \text{cube edge length}$$

Solving: l = edge length of unit cell = 3.28×10^{-8} cm = 328 pm

Assume Ti atoms just touch along the body diagonal of the cube, so body diagonal = 4 r.

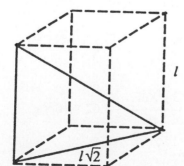

The triangle we need to solve is:

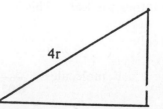

$(4r)^2 = (3.28 \times 10^{-8} \text{ cm})^2 + [\sqrt{2}(3.28 \times 10^{-8} \text{ cm})]^2$, $r = 1.42 \times 10^{-8}$ cm = 142 pm = 1.42 Å

For a body centered unit cell, the radius of the atom is related to the cube edge length by $4r = \sqrt{3}\, l$.

46.   If fcc structure: 4 atoms/unit cell

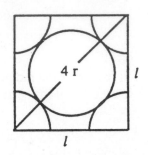

$2\, l^2 = 16\, r^2$

$l = r\sqrt{8} = 144 \text{ pm } \sqrt{8} = 407$ pm

$l = 407 \times 10^{-12}$ m = 407×10^{-10} cm

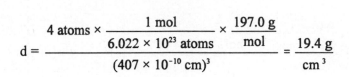

$$d = \frac{4 \text{ atoms} \times \dfrac{1 \text{ mol}}{6.022 \times 10^{23} \text{ atoms}} \times \dfrac{197.0 \text{ g}}{\text{mol}}}{(407 \times 10^{-10} \text{ cm})^3} = \frac{19.4 \text{ g}}{\text{cm}^3}$$

If bcc: 2 atoms/unit cell

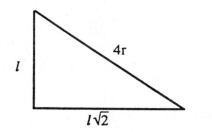

$16\, r^2 = l^2 + 2\, l^2$

$l = r\sqrt{16/3} = 333 \text{ pm} = 333 \times 10^{-10}$ cm

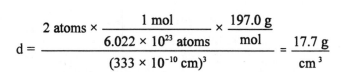

$$d = \frac{2 \text{ atoms} \times \dfrac{1 \text{ mol}}{6.022 \times 10^{23} \text{ atoms}} \times \dfrac{197.0 \text{ g}}{\text{mol}}}{(333 \times 10^{-10} \text{ cm})^3} = \frac{17.7 \text{ g}}{\text{cm}^3}$$

The measured density is consistent with a face centered cubic unit cell.

49.   a.   8 corners $\times \dfrac{1/8 \text{ Xe}}{\text{corner}}$ + 1 Xe inside cell = 2 Xe; 8 edges $\times \dfrac{1/4 \text{ F}}{\text{edges}}$ + 2 F inside cell = 4 F

Empirical formula is XeF_2. This is also the molecular formula.

b.   For a unit cell:

$$\text{mass} = 2 \text{ XeF}_2 \text{ molecules} \times \frac{1 \text{ mol XeF}_2}{6.022 \times 10^{23} \text{ molecules}} \times \frac{169.3 \text{ g XeF}_2}{\text{mol XeF}_2} = 5.62 \times 10^{-22} \text{ g}$$

$$\text{volume} = (702 \times 10^{-12} \text{ m})(432 \times 10^{-12} \text{ m})(432 \times 10^{-12} \text{ m}) = 1.31 \times 10^{-28} \text{ m}^3$$

$$\text{volume} = 1.31 \times 10^{-28} \text{ m}^3 \times \left(\frac{100 \text{ cm}}{\text{m}}\right)^3 = 1.31 \times 10^{-22} \text{ cm}^3$$

$$\text{density} = d = \frac{\text{mass}}{\text{volume}} = \frac{5.62 \times 10^{-22} \text{ g}}{1.31 \times 10^{-22} \text{ cm}^3} = 4.29 \text{ g/cm}^3$$

51.   a.   The unit cell consists of Ni at the cube corners and Ti at the body center, or Ti at the cube corners and Ni at the body center.

   b. $8 \times 1/8 = 1$ atom from corners + 1 atom at body center; Empirical formula = NiTi

   c.   Both have coordination numbers of 8.

52.   a.   1 Ti at body center; 8 corners $\times \dfrac{1/8 \text{ Ca}}{\text{corner}} = 1$ Ca atom

   6 face centers $\times \dfrac{1/2 \text{ oxygen}}{\text{face center}} = 3$ O atoms; Formula = $CaTiO_3$

   b.   The Ti atoms are at the corners of each unit cell and the oxygen atoms are at the center of each edge in the unit cell.

   Since each of the 12 cube edges is shared by 4 unit cells:

   $12 \times 1/4 = 3$ O atoms; $8 \times 1/8 = 1$ Ti atom; 1 Ca at center; Formula = $CaTiO_3$

   c.   Six oxygen atoms surround each Ti atom.

55.   Conductor: Partially filled valence band; Electrons can move through the valence band (from filled to unfilled orbitals).

   Insulator: Filled valence band, large band gap; Electrons cannot move in the valence band and cannot jump to the conduction band.

   Semiconductor: Filled valence band, small band gap; Electrons cannot move in the valence band but can jump to the conduction band.

56.   a.   As the temperature is increased, more electrons in the valence band have sufficient kinetic energy to jump from the valence band to the conduction band.

   b.   A photon of light is absorbed by an electron which then has sufficient energy to jump from the valence band to the conduction band.

   c.   An impurity either adds electrons at an energy near that of the conduction band (n-type) or creates holes (empty energy levels) at energies in the valence band (p-type).

58.   To make a p-type semiconductor we need to dope the material with atoms with fewer valence electrons. The average number of valence electrons is four. We could dope with more of the Group 3A elements or with atoms of Zn or Cd. Cadmium is the most common impurity used to produce p-type GaAs semiconductors. To make a n-type GaAs semiconductor, dope with an excess group 5 element or dope with a Group 6 element such as sulfur.

59. $E = 2.5 \text{ eV} \times (1.6 \times 10^{-19} \text{ J/eV}) = 4.0 \times 10^{-19} \text{ J}$

$E = \dfrac{hc}{\lambda}, \; \lambda = \dfrac{hc}{E} = \dfrac{(6.63 \times 10^{-34} \text{ J s}) (3.00 \times 10^8 \text{ m/s})}{4.0 \times 10^{-19} \text{ J}} = 5.0 \times 10^{-7} \text{ m} = 5.0 \times 10^2 \text{ nm}$

Phase Changes and Phase Diagrams

62.   Equilibrium: There is no change in composition; the vapor pressure is constant.

Dynamic: Two processes, vapor → liquid and liquid → vapor, are both occurring with equal rates.

63.   At 100.°C (373 K), the vapor pressure of H_2O is 1.00 atm. For water, $\Delta H_{vap} = 40.7$ kJ/mol.

$$\ln\left(\frac{P_1}{P_2}\right) = \frac{\Delta H_{vap}}{R}\left(\frac{1}{T_2} - \frac{1}{T_1}\right) \text{ or } \ln\left(\frac{P_2}{P_1}\right) = \frac{\Delta H_{vap}}{R}\left(\frac{1}{T_1} - \frac{1}{T_2}\right)$$

$$\ln\left(\frac{P_2}{1.00 \text{ atm}}\right) = \frac{40.7 \times 10^3 \text{ J/mol}}{8.3145 \text{ J K}^{-1} \text{ mol}^{-1}}\left(\frac{1}{373 \text{ K}} - \frac{1}{388 \text{ K}}\right), \; \ln P_2 = 0.51, \; P_2 = e^{0.51} = 1.7 \text{ atm}$$

$$\ln\left(\frac{3.50}{1.00}\right) = \frac{40.7 \times 10^3 \text{ J/mol}}{8.3145 \text{ J K}^{-1} \text{ mol}^{-1}}\left(\frac{1}{373 \text{ K}} - \frac{1}{T_2}\right) = 1.253, \; 2.56 \times 10^{-4} = \left(\frac{1}{373} - \frac{1}{T_2}\right)$$

$$2.56 \times 10^{-4} = 2.68 \times 10^{-3} - \frac{1}{T_2}, \; \frac{1}{T_2} = 2.42 \times 10^{-3}, \; T_2 = \frac{1}{2.42 \times 10^{-3}} = 413 \text{ K or } 140.°C$$

65. $H_2O(s, -20.°C) \rightarrow H_2O(s, 0°C)$

$q_1 = s_{ice} \times m \times \Delta T = 2.1 \dfrac{J}{g \, °C} \times 5.00 \times 10^2 \text{ g} \times 20.°C = 2.1 \times 10^4 \text{ J} = 21 \text{ kJ}$

$H_2O(s, 0°C) \rightarrow H_2O(l, 0°C), \; q_2 = 5.00 \times 10^2 \text{ g } H_2O \times \dfrac{1 \text{ mol}}{18.02 \text{ g}} \times \dfrac{6.01 \text{ kJ}}{\text{mol}} = 167 \text{ kJ}$

$H_2O(l, 0°C) \rightarrow H_2O(l, 100.°C), \; q_3 = 4.2 \dfrac{J}{g \, °C} \times 5.00 \times 10^2 \text{ g} \times 100.°C = 2.1 \times 10^5 \text{ J} = 210 \text{ kJ}$

$H_2O(l, 100.°C) \rightarrow H_2O(g, 100.°C), \; q_4 = 5.00 \times 10^2 \text{ g} \times \dfrac{1 \text{ mol}}{18.02 \text{ g}} \times \dfrac{40.7 \text{ kJ}}{\text{mol}} = 1130 \text{ kJ}$

$H_2O(g, 100.°C) \rightarrow H_2O(g, 250.°C), \; q_5 = 2.0 \dfrac{J}{g \, °C} \times 5.00 \times 10^2 \text{ g} \times 150.°C = 1.5 \times 10^5 \text{ J} = 150 \text{ kJ}$

$q_{total} = q_1 + q_2 + q_3 + q_4 + q_5 = 21 + 167 + 210 + 1130 + 150 = 1680 \text{ kJ}$

67. $1.00 \text{ lb} \times \dfrac{454 \text{ g}}{\text{lb}} = 454 \text{ g } H_2O$; A change of $1.00°F$ is equal to a change of $5/9°C$.

The amount of heat in J in 1 Btu is: $\dfrac{4.18 \text{ J}}{\text{g } °C} \times 454 \text{ g} \times \dfrac{5}{9} °C = 1.05 \times 10^3 \text{ J} = 1.05 \text{ kJ}$

It takes 40.7 kJ to vaporize 1 mol H_2O (ΔH_{vap}). Combining these:

$$\dfrac{1.00 \times 10^4 \text{ Btu}}{\text{hr}} \times \dfrac{1.05 \text{ kJ}}{\text{Btu}} \times \dfrac{1 \text{ mol } H_2O}{40.7 \text{ kJ}} = 258 \text{ mol/hr}$$

or $\dfrac{258 \text{ mol}}{\text{hr}} \times \dfrac{18.02 \text{ g}}{\text{mol}} = 4650 \text{ g/hr} = 4.65 \text{ kg/hr}$

68.   We want to graph ln P vs 1/T. The slope of the resulting straight line will be $-\Delta H/R$.

P	ln P	T (Li)	1/T	T (Mg)	1/T
1 torr	0	1023 K	$9.775 \times 10^{-4} \text{ K}^{-1}$	893 K	$11.2 \times 10^{-4} \text{ K}^{-1}$
10.	2.30	1163	8.598×10^{-4}	1013	9.872×10^{-4}
100.	4.605	1353	7.391×10^{-4}	1173	8.525×10^{-4}
400.	5.991	1513	6.609×10^{-4}	1313	7.616×10^{-4}
760.	6.633	1583	6.317×10^{-4}	1383	7.231×10^{-4}

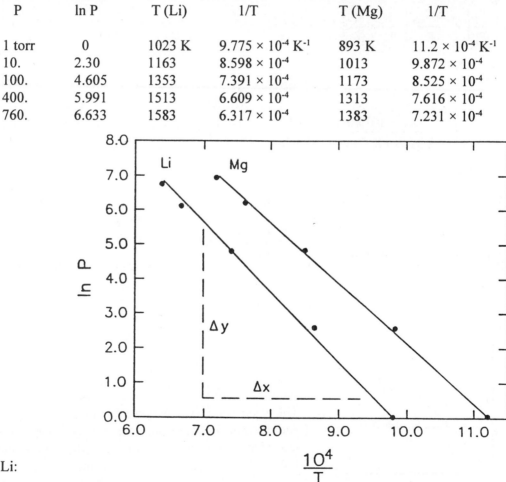

For Li:

We get the slope by taking two points (x, y) that are on the line we draw, not data points.
There may be experimental error and individual data points may not fall directly on the best
fit line. For a line:

$$\text{slope} = \dfrac{\Delta y}{\Delta x} = \dfrac{y_2 - y_1}{x_2 - x_1}$$

or we can fit the straight line using a computer or calculator.

The equation of this line is: $\ln P = -1.90 \times 10^4 (1/T) + 18.6$, slope $= -1.90 \times 10^4$ K

Slope $= -\Delta H/R$, $\Delta H = -$slope $\times R = 1.90 \times 10^4$ K $\times 8.3145$ J K^{-1} mol^{-1}

$\Delta H = 1.58 \times 10^5$ J/mol $= 158$ kJ/mol

For Mg:

The equation of the line is: $\ln P = -1.67 \times 10^4 (1/T) + 18.7$, slope $= -1.67 \times 10^4$ K

$\Delta H = -$slope $\times R = 1.67 \times 10^4$ K $\times 8.3145$ J K^{-1} mol^{-1}, $\Delta H = 1.39 \times 10^5$ J/mol $= 139$ kJ/mol

The bonding is stronger in Li since ΔH_{vap} is larger for Li.

69. $\ln\left(\dfrac{P_1}{P_2}\right) = \dfrac{\Delta H_{vap}}{R}\left(\dfrac{1}{T_2} - \dfrac{1}{T_1}\right)$

At normal boiling point, $P_1 = 760.$ torr, $T_1 = 56.5°C = 329.7$ K; $T_2 = 25.0°C = 298.2$ K, $P_2 = ?$

$\ln\left(\dfrac{760.}{P_2}\right) = \dfrac{32.0 \times 10^3 \text{ J/mol}}{8.3145 \text{ J K}^{-1}\text{ mol}^{-1}}\left(\dfrac{1}{298.2} - \dfrac{1}{329.7}\right)$, $6.633 - \ln P_2 = 1.23$

$\ln P_2 = 5.40$, $P_2 = e^{5.40} = 221$ torr

72.   a.   As the intermolecular forces increase, the rate of evaporation decreases.

b.   Increase T, increase rate

c.   Increase surface area, increase rate

73.

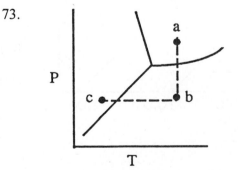

As P is lowered, we go from a to b on the phase diagram. The water boils. The evaporation of the water is endothermic and the water is cooled (b → c), leaving some ice. If the pump is left on, the ice will sublime until none is left. This is the basis of freeze drying.

74.   A: solid;   B: liquid;   C: vapor

D: solid + vapor;   E: solid + liquid + vapor

F: liquid + vapor;   G: liquid + vapor;   H: vapor

triple point: E;   critical point: G

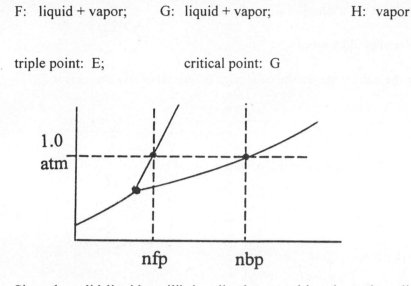

Since the solid-liquid equilibrium line has a positive slope, the solid phase is denser than the liquid phase.

78.   Heat released = 0.250 g Na $\times \dfrac{1 \text{ mol}}{22.99 \text{ g}} \times \dfrac{368 \text{ kJ}}{2 \text{ mol}}$ = 2.00 kJ

To melt 50.0 g of ice requires: 50.0 g ice $\times \dfrac{1 \text{ mol } H_2O}{18.02 \text{ g}} \times \dfrac{6.01 \text{ kJ}}{\text{mol}}$ = 16.7 kJ

The reaction doesn't release enough heat to melt all of the ice. The temperature will remain at 0°C.

79.   a. 3

       b. Triple point at 95.31°C: rhombic, monoclinic, gas
           Triple point at 115.18°C: monoclinic, liquid, gas
           Triple point at 153°C: rhombic, monoclinic, liquid

       c. Rhombic is stable at T = 20°C and P = 1 atm.

       d. Yes, monoclinic sulfur and vapor (gas) share a common boundary line in the phase diagram.

       e. 444.6°C; The normal boiling point occurs at P = 1 atm.

       f. Rhombic, since the rhombic-monoclinic equilibrium line has a positive slope.

Additional Exercises

80.   One B atom and one N atom together have the same number of electrons as two C atoms. The description of physical properties sound a lot like the properties of graphite and diamond, the two solid forms of carbon. The two forms of BN have structures similar to graphite and diamond.

83.   There is one atom (radius = R) in a simple cubic unit cell.

$V_{occ} = 4/3\pi R^3$ = volume occupied by atom

The atom touches along the cube edge, so the cube edge length (l) of the unit cell is 2R.

$V_{tot} = l^3 = (2R)^3 = 8R^3$

$$\frac{V_{occ}}{V_{tot}} = \frac{4/3\pi R^3}{8R^3} = \frac{4\pi}{24} = 0.524 \text{ or } 52.4 \% \text{ of the volume is occupied.}$$

84.

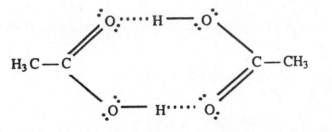

86.   The unit cell is a parallelpiped. There are three parallelpiped unit cells in a hexagon. In each parallelpiped, there are atoms at each of the 8 corners (shared by eight unit cells) plus one atom inside the unit cell: 2/3 of one atom plus 1/6 from each of two others. Thus, there are two atoms in the unit cell.

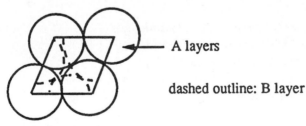

A layers

dashed outline: B layer

88.   Total mass H_2O = 18 cubes × $\dfrac{30.0 \text{ g}}{\text{cube}}$ = 540. g;   540. g H_2O × $\dfrac{1 \text{ mol } H_2O}{18.02 \text{ g}}$ = 30.0 mol H_2O

Heat needed to produce ice at -5.0°C:

$$\frac{4.18 \text{ J}}{\text{g °C}} \times 540. \text{ g} \times 22.0 \text{ °C} + \frac{6.01 \times 10^3 \text{ J}}{\text{mol}} \times 30.0 \text{ mol} + \frac{2.08 \text{ J}}{\text{g °C}} \times 540. \text{ g} \times 5.0 \text{ °C}$$

$$= 4.97 \times 10^4 \text{ J} + 1.80 \times 10^5 \text{ J} + 5.6 \times 10^3 \text{ J} = 2.35 \times 10^5 \text{ J}$$

$2.35 \times 10^5 \text{ J} \times \dfrac{1 \text{ g } CF_2Cl_2}{158 \text{ J}} = 1.49 \times 10^3 \text{ g } CF_2Cl_2$ must be vaporized.

91.   CsCl is a simple cubic array of Cl⁻ ions with Cs⁺ in the middle of each unit cell. There is one Cs⁺ and one Cl⁻ ion in each unit cell. Cs⁺ and Cl⁻ touch along the body diagonal.

body diagonal = $2r_{Cs^+} + 2r_{Cl^-} = \sqrt{3}\, l$, l = length of cube edge

In each unit cell:

mass = 1 CsCl molecule (1 mol/6.022 × 10²³ molecules) (168.4 g/mol) = 2.796 × 10⁻²² g

volume = l^3 = mass/density = 2.796 × 10⁻²² g/3.97 g cm⁻³ = 7.04 × 10⁻²³ cm³

l^3 = 7.04 × 10⁻²³ cm³, l = 4.13 × 10⁻⁸ cm = 413 pm = length of cube edge

$2r_{Cs^+} + 2r_{Cl^-} = \sqrt{3}\, l = \sqrt{3}(413$ pm$) = 715$ pm

The distance between ion centers = $r_{Cs^+} + r_{Cl^-}$ = 715 pm/2 = 358 pm

From ionic radius: r_{Cs^+} = 169 pm and r_{Cl^-} = 181 pm; $r_{Cs^+} + r_{Cl^-}$ = 169 + 181 = 350. pm

The actual distance is 8 pm (2.3%) greater than that calculated from tables of ionic radii.

93.   There are 2 tetrahedral holes per packing atom. Let f = fraction of tetrahedral holes filled

K_2O: cation to anion ratio = $\dfrac{2}{1} = \dfrac{2f}{1}$, f = 1; All tetrahedral holes are filled.

CuI: cation to anion ratio = $\dfrac{1}{1} = \dfrac{2f}{1}$, f = $\dfrac{1}{2}$; $\dfrac{1}{2}$ of the tetrahedral holes are filled.

ZrI_4:   cation to anion ratio = $\dfrac{1}{4} = \dfrac{2f}{1}$, f = $\dfrac{1}{8}$; $\dfrac{1}{8}$ of the tetrahedral holes are filled.

96.   Ar is cubic closest packed. There are 4 Ar atoms per unit cell and with a face centered unit cell, the atoms touch along the face diagonal.

face diagonal = 4r = $\sqrt{2}\, l$, l = length of cube edge; l = 4(190. pm)/$\sqrt{2}$ = 537 pm = 5.37 × 10⁻⁸ cm

$$d = \frac{mass}{volume} = \frac{4 \text{ atoms} \times \dfrac{1 \text{ mol}}{6.022 \times 10^{23} \text{ atoms}} \times \dfrac{39.95 \text{ g}}{mol}}{(5.37 \times 10^{-8} \text{ cm})^3} = 1.71 \text{ g/cm}^3$$

98.   Re at 8 corners: 8(1/8) = 1 Re; O at 12 edges: 12(1/4) = 3 O

Formula is ReO_3. If O has 2- charge, then charge on Re is +6.

100.   Total charge of all Fe is +2 to balance the -2 charge from the one O atom. Sum of Fe is 0.950.

Setting up two equations: $x + y = 0.950$ and $2x + 3y = 2.000$

Solving: $2x + 3(0.950 - x) = 2.000$, $x = 0.85$ and $y = 0.10$

$\dfrac{0.10}{0.95} = 0.11 = $ fraction of Fe as Fe^{3+}

If all Fe^{2+}, then $1.000\ Fe^{2+}/O^{2-}$; $1.000 - 0.950 = 0.050 = $ vacant sites

5.0% of Fe sites are vacant.

102.   For water vapor at 30.0°C and 31.824 torr:

$$\text{density} = \frac{P(\text{molar mass})}{RT} = \frac{\left(\dfrac{31.824\ \text{atm}}{760}\right)\left(\dfrac{18.015\ \text{g}}{\text{mol}}\right)}{\dfrac{0.08206\ \text{L atm}}{\text{mol K}} \times 303.2\ \text{K}} = 0.03032\ \text{g/L}$$

The volume of one molecule is proportional to d^3 where d is the average distance between molecules. For a large sample of molecules, the volume is still proportional to d^3. So:

$$\frac{V_{gas}}{V_{liq}} = \frac{d_{gas}^3}{d_{liq}^3}$$

If we have 0.99567 g H_2O then $V_{liq} = 1.0000\ \text{cm}^3 = 1.0000 \times 10^{-3}$ L.

$V_{gas} = 0.99567$ g $\times$ 1 L/0.03032 g $= 32.84$ L

$$\frac{d_{gas}^3}{d_{liq}^3} = \frac{32.84\ \text{L}}{1.0000 \times 10^{-3}\ \text{L}} = 3.284 \times 10^4, \quad \frac{d_{gas}}{d_{liq}} = (3.284 \times 10^4)^{1/3} = 32.02, \quad \frac{d_{liq}}{d_{gas}} = 0.03123$$

104. 100.0 g $N_2 \times \dfrac{1\ \text{mol}\ N_2}{28.014\ \text{g}\ N_2} = 3.570$ mol N_2; $P_{H_2O} = \chi_{H_2O}P_{tot}$, $\chi_{H_2O} = \dfrac{23.8\ \text{torr}}{700.\ \text{torr}} = 0.0340$

$\chi_{H_2O} = 0.0340 = \dfrac{n_{H_2O}}{n_{N_2} + n_{H_2O}} = \dfrac{n_{H_2O}}{3.570 + n_{H_2O}}$, $n_{H_2O} = 0.121 + 0.0340\ n_{H_2O}$

$n_{H_2O} = 0.125$ mol; 0.125 mol $\times 18.02$ g/mol $= 2.25$ g H_2O

107.   Mn at 8 corners × (1/8) + 1 Mn at body center = 2 Mn; There are 2 Mn atoms in each unit cell. The coordination number of Mn is 8.

For Mn at center: coordination # is from 8 Mn at corners.

For Mn at corner: coordination # is from 8 Mn at the center of 8 different cubes that touch each corner Mn.

109.   A face centered cubic unit cell contains 4 atoms. For a unit cell:

mass of X = volume × density = $(4.09 \times 10^{-8} \text{ cm})^3 \times 10.5 \text{ g/cm}^3 = 7.18 \times 10^{-22}$ g

mol X = 4 atoms X × $\dfrac{1 \text{ mol X}}{6.022 \times 10^{23} \text{ atoms}}$ = 6.642×10^{-24} mol X

Atomic mass = $\dfrac{7.18 \times 10^{-22} \text{ g X}}{6.642 \times 10^{-24} \text{ mol X}}$ = 108 g/mol; The metal is silver (Ag).

CHAPTER SEVENTEEN

PROPERTIES OF SOLUTIONS

1. $125 \text{ g sucrose} \times \dfrac{1 \text{ mol}}{342.3 \text{ g}} = 0.365 \text{ mol}; \quad M = \dfrac{0.365 \text{ mol}}{1.00 \text{ L}} = \dfrac{0.365 \text{ mol sucrose}}{L}$

2. $0.250 \text{ L} \times \dfrac{0.100 \text{ mol}}{L} \times \dfrac{134.0 \text{ g}}{\text{mol}} = 3.35 \text{ g } Na_2C_2O_4$

3. $25.00 \times 10^{-3} \text{ L} \times \dfrac{0.308 \text{ mol}}{L} = 7.70 \times 10^{-3} \text{ mol}; \quad \dfrac{7.70 \times 10^{-3} \text{ mol}}{0.500 \text{ L}} = \dfrac{1.54 \times 10^{-2} \text{ mol } NiCl_2}{L}$

   $NiCl_2(s) \rightarrow Ni^{2+}(aq) + 2 \text{ Cl}^-(aq); \quad M_{Ni^{2+}} = \dfrac{1.54 \times 10^{-2} \text{ mol}}{L}; \quad M_{Cl^-} = \dfrac{3.08 \times 10^{-2} \text{ mol}}{L}$

4. a. $158.5 \times 10^{-3} \text{ g Cu} \times \dfrac{1 \text{ mol}}{63.55 \text{ g}} = 2.494 \times 10^{-3} \text{ mol Cu}$

   $M_{Cu^{2+}} = \dfrac{2.494 \times 10^{-3} \text{ mol}}{1.00 \text{ L}} = \dfrac{2.49 \times 10^{-3} \text{ mol}}{L}$

   b. $ppm = \dfrac{\text{g Cu}}{\text{g solution}} \times 10^6 = \dfrac{0.1585 \text{ g}}{1.0 \times 10^3 \text{ g}} \times 10^6 = 158.5 \text{ ppm} \approx 160 \text{ ppm Cu}$

5. a. $\dfrac{2.8 \times 10^{-3} \text{ g}}{1.0 \text{ g}} \times 10^6 = 2800 \text{ ppm Cd}^{2+}$ (assuming density = 1.0 g/mL)

   $2800 \text{ ppm} = 2.8 \times 10^6 \text{ ppb Cd}^{2+}$

   b. $\dfrac{2.8 \times 10^{-3} \text{ g}}{1.0 \times 10^{-3} \text{ L}} \times \dfrac{1 \text{ mol}}{112.4 \text{ g}} = \dfrac{2.5 \times 10^{-2} \text{ mol Cd}^{2+}}{L}$

6. a. $Ca(NO_3)_2(s) \rightarrow Ca^{2+}(aq) + 2 \text{ NO}_3^-(aq); \quad M_{Ca^{2+}} = \dfrac{1.06 \times 10^{-3} \text{ mol}}{L}; \quad M_{NO_3^-} = \dfrac{2.12 \times 10^{-3} \text{ mol}}{L}$

   b. $1.0 \times 10^{-3} \text{ L} \times \dfrac{1.06 \times 10^{-3} \text{ mol Ca}^{2+}}{L} \times \dfrac{40.08 \text{ g Ca}^{2+}}{\text{mol}} = 4.2 \times 10^{-5} \text{ g Ca}^{2+}$

c. $1.0 \times 10^{-6} \text{ L} \times \dfrac{2.12 \times 10^{-3} \text{ mol NO}_3^-}{\text{L}} \times \dfrac{6.02 \times 10^{23} \text{ NO}_3^- \text{ ions}}{\text{mol NO}_3^-} = 1.3 \times 10^{15} \text{ NO}_3^- \text{ ions}$

7. $1.00 \text{ L} \times \dfrac{0.040 \text{ mol HCl}}{\text{L}} = 0.040 \text{ mol HCl};\ \ 0.040 \text{ mol HCl} \times \dfrac{1 \text{ L}}{0.25 \text{ mol HCl}} = 0.16 \text{ L} = 160 \text{ mL}$

Concentration of Solutions

9. $\text{molarity} = \dfrac{3.0 \text{ g H}_2\text{O}_2}{100.0 \text{ g soln}} \times \dfrac{1.0 \text{ g soln}}{\text{cm}^3 \text{ soln}} \times \dfrac{1000 \text{ cm}^3}{\text{L}} \times \dfrac{1 \text{ mol H}_2\text{O}_2}{34.0 \text{ g H}_2\text{O}_2} = 0.88 \text{ mol/L}$

$\text{molality} = \dfrac{\text{mol H}_2\text{O}_2}{\text{kg H}_2\text{O}} = \dfrac{3.0 \text{ g H}_2\text{O}_2}{97.0 \text{ g H}_2\text{O}} \times \dfrac{1000 \text{ g}}{\text{kg}} \times \dfrac{1 \text{ mol H}_2\text{O}_2}{34.0 \text{ g H}_2\text{O}_2} = 0.91 \text{ mol/kg}$

$3.0 \text{ g H}_2\text{O}_2 \times \dfrac{1 \text{ mol}}{34.0 \text{ g}} = 8.8 \times 10^{-2} \text{ mol H}_2\text{O}_2;\ \ 97.0 \text{ g H}_2\text{O} \times \dfrac{1 \text{ mol}}{18.02 \text{ g}} = 5.38 \text{ mol H}_2\text{O}$

$\text{mole fraction of H}_2\text{O}_2 = \chi_{\text{H}_2\text{O}_2} = \dfrac{\text{mol H}_2\text{O}_2}{\text{total mol}} = \dfrac{8.8 \times 10^{-2}}{5.38 + 0.088} = 1.6 \times 10^{-2}$

10.   Hydrochloric acid:

$\text{molarity} = \dfrac{38 \text{ g HCl}}{100. \text{ g soln}} \times \dfrac{1.19 \text{ g soln}}{\text{cm}^3 \text{ soln}} \times \dfrac{1000 \text{ cm}^3}{\text{L}} \times \dfrac{1 \text{ mol HCl}}{36.5 \text{ g}} = 12 \text{ mol/L}$

$\text{molality} = \dfrac{38 \text{ g HCl}}{62 \text{ g solvent}} \times \dfrac{1000 \text{ g}}{\text{kg}} \times \dfrac{1 \text{ mol HCl}}{36.5 \text{ g}} = 17 \text{ mol/kg}$

$38 \text{ g HCl} \times \dfrac{1 \text{ mol}}{36.5 \text{ g}} = 1.0 \text{ mol HCl};\ \ 62 \text{ g H}_2\text{O} \times \dfrac{1 \text{ mol}}{18.0 \text{ g}} = 3.4 \text{ mol H}_2\text{O}$

$\text{mole fraction of HCl} = \chi_{\text{HCl}} = \dfrac{1.0}{3.4 + 1.0} = 0.23$

Nitric acid:

$\dfrac{70. \text{ g HNO}_3}{100. \text{ g soln}} \times \dfrac{1.42 \text{ g soln}}{\text{cm}^3 \text{ soln}} \times \dfrac{1000 \text{ cm}^3}{\text{L}} \times \dfrac{1 \text{ mol HNO}_3}{63.0 \text{ g}} = 16 \text{ mol/L}$

$\dfrac{70. \text{ g HNO}_3}{30. \text{ g solvent}} \times \dfrac{1000 \text{ g}}{\text{kg}} \times \dfrac{1 \text{ mol HNO}_3}{63.0 \text{ g}} = 37 \text{ mol/kg}$

$70. \text{ g HNO}_3 \times \dfrac{1 \text{ mol}}{63.0 \text{ g}} = 1.1 \text{ mol HNO}_3;\ \ 30. \text{ g H}_2\text{O} \times \dfrac{1 \text{ mol}}{18.0 \text{ g}} = 1.7 \text{ mol H}_2\text{O}$

$\chi_{\text{HNO}_3} = \dfrac{1.1}{1.7 + 1.1} = 0.39$

Sulfuric acid:

$$\frac{95 \text{ g H}_2\text{SO}_4}{100. \text{ g soln}} \times \frac{1.84 \text{ g soln}}{\text{cm}^3 \text{ soln}} \times \frac{1000 \text{ cm}^3}{\text{L}} \times \frac{1 \text{ mol H}_2\text{SO}_4}{98.1 \text{ g H}_2\text{SO}_4} = 18 \text{ mol/L}$$

$$\frac{95 \text{ g H}_2\text{SO}_4}{5 \text{ g H}_2\text{O}} \times \frac{1000 \text{ g}}{\text{kg}} \times \frac{1 \text{ mol}}{98.1 \text{ g}} = 194 \text{ mol/kg} \approx 200 \text{ mol/kg}$$

$$95 \text{ g H}_2\text{SO}_4 \times \frac{1 \text{ mol}}{98.1 \text{ g}} = 0.97 \text{ mol H}_2\text{SO}_4; \quad 5 \text{ g H}_2\text{O} \times \frac{1 \text{ mol}}{18.0 \text{ g}} = 0.3 \text{ mol H}_2\text{O}$$

$$\chi_{\text{H}_2\text{SO}_4} = \frac{0.97}{0.97 + 0.3} = 0.76$$

Acetic Acid:

$$\frac{99 \text{ g CH}_3\text{CO}_2\text{H}}{100. \text{ g soln}} \times \frac{1.05 \text{ g soln}}{\text{cm}^3 \text{ soln}} \times \frac{1000 \text{ cm}^3}{\text{L}} \times \frac{1 \text{ mol}}{60.05 \text{ g}} = 17 \text{ mol/L}$$

$$\frac{99 \text{ g CH}_3\text{CO}_2\text{H}}{1 \text{ g H}_2\text{O}} \times \frac{1000 \text{ g}}{\text{kg}} \times \frac{1 \text{ mol}}{60.05 \text{ g}} = 1600 \text{ mol/kg} \approx 2000 \text{ mol/kg}$$

$$99 \text{ g HOAc} \times \frac{1 \text{ mol}}{60.05 \text{ g}} = 1.6 \text{ mol HOAc}; \quad 1 \text{ g H}_2\text{O} \times \frac{1 \text{ mol}}{18.0 \text{ g}} = 0.06 \text{ mol H}_2\text{O}$$

$$\chi_{\text{HOAc}} = \frac{1.6}{1.6 + 0.06} = 0.96$$

Ammonia:

$$\frac{28 \text{ g NH}_3}{100. \text{ g soln}} \times \frac{0.90 \text{ g}}{\text{cm}^3} \times \frac{1000 \text{ cm}^3}{\text{L}} \times \frac{1 \text{ mol}}{17.0 \text{ g}} = 15 \text{ mol/L}$$

$$\frac{28 \text{ g NH}_3}{72 \text{ g H}_2\text{O}} \times \frac{1000 \text{ g}}{\text{kg}} \times \frac{1 \text{ mol}}{17.0 \text{ g}} = 23 \text{ mol/kg}$$

$$28 \text{ g NH}_3 \times \frac{1 \text{ mol}}{17.0 \text{ g}} = 1.6 \text{ mol NH}_3; \quad 72 \text{ g H}_2\text{O} \times \frac{1 \text{ mol}}{18.0 \text{ g}} = 4.0 \text{ mol H}_2\text{O}$$

$$\chi_{\text{NH}_3} = \frac{1.6}{4.0 + 1.6} = 0.29$$

11. $50.0 \text{ mL toluene} \times \dfrac{0.867 \text{ g}}{\text{mL}} = 43.4 \text{ g toluene}; \quad 125 \text{ mL benzene} \times \dfrac{0.874 \text{ g}}{\text{mL}} = 109 \text{ g benzene}$

$$\text{mass \% toluene} = \frac{\text{mass of toluene}}{\text{total mass}} \times 100 = \frac{43.4}{43.4 + 109} \times 100 = 28.5\%$$

$$\frac{43.4 \text{ g toluene}}{175 \text{ mL soln}} \times \frac{1000 \text{ mL}}{L} \times \frac{1 \text{ mol toluene}}{92.13 \text{ g toluene}} = 2.69 \text{ mol/L}$$

$$\frac{43.4 \text{ g toluene}}{109 \text{ g benzene}} \times \frac{1000 \text{ g}}{kg} \times \frac{1 \text{ mol toluene}}{92.13 \text{ g toluene}} = 4.32 \text{ mol/kg}$$

$$43.4 \text{ g toluene} \times \frac{1 \text{ mol}}{92.13 \text{ g}} = 0.471 \text{ mol toluene}$$

$$109 \text{ g benzene} \times \frac{1 \text{ mol benzene}}{78.11 \text{ g benzene}} = 1.40 \text{ mol benzene}$$

$$\chi_{toluene} = \frac{0.471}{0.471 + 1.40} = 0.252$$

14. $$\text{Molarity} = \frac{\text{moles solute}}{\text{L solution}}; \quad \text{Molality} = \frac{\text{moles solute}}{\text{kg solvent}}$$

Since volume is temperature dependent and mass isn't, then molarity is temperature dependent and molality is temperature independent. When determining ΔT_f and ΔT_b, we are interested in how temperature depends on composition. Thus, we don't want our expression of composition to also be dependent on temperature.

15. $$\frac{1.00 \text{ mol acetone}}{1.00 \text{ kg ethanol}} = 1.00 \text{ molal}; \quad 1.00 \times 10^3 \text{ g } C_2H_5OH \times \frac{1 \text{ mol}}{46.07 \text{ g}} = 21.7 \text{ mol } C_2H_5OH$$

$$\chi_{acetone} = \frac{1.00}{1.00 + 21.7} = 0.0441$$

$$1.00 \text{ mol } CH_3COCH_3 \times \frac{58.08 \text{ g } CH_3COCH_3}{\text{mol } CH_3COCH_3} \times \frac{1 \text{ mL}}{0.788 \text{ g}} = 73.7 \text{ mL}$$

$$1.00 \times 10^3 \text{ g ethanol} \times \frac{1 \text{ mL}}{0.789 \text{ g}} = 1270 \text{ mL}; \quad \text{Total V} = 1270 + 73.7 = 1340 \text{ mL}$$

$$\text{molarity} = \frac{1.00 \text{ mol}}{1.34 \text{ L}} = 0.746 \ M$$

17. $$1.0 \text{ L} \times \frac{1000 \text{ mL}}{L} \times \frac{1.0 \text{ g}}{mL} = 1.0 \times 10^3 \text{ g solution}$$

$$\text{mass \% NaCl} = \frac{25 \text{ g NaCl}}{1.0 \times 10^3 \text{ g solution}} \times 100 = 2.5\%$$

$$\frac{25 \text{ g NaCl}}{L} \times \frac{1 \text{ mol NaCl}}{58.4 \text{ g NaCl}} = 0.43 \ M$$

1.0×10^3 g solution contains 25 g NaCl and 975 g $H_2O \approx 980$ g H_2O.

$$\text{molality} = \frac{0.43 \text{ mol NaCl}}{0.98 \text{ kg solvent}} = 0.44 \text{ molal}$$

0.43 mol NaCl; 980 g $\times \dfrac{1 \text{ mol}}{18.0 \text{ g}} = 54$ mol H_2O; $\chi_{NaCl} = \dfrac{0.43}{0.43 + 54} = 7.9 \times 10^{-3}$

Thermodynamics of Solutions and Solubility

19.   The nature of the interparticle forces. Polar solutes and ionic solutes dissolve in polar solvents and nonpolar solutes dissolve in nonpolar solvents.

20.   As the length of the hydrocarbon chain increases, the solubility decreases. The –OH end of the alcohols can hydrogen bond with water. The hydrocarbon chain, however, is relatively nonpolar and interacts poorly with water. As the chain gets longer, a greater portion of the molecule cannot interact with the water molecules and the solubility decreases, i.e., the effect of the –OH group decreases as the compounds get larger.

21.   a. Mg^{2+}; smaller, higher charge   b. Be^{2+}; smaller

        d. F^-; smaller   e. Cl^-; smaller

22. $KCl(s) \rightarrow K^+(g) + Cl^-(g)$ $\Delta H = -\Delta H_{LE} = -(-715 \text{ kJ/mol})$
        $K^+(g) + Cl^-(g) \rightarrow K^+(aq) + Cl^-(aq)$ $\Delta H = \Delta H_{hyd} = -684 \text{ kJ/mol}$
        _____
                $KCl(s) \rightarrow K^+(aq) + Cl^-(aq)$ $\Delta H_{soln} = 31 \text{ kJ/mol}$

23. $CsI(s) \rightarrow Cs^+(g) + I^-(g)$ $\Delta H = -\Delta H_{LE} = 604 \text{ kJ}$
        $Cs^+(g) + I^-(g) \rightarrow Cs^+(aq) + I^-(aq)$ $\Delta H = \Delta H_{hyd}$
        _____
                $CsI(s) \rightarrow Cs^+(aq) + I^-(aq)$ $\Delta H_{soln} = 33 \text{ kJ}$

        33 kJ = 604 kJ + ΔH_{hyd}, $\Delta H_{hyd} = -571$ kJ

                $CsOH(s) \rightarrow Cs^+(g) + OH^-(g)$ $\Delta H = -\Delta H_{LE} = 724 \text{ kJ}$
        $Cs^+(g) + OH^-(g) \rightarrow Cs^+(aq) + OH^-(aq)$ $\Delta H = \Delta H_{hyd}$
        _____
                $CsOH(s) \rightarrow Cs^+(aq) + OH^-(aq)$ $\Delta H_{soln} = -72 \text{ kJ}$

        -72 kJ = 724 kJ + ΔH_{hyd}, $\Delta H_{hyd} = -796$ kJ

25.   Water is a polar molecule capable of hydrogen bonding. Polar molecules, molecules capable of hydrogen bonding, and ions can be hydrated. For covalent compounds, as polarity increases, hydration increases. For ionic compounds, as the size of an ion decreases and/or the charge increases, hydration increases.

a. CH_3CH_2OH; CH_3CH_2OH is polar while $CH_3CH_2CH_3$ is nonpolar.

b. $CHCl_3$; $CHCl_3$ is polar while CCl_4 is nonpolar.

c. CH_3CO_2H; CH_3CO_2H is much more polar than $CH_3(CH_2)_{14}CO_2H$.

d. Na_2S; Most sulfides are insoluble. However, Na_2S is an exception.

26.   a. Water; $Cu(NO_3)_2$ is an ionic solid.

b. CCl_4; CS_2 is a nonpolar molecule.   c. Water; CH_3CO_2H is polar.

d. CCl_4; The long nonpolar hydrocarbon chain favors a nonpolar solvent.

27.   Both $Al(OH)_3$ and NaOH are ionic. Since the lattice energy is proportional to charge, the lattice energy of aluminum hydroxide is greater than that of sodium hydroxide. The attraction of water molecules for Al^{3+} and OH^- cannot overcome the larger lattice energy and $Al(OH)_3$ is insoluble. For NaOH, the hydration energy is large enough to overcome the smaller lattice energy and NaOH is soluble.

30.   hydrophobic: water hating; hydrophilic: water loving

31. $CO_2 + OH^- \rightarrow HCO_3^-$; No, the reaction of CO_2 with OH^- greatly increases the solubility of CO_2 in basic solution by forming the soluble bicarbonate ion.

32. $P_{gas} = kC$, $120 \text{ torr} \times \dfrac{1 \text{ atm}}{760 \text{ torr}} = \dfrac{780 \text{ atm}}{M} \times C$, $C = 2.0 \times 10^{-4}$ mol/L

Vapor Pressures of Solutions

34. $P_{H_2O} = \chi_{H_2O}^L P_{H_2O}^\bullet$; $\chi_{H_2O}^L = \dfrac{\text{mol } H_2O \text{ in solution}}{\text{total mol in solution}}$

50.0 g $C_6H_{12}O_6 \times \dfrac{1 \text{ mol } C_2H_{12}O_6}{180.16 \text{ g } C_6H_{12}O_6} = 0.278$ mol glucose

600.0 g $H_2O \times \dfrac{1 \text{ mol}}{18.015 \text{ g}} = 33.31$ mol H_2O

$\chi_{H_2O}^L = \dfrac{33.31}{33.59} = 0.9917$; $P_{H_2O} = \chi_{H_2O}^L P_{H_2O}^\bullet = 0.9917 \times 23.8 \text{ torr} = 23.6$ torr

35.   50.0 g $CH_3COCH_3 \times \dfrac{1 \text{ mol}}{58.08 \text{ g}} = 0.861$ mol acetone

50.0 g $CH_3OH \times \dfrac{1 \text{ mol}}{32.04 \text{ g}} = 1.56$ mol methanol

$$\chi_{acetone}^{L} = \frac{0.861}{0.861 + 1.56} = 0.356; \quad \chi_{methanol}^{L} = 1 - \chi_{acetone}^{L} = 0.644$$

$$P_{total} = P_{methanol} + P_{acetone} = 0.644(143 \text{ torr}) + 0.356(271 \text{ torr}) = 92.1 \text{ torr} + 96.5 \text{ torr} = 188.6 \text{ torr}$$

Since partial pressures are proportional to the number of moles, then in the vapor phase:

$$\chi_{acetone}^{V} = \frac{P_{acetone}}{P_{total}} = \frac{96.5 \text{ torr}}{188.6 \text{ torr}} = 0.512; \quad \chi_{methanol}^{V} = 1.000 - 0.512 = 0.488$$

It is probably not a good assumption that this solution is ideal because of methanol-acetone hydrogen bonding, resulting in stronger forces in solution as compared to the separate phases.

36.   Compared to H_2O, solution d (methanol/water) will have the highest vapor pressure since methanol is more volatile than water. Both solution b (glucose/water) and solution c (NaCl/water) will have a lower vapor pressure than water by Raoult's law. NaCl dissolves to give Na^+ ions and Cl^- ions; glucose is a nonelectrolyte. Since there are more particles in solution c, the vapor pressure of solution c will be the lowest.

37.   If solute-solvent attractions > solvent-solvent and solute-solute attractions, then there is a negative deviation from Raoult's law. If solute-solvent attractions < solvent-solvent and solute-solute attractions, then there is a positive deviation from Raoult's law.

38.   A positive deviation from Raoult's law means the vapor pressure of the solution is greater than if the solution were ideal. At the boiling point, the vapor pressure equals atmospheric pressure. For a solution with positive deviations, it will take a lower temperature to achieve a vapor pressure of one atmosphere. Therefore, the boiling point is lower than if the solution were ideal.

39.   a. CF_3CF_3 and $CF_3CF_2CF_3$; Solutions will be ideal when the intermolecular forces between the two substances are about equal. This usually occurs for two nonpolar substances of similar size since the strength of the London dispersion forces will be similar. CF_3CF_3 and $CF_3CF_2CF_3$ are both relatively nonpolar with similar size. Hydrogen bonding will be important in water/acetone solutions and will likely form solutions with a negative deviation from Raoult's law.

       b. C_7H_{16} and C_6H_{14}; Both are nonpolar with similar size. The LD forces are approximately equal. Dipole forces are present in both CHF_3 and CH_3OCH_3 and it is unlikely that the dipole forces in solution are the same as in the two pure substances.

40. $25.8 \text{ g } CH_4N_2O \times \dfrac{1 \text{ mol}}{60.06 \text{ g}} = 0.430 \text{ mol}; \quad 275 \text{ g } H_2O \times \dfrac{1 \text{ mol}}{18.02 \text{ g}} = 15.3 \text{ mol}$

$$\chi_{H_2O}^{L} = \frac{15.3}{15.3 + 0.430} = 0.973; \quad P_{H_2O} = \chi_{H_2O}^{L} P_{H_2O}^{\bullet} = 0.973 \,(23.8 \text{ torr}) = 23.2 \text{ torr at } 25°C$$

$$P_{H_2O} = 0.973 \,(71.9 \text{ torr}) = 70.0 \text{ torr at } 45°C$$

42.   a. $25 \text{ mL C}_5\text{H}_{12} \times \dfrac{0.63 \text{ g}}{\text{mL}} \times \dfrac{1 \text{ mol}}{72.1 \text{ g}} = 0.22 \text{ mol C}_5\text{H}_{12}$

$45 \text{ mL C}_6\text{H}_{14} \times \dfrac{0.66 \text{ g}}{\text{mL}} \times \dfrac{1 \text{ mol}}{86.2 \text{ g}} = 0.34 \text{ mol C}_6\text{H}_{14}$

$\chi_{pen}^{L} = \dfrac{\text{mol pentane in solution}}{\text{total mol in solution}} = \dfrac{0.22}{0.56} = 0.39, \quad \chi_{hex}^{L} = 1.00 - 0.39 = 0.61$

$P_{pen} = \chi_{pen}^{L} P_{pen}^{\bullet} = 0.39(511 \text{ torr}) = 2.0 \times 10^2 \text{ torr}; \quad P_{hex} = 0.61(150. \text{ torr}) = 92 \text{ torr}$

$P_{total} = P_{pen} + P_{hex} = 2.0 \times 10^2 + 92 = 292 \text{ torr} \approx 290 \text{ torr}$

b.   In the vapor phase:

$\chi_{pen}^{V} = \dfrac{P_{pen}}{P_{total}} = \dfrac{2.0 \times 10^2 \text{ torr}}{290 \text{ torr}} = 0.69$

Colligative Properties

44. $m = \dfrac{4.9 \text{ g sucrose}}{175 \text{ g solvent}} \times \dfrac{1000 \text{ g}}{\text{kg}} \times \dfrac{1 \text{ mol C}_{12}\text{H}_{22}\text{O}_{11}}{342.3 \text{ g C}_{12}\text{H}_{22}\text{O}_{11}} = 0.082 \text{ molal}$

$\Delta T_b = K_b m = \dfrac{0.51 °C}{\text{molal}} \times 0.082 \text{ molal} = 0.042 °C; \quad T_b = 100.042 °C$ at 1 atm barometric pressure

$\Delta T_f = K_f m = \dfrac{1.86 °C}{\text{molal}} \times 0.082 \text{ molal} = 0.15 °C; \quad T_f = -0.15 °C$

$\pi = MRT$; In dilute aqueous solutions the density of the solution is about 1.0 g/mL, thus we can assume that molarity = M = molality = 0.082.

$\pi = \dfrac{0.082 \text{ mol}}{\text{L}} \times \dfrac{0.08206 \text{ L atm}}{\text{mol K}} \times 298 \text{ K} = 2.0 \text{ atm}$

45.   Assume molarity and molality are equal since solution is dilute.

$M = m = \dfrac{1.0 \text{ g}}{\text{L}} \times \dfrac{1 \text{ mol}}{9.0 \times 10^4 \text{ g}} = 1.1 \times 10^{-5} \text{ mol/L}; \quad \pi = MRT$

At 298 K: $\pi = \dfrac{1.1 \times 10^{-5} \text{ mol}}{\text{L}} \times \dfrac{0.08206 \text{ L atm}}{\text{mol K}} \times 298 \text{ K} \times \dfrac{760 \text{ mm Hg}}{\text{atm}}, \quad \pi = 0.20 \text{ mm Hg}$

$\Delta T_f = K_f m = \dfrac{1.86 °C}{\text{molal}} \times 1.1 \times 10^{-5} \text{ molal} = 2.0 \times 10^{-5} °C$

46.   Osmotic pressure is better for determining the molar mass of large molecules. A temperature change of $10^{-5} °C$ is very difficult to measure. A change in height of a column of mercury by 0.2 mm is not as hard to measure precisely.

48. $\Delta T_f = K_f m, \quad m = \dfrac{\Delta T_f}{K_f} = \dfrac{2.63\,°C}{40.\,°C \ kg \ mol^{-1}} = \dfrac{6.6 \times 10^{-2} \ mol \ reserpine}{kg \ solvent}$

$\dfrac{6.6 \times 10^{-2} \ mol \ reserpine}{kg \ solvent} = \dfrac{1.00 \ g \ reserpine}{25.0 \ g \ solvent} \times \dfrac{1}{MM} \times \dfrac{1000 \ g \ solvent}{kg \ solvent}$

$MM = molar \ mass \ of \ reserpine = \dfrac{1000}{25.0 \times (6.6 \times 10^{-2})} = 606 \ g/mol \approx 610 \ g/mol$

50. $\Delta T_f = 5.51 - 2.81 = 2.70°C; \quad m = \dfrac{\Delta T_f}{K_f} = \dfrac{2.70°C}{5.12°C/molal} = 0.527 \ molal$

Let x = mass of naphthalene (molar mass = 128.2 g/mol). Then $1.60 - x$ = mass of anthracene (molar mass = 178.2 g/mol).

$\dfrac{x}{128.2} = moles \ naphthalene$ and $\dfrac{1.60 - x}{178.2} = moles \ anthracene$

$\dfrac{0.527 \ moles \ solute}{kg \ solvent} = \dfrac{\dfrac{x}{128.2} + \dfrac{1.60 - x}{178.2}}{0.0200 \ kg \ solvent}, \quad 1.05 \times 10^{-2} = \dfrac{178.2 \ x + 1.60(128.2) - 128.2 \ x}{128.2(178.2)}$

$50.0 \ x + 205 = 240., \ 50.0 \ x = 240. - 205, \ 50.0 \ x = 35, \ x = 0.70 \ g \ naphthalene$

So the mixture is:

$\dfrac{0.70 \ g}{1.60 \ g} \times 100 = 44\% \ naphthalene \ by \ mass$ and 56% anthracene by mass

53. $m = \dfrac{\Delta T_f}{K_f} = \dfrac{30.0°C}{1.86°C \ kg \ mol^{-1}} = 16.1 \ mol \ C_2H_6O_2/kg$

Since the density of water is 1.00 g/cm^3, the moles of $C_2H_6O_2$ needed are:

$15.0 \ L \ H_2O \times \dfrac{1.00 \ kg \ H_2O}{L \ H_2O} \times \dfrac{16.1 \ mol \ C_2H_6O_2}{kg \ H_2O} = 242 \ mol \ C_2H_6O_2$

Volume $C_2H_6O_2$ = 242 mol $C_2H_6O_2 \times \dfrac{62.07 \ g}{mol} \times \dfrac{1 \ cm^3}{1.11 \ g} = 13,500 \ cm^3 = 13.5 \ L$

$\Delta T_b = K_b m = \dfrac{0.51°C}{molal} \times 16.1 \ molal = 8.2°C; \ T_b = 100.0°C + 8.2°C = 108.2°C$

Properties of Electrolyte Solutions

54. $NaCl(s) \rightarrow Na^+(aq) + Cl^-(aq)$; The total concentration of particles is 2(0.6 M) = 1.2 M.

$$\pi = MRT = \frac{1.2 \text{ mol}}{L} \times \frac{0.08206 \text{ L atm}}{\text{mol K}} \times 298 \text{ K} = 29.3 \text{ atm} = 29 \text{ atm}$$

A pressure greater than 30. atm should be applied to insure purification by reverse osmosis.

55.   a.   Water would migrate from right to left. The level of liquid in the right arm would go down and the level in the left arm would go up.

      b.   The levels would be equal. The concentration of NaCl would be equal in both chambers.

56. $MgCl_2$ and NaCl are strong electrolytes, HOCl is a weak electrolyte and glucose is a nonelectrolyte. The effective particle concentrations are ~3.0 m $MgCl_2$, ~2.0 m NaCl, 2.0 < m HOCl < 1.0, and 1.0 m glucose. The order of freezing point depressions ($\Delta T_f = K_f m$) from lowest to highest are: glucose < HOCl < NaCl < $MgCl_2$.

58. $Ca(NO_3)_2(s) \rightarrow Ca^{2+}(aq) + 2 \ NO_3^-(aq)$; i = 3 mol particles/mol $Ca(NO_3)_2$

$$\Delta T_f = iK_f m = 3 \times \frac{1.86°C}{\text{molal}} \times 0.5 \text{ molal} = 2.8°C \approx 3°C; \ T_f = -3°C$$

59.   The measured freezing point should be higher. Due to ion pairing, the depression of the freezing point will be less than expected since the effective particle concentration is less than 3(0.5) molal. This results in a higher freezing point.

61.   Ion pairing can occur, resulting in fewer particles than expected. This results in smaller freezing point depressions and smaller boiling point elevations ($\Delta T = Km$). Ion pairing will increase as the concentration of electrolyte increases.

64.   a.   °C = 5(°F - 32)/9 = 5(-29 -32)/9 = -34°C

      Assuming the solubility of $CaCl_2$ is temperature independent, the molality of a saturated $CaCl_2$ solution is:

$$\frac{74.5 \text{ g } CaCl_2}{100.0 \text{ mL } H_2O} \times \frac{1.00 \text{ mL } H_2O}{1.00 \text{ g } H_2O} \times \frac{1000 \text{ g}}{\text{kg}} \times \frac{1 \text{ mol } CaCl_2}{111.0 \text{ g } CaCl_2} = \frac{6.71 \text{ mol } CaCl_2}{\text{kg } H_2O}$$

$$\Delta T_f = iK_f m = 3(1.86°C \text{ kg mol}^{-1}) (6.71 \text{ mol kg}^{-1}) = 37.4°C$$

      Assuming i = 3, a saturated solution of $CaCl_2$ can lower the freezing point of water to -37.4°C. Assuming these conditions, a saturated $CaCl_2$ solution should melt ice at -34°C (-29°F).

      b.   From Exercise 62, i ≈ 2.6; $\Delta T_f = iK_f m = 2.6(1.86) (6.71) = 32°C$; $T_f = -32°C$

      Assuming i = 2.6, a saturated $CaCl_2$ solution will not melt ice at -34°C(-29°F).

Additional Exercises

65.

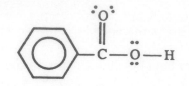

Benzoic acid is capable of hydrogen bonding. However, it is more soluble in nonpolar benzene than in water. In benzene, a nonpolar hydrogen bonded dimer forms.

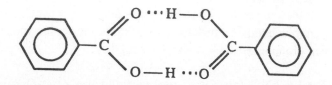

The dimer is relatively nonpolar and thus more soluble in benzene than in water. Since benzoic acid forms dimers in benzene, the effective solute particle concentration will be less than 1.0 molal. Therefore, the freezing point depression would be less than 5.12°C ($\Delta T_f = K_f m$).

66.   Benzoic acid would be more soluble in a basic solution because of the reaction:

$$C_6H_5CO_2H + OH^- \rightarrow C_6H_5CO_2^- + H_2O$$

67.   a.   The average values for each ion are:

300. mg Na^+; 15.7 mg K^+; 5.45 mg Ca^{2+}; 388 mg Cl^-; 246 mg lactate, $C_3H_5O_3^-$

Note: Since we can precisely weigh to ± 0.1 mg on an analytical balance, we'll carry extra significant figures and calculate results to ± 0.1 mg.

The only source of lactate is $NaC_3H_5O_3$.

$$246 \text{ mg lactate} \times \frac{112.06 \text{ mg } NaC_3H_5O_3}{89.07 \text{ mg } C_3H_5O_3^-} = 309.5 \text{ mg sodium lactate}$$

The only source of Ca^{2+} is $CaCl_2 \cdot 2H_2O$.

$$5.45 \text{ mg } Ca^{2+} \times \frac{147.0 \text{ mg } CaCl_2 \cdot 2H_2O}{40.08 \text{ mg } Ca^{2+}} = 19.99 \text{ or } 20.0 \text{ mg } CaCl \cdot 2H_2O$$

The only source of K^+ is KCl.

$$15.7 \text{ mg } K^+ \times \frac{74.55 \text{ mg KCl}}{39.10 \text{ mg } K^+} = 29.9 \text{ mg KCl}$$

From what we have used already, let's calculate the mass of Na^+ and Cl^- added.

309.5 mg sodium lactate = 246.0 mg lactate + 63.5 mg Na^+

Thus, we need to add an additional 236.5 mg Na^+ to get the desired 300. mg.

$$236.5 \text{ mg } Na^+ \times \frac{58.44 \text{ mg NaCl}}{22.99 \text{ mg } Na^+} = 601.2 \text{ mg NaCl}$$

Let's check the mass of Cl^- added:

$$20.0 \text{ mg } CaCl_2 \cdot 2H_2O \times \frac{70.90 \text{ mg } Cl^-}{147.0 \text{ mg } CaCl_2 \cdot 2H_2O} = 9.6 \text{ mg } Cl^-$$

20.0 mg $CaCl_2 \cdot 2H_2O$ = 9.6 mg Cl^-

29.9 mg KCl - 15.7 mg K^+ = 14.2 mg Cl^-

$\underline{601.2 \text{ mg NaCl} - 236.5 \text{ mg } Na^+ = 364.7 \text{ mg } Cl^-}$

Total Cl^- = 388.5 mg Cl^-

This is the quantity of Cl^- we want (the average amount of Cl^-).

An analytical balance can weigh to the nearest 0.1 mg. We would use 309.5 mg sodium lactate, 20.0 mg $CaCl_2 \cdot 2H_2O$, 29.9 mg KCl and 601.2 mg NaCl.

b. To get the range of osmotic pressure, we need to calculate the molar concentration of each ion at its minimum and maximum values. At minimum concentrations, we have:

$$\frac{285 \text{ mg } Na^+}{100. \text{ mL}} \times \frac{1 \text{ mmol}}{22.99 \text{ mg}} = 0.124 \ M; \quad \frac{14.1 \text{ mg } K^+}{100. \text{ mL}} \times \frac{1 \text{ mmol}}{39.10 \text{ mg}} = 0.00361 \ M$$

$$\frac{4.9 \text{ mg } Ca^{2+}}{100. \text{ mL}} \times \frac{1 \text{ mmol}}{40.08 \text{ mg}} = 0.0012 \ M; \quad \frac{368 \text{ mg } Cl^-}{100. \text{ mL}} \times \frac{1 \text{ mmol}}{35.45 \text{ mg}} = 0.104 \ M$$

$$\frac{231 \text{ mg lactate}}{100. \text{ mL}} \times \frac{1 \text{ mmol}}{89.07 \text{ mg}} = 0.0259 \ M$$

Total = 0.124 + 0.00361 + 0.0012 + 0.104 + 0.0259 = 0.259 M

$$\pi = MRT = \frac{0.259 \text{ mol}}{L} \times \frac{0.08206 \text{ L atm}}{\text{mol K}} \times 310. \text{ K} = 6.59 \text{ atm}$$

Similarly at maximum concentrations, the concentration of each ion is:

Na^+: 0.137 M; K^+: 0.00442 M; Ca^{2+}: 0.0015 M; Cl^-: 0.115 M; $C_3H_5O_3^-$: 0.0293 M

The total concentration of all ions is the sum, 0.287 M.

$$\pi = \frac{0.287 \text{ mol}}{L} \times \frac{0.08206 \text{ L atm}}{\text{mol K}} \times 310. \text{ K} = 7.30 \text{ atm}$$

Osmotic pressure ranges from 6.59 atm to 7.30 atm.

68.   No, the solution is not ideal. For an ideal solution, the strength of interparticle forces in the solution are the same as in the pure solute and pure solvent. This results in $\Delta H_{soln} = 0$ for an ideal solution. ΔH_{soln} for methanol/water is not zero. Since $\Delta H_{soln} < 0$, this solution shows negative deviation from Raoult's law.

72. $14.22 \text{ mg CO}_2 \times \dfrac{12.011 \text{ mg C}}{44.009 \text{ mg CO}_2} = 3.881 \text{ mg C};\ \ \% \text{ C} = \dfrac{3.881}{4.80} \times 100 = 80.9\% \text{ C}$

$1.66 \text{ mg H}_2\text{O} \times \dfrac{2.016 \text{ mg H}}{18.02 \text{ mg H}_2\text{O}} = 0.186 \text{ mg H};\ \ \% \text{ H} = \dfrac{0.186}{4.80} \times 100 = 3.88\% \text{ H}$

% O = 100.00 - (80.9 + 3.88) = 15.2% O

Out of 100.00 g:

$80.9 \text{ g C} \times \dfrac{1 \text{ mol}}{12.01 \text{ g}} = 6.74 \text{ mol C};\ \ \dfrac{6.74}{0.950} = 7.09 \approx 7$

$3.88 \text{ g H} \times \dfrac{1 \text{ mol}}{1.008 \text{ g}} = 3.85 \text{ mol H};\ \ \dfrac{3.85}{0.950} = 4.05 \approx 4$

$15.2 \text{ g O} \times \dfrac{1 \text{ mol}}{16.00 \text{ g}} = 0.950 \text{ mol O};\ \ \dfrac{0.950}{0.950} = 1$

Therefore, the empirical formula is C_7H_4O.

$$\Delta T_f = K_f m, \quad m = \frac{\Delta T_f}{K_f} = \frac{22.3 °C}{40. °C/\text{molal}} = 0.56 \text{ molal}$$

$$0.56 \text{ molal} = \frac{1.32 \text{ g anthraquinone}}{0.0114 \text{ kg camphor}} \times \frac{1}{MM}, \quad MM = \text{molar mass anthraquinone}$$

$$MM = \frac{1.32}{0.0114 \times 0.56} = 210 \text{ g/mol}$$

The empirical mass of C_7H_4O is: $7(12) + 4(1) + 16 \approx 104 \text{ g/mol}$. Since the molar mass is twice the empirical mass, then the molecular formula is $C_{14}H_8O_2$.

75.   Out of 100.00 g, there are:

$31.57 \text{ g C} \times \dfrac{1 \text{ mol}}{12.011 \text{ g}} = 2.628 \text{ mol C};\ \ \dfrac{2.628}{2.628} = 1.000$

$$5.30 \text{ g H} \times \frac{1 \text{ mol}}{1.008 \text{ g}} = 5.26 \text{ mol H}; \qquad \frac{5.26}{2.628} = 2.00$$

$$63.13 \text{ g O} \times \frac{1 \text{ mol}}{15.999 \text{ g}} = 3.946 \text{ mol O}; \qquad \frac{3.946}{2.628} = 1.502$$

Empirical formula: $C_2H_4O_3$

$$m = \frac{\Delta T_f}{K_f} = \frac{5.20°C}{1.86°C/molal} = 2.80 \text{ molal}; \qquad \frac{2.80 \text{ mol}}{kg} = \frac{10.56 \text{ g}}{0.0250 \text{ kg H}_2O} \times \frac{1}{MM}$$

MM = 151 g/mol = experimental molar mass of compound

The empirical mass of $C_2H_4O_3$ = 76.051 g/mol. Since the molar mass is about twice the empirical mass, then the molecular formula is $C_4H_8O_6$ which has a molar mass of 152.101 g/mol.

Note: We use the experimental molar mass to get the molecular formula. Knowing this, we calculate the molar mass precisely from the molecular formula.

77.   If there are 100.0 mL of wine:

$$12.5 \text{ mL } C_2H_5OH \times \frac{0.79 \text{ g}}{mL} = 9.9 \text{ g } C_2H_5OH \text{ and } 87.5 \text{ mL H}_2O \times \frac{1.0 \text{ g}}{mL} = 87.5 \text{ g H}_2O$$

$$\text{mass \% ethanol} = \frac{9.9}{87.5 + 9.9} \times 100 = 10.\% \text{ by mass}$$

$$m = \frac{9.9 \text{ g } C_2H_5OH}{0.0875 \text{ kg H}_2O} \times \frac{1 \text{ mol}}{46.07 \text{ g}} = 2.5 \text{ molal}$$

80. $\pi = MRT, \; M = \dfrac{\pi}{RT} = \dfrac{15}{(0.08206)(298)} = 0.61 \; M; \quad \dfrac{0.61 \text{ mol}}{L} \times \dfrac{342.3 \text{ g}}{mol} = 209 \text{ g/L} \approx 210 \text{ g/L}$

Dissolve 209 g sucrose in water and dilute to 1.0 L in a volumetric flask. To get 0.61 ± 0.01 mol/L, we need 209 ± 3 g sucrose.

81. $\Delta T = 25.50°C - 24.59°C = 0.91°C = K_f m, \; m = \dfrac{0.91°C}{9.1°C/molal} = 0.10 \text{ molal}$

$$\text{mass H}_2O = 0.0100 \text{ kg t-butanol} \left(\frac{0.10 \text{ mol H}_2O}{\text{kg t-butanol}} \right) \left(\frac{18.0 \text{ g H}_2O}{\text{mol H}_2O} \right) = 0.018 \text{ g H}_2O$$

82.   a. $m = \dfrac{5.0 \text{ g } C_6H_{12}O_6}{0.025 \text{ kg}} \times \dfrac{1 \text{ mol}}{180.2 \text{ g}} = 1.1 \text{ molal}$

$$\Delta T_f = K_f m = \frac{1.86°C}{molal} \times 1.1 \text{ molal} = 2.0°C; \; T_f = -2.0°C$$

b. $m = \dfrac{5.0 \text{ g NaCl}}{0.025 \text{ kg}} \times \dfrac{1 \text{ mol}}{58.44 \text{ g}} = 3.4 \text{ molal};$ NaCl is a strong electrolyte with i = 2.

$\Delta T_f = iK_f m = 2 \times 1.86°\text{C/molal} \times 3.4 \text{ molal} = 13°\text{C};\ \ T_f = -13°\text{C}$

84. $m = \dfrac{24.0 \text{ g} \times \dfrac{1 \text{ mol}}{58.0 \text{ g}}}{0.600 \text{ kg}} = 0.690 \text{ mol/kg};\ \ \Delta T_b = K_b m = (0.51°\text{C kg mol}^{-1})(0.690 \text{ mol/kg}) = 0.35°\text{C}$

$T_b = 99.725°\text{C} + 0.35°\text{C} = 100.08°\text{C}$

87. $M = \dfrac{1.75 \text{ g} \times \dfrac{1 \text{ mol}}{342.3 \text{ g}}}{0.150 \text{ L}} = 0.0341 \text{ mol/L}$

$\pi = MRT = \dfrac{0.0341 \text{ mol}}{\text{L}} \times \dfrac{0.08206 \text{ L atm}}{\text{mol K}} \times 290.2 \text{ K} = 0.812 \text{ atm} = 617 \text{ torr}$

90. $m = \dfrac{0.100 \text{ g} \times \dfrac{1 \text{ mol}}{100.0 \text{ g}}}{0.5000 \text{ kg}} = 2.00 \times 10^{-3} \text{ mol/kg} \approx 2.00 \times 10^{-3} \text{ mol/L}$ (dilute solution)

$\Delta T_f = iK_f m,\ \ 0.0056°\text{C} = i(1.86°\text{C/molal})(2.00 \times 10^{-3} \text{ molal}),\ \ i = 1.5$

If i = 1.0, % dissociation = 0% and if i = 2.0, % dissociation = 100%. Since i = 1.5, then the weak acid is 50.% dissociated.

$\text{HA} \rightleftharpoons \text{H}^+ + \text{A}^- \qquad K_a = \dfrac{[\text{H}^+][\text{A}^-]}{[\text{HA}]}$

Since the weak acid is 50.% dissociated, then:

$[\text{H}^+] = [\text{A}^-] = [\text{HA}]_o \times 0.50 = 2.00 \times 10^{-3} M \times 0.50 = 1.0 \times 10^{-3} M$

$[\text{HA}] = 2.00 \times 10^{-3} M - 1.0 \times 10^{-3} M = 1.0 \times 10^{-3} M$

$K_a = \dfrac{[\text{H}^+][\text{A}^-]}{[\text{HA}]} = \dfrac{(1.0 \times 10^{-3})(1.0 \times 10^{-3})}{1.0 \times 10^{-3}} = 1.0 \times 10^{-3}$

91.   If ideal, NaCl dissociates completely and i = 2. $\Delta T_f = iK_f m$

$1.28°\text{C} = 2 \times 1.86°\text{C kg/mol} \times m,\ \ m = 0.344 \text{ mol NaCl/kg H}_2\text{O}$

$0.344 \text{ mol NaCl} \times 58.44 \text{ g/mol} = 20.1 \text{ g NaCl};\ \ \text{mass \% NaCl} = \dfrac{20.1 \text{ g}}{1.00 \times 10^3 \text{ g} + 20.1 \text{ g}} \times 100 = 1.97\%$

93. $P_{CS_2} = \chi^V_{CS_2} P_{tot} = 0.855 \, (263 \text{ torr}) = 225 \text{ torr}$

$P_{CS_2} = \chi^L_{CS_2} P^{\bullet}_{CS_2}, \quad \chi^L_{CS_2} = \dfrac{P_{CS_2}}{P^{\bullet}_{CS_2}} = \dfrac{225 \text{ torr}}{375 \text{ torr}} = 0.600$

94. $iM = \dfrac{\pi}{RT} = \dfrac{0.3950 \text{ atm}}{0.08206 \text{ L atm mol}^{-1}\text{K}^{-1} \, (298.2 \text{ K})} = 0.01614 \text{ mol/L} = \text{total ion concentration}$

$0.01614 \, M = C_{Mg^{2+}} + C_{Na^+} + C_{Cl^-}; \quad C_{Cl^-} = 2 \, C_{Mg^{2+}} + C_{Na^+}$ (charge balance)

Combining: $0.01614 = 3 \, C_{Mg^{2+}} + 2 \, C_{Na^+}$

Let x = mass $MgCl_2$ and y = mass NaCl, then $x + y = 0.5000$ g.

$C_{Mg^{2+}} = \dfrac{x}{95.218}$ and $C_{Na^+} = \dfrac{y}{58.443}$ (Since V = 1.000 L)

Total ion concentration = $\dfrac{3 \, x}{95.218} + \dfrac{2 \, y}{58.443} = 0.01614 \, M;$ Rearranging: $3 \, x + 3.2585 \, y = 1.537$

Solving by simultaneous equations:

$$
\begin{aligned}
3 \, x \quad + \quad 3.2585 \, y &= 1.537 \\
-3 \, (x \quad + \qquad\quad y) &= -3(0.5000) \\
\hline
0.2585 \, y &= 0.037, \quad y = 0.14 \text{ g NaCl}
\end{aligned}
$$

mass $MgCl_2$ = 0.5000 g - 0.14 g = 0.36 g; mass % $MgCl_2 = \dfrac{0.36 \text{ g}}{0.5000 \text{ g}} \times 100 = 72\%$

CHAPTER EIGHTEEN

THE REPRESENTATIVE ELEMENTS: GROUPS 1A THROUGH 4A

Group 1A Elements

2. a. $\Delta H° = -110.5 - [-242 - 75] = 207$ kJ; $\Delta S° = 3(131) + 198 - [186 + 189] = 216$ J/K

    b. $\Delta G° = \Delta H° - T\Delta S°$; $\Delta G° = 0$ when $T = \dfrac{\Delta H°}{\Delta S°} = \dfrac{207 \times 10^3 \text{ J}}{216 \text{ J/K}} = 958$ K

    At T > 958 K and standard pressures, the favorable $\Delta S°$ term dominates and the reaction is spontaneous ($\Delta G° < 0$).

3. For $3 Fe(s) + 4 H_2O(g) \rightarrow Fe_3O_4(s) + 4 H_2(g)$

    a. $\Delta H° = -1117 - [4(-242)] = -149$ kJ; $\Delta S° = 146 + 4(131) - [3(27) + 4(189)] = -167$ J/K

    b. $\Delta G° = 0$ when $T = \dfrac{\Delta H°}{\Delta S°} = \dfrac{-149 \times 10^3 \text{ J}}{-167 \text{ J/K}} = 892$ K

    At T < 892 K and standard pressures, the favorable $\Delta H°$ term dominates and the reaction is spontaneous ($\Delta G° < 0$).

    For $C(s) + H_2O(g) \rightarrow CO(g) + H_2(g)$

    a. $\Delta H° = -110.5 - (-242) = 132$ kJ; $\Delta S° = 198 + 131 - [6 + 189] = 134$ J/K

    $T = \dfrac{\Delta H°}{\Delta S°} = \dfrac{132 \times 10^3 \text{ J}}{134 \text{ J/K}} = 985$ K

    b. This reaction is spontaneous when the favorable $\Delta S°$ term dominates, which occurs at T > 985 K (assuming standard pressures).

4. 1. Ammonia production and 2. Hydrogenation of vegetable oils

7. a. $Li_3N(s) + 3\ HCl(aq) \rightarrow 3\ LiCl(aq) + NH_3(aq)$ b. $Rb_2O(s) + H_2O(l) \rightarrow 2\ RbOH(aq)$

    c. $Cs_2O_2(s) + 2\ H_2O(l) \rightarrow 2\ CsOH(aq) + H_2O_2(aq)$

    d. $NaH(s) + H_2O(l) \rightarrow NaOH(aq) + H_2(g)$

8. $K^+(out) \rightarrow K^+(in);\ \ E = E° - \dfrac{0.0592}{1} \log\left(\dfrac{[K^+]_{in}}{[K^+]_{out}}\right);\ \ E° = 0$

    $E = -0.0592 \log\left(\dfrac{0.15}{5.0 \times 10^{-3}}\right) = -0.087\ V$

    $\Delta G = work = -nFE = -(1\ mol\ e^-)(96{,}485\ C/mol\ e^-)(-0.087\ J/C) = 8400\ J = 8.4\ kJ = work$

10. $2\ Li(s) + 2\ C_2H_2(g) \rightarrow 2\ LiC_2H(s) + H_2(g);$ This is an oxidation-reduction reaction.

13. a. $K(s) + O_2(g) \rightarrow KO_2(s)$ b. $16\ K(s) + S_8(s) \rightarrow 8\ K_2S(s)$

     c. $12\ K(s) + P_4(s) \rightarrow 4\ K_3P(s)$ d. $2\ K(s) + H_2(g) \rightarrow 2\ KH(s)$

     e. $2\ K(s) + 2\ H_2O(l) \rightarrow H_2(g) + 2\ KOH(aq)$

14. a. sodium oxide: Na_2O; b. sodium superoxide: NaO_2; c. sodium peroxide: Na_2O_2

Group 2A Elements

17.

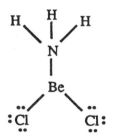

Geometry is trigonal planar.

Be uses sp^2 hybrid orbitals.

N uses sp^3 hybrid orbitals.

$BeCl_2$ is a Lewis acid.

19. $BeCl_2(NH_3)_2$ would form in excess ammonia. $BeCl_2(NH_3)_2$ has $2 + 2(7) + 2(5) + 6(1) = 32$ valence electrons. A structure for this molecule can be drawn that obeys the octet rule.

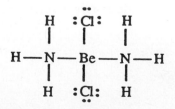

23. $Mg_3N_2(s) + 6\ H_2O(l) \rightarrow 2\ NH_3(g) + 3\ Mg^{2+}(aq) + 6\ OH^-(aq)$

$Mg_3P_2(s) + 6\ H_2O(l) \rightarrow 2\ PH_3(g) + 3\ Mg^{2+}(aq) + 6\ OH^-(aq)$

24. $1.00 \times 10^3\ kg \times \dfrac{1000\ g}{kg} \times \dfrac{1\ mol\ Ca}{40.08\ g} \times \dfrac{2\ mol\ e^-}{mol\ Ca} \times \dfrac{96,485\ C}{mol\ e^-} = 4.81 \times 10^9\ C$

$current = \dfrac{4.81 \times 10^9\ C}{8.00\ hr} \times \dfrac{1\ hr}{60\ min} \times \dfrac{1\ min}{60\ s} = \dfrac{1.67 \times 10^5\ C}{s} = 1.67 \times 10^5\ A$

$1.00 \times 10^3\ kg\ Ca \times \dfrac{70.90\ g\ Cl_2}{40.08\ g\ Ca} = 1.77 \times 10^3\ kg\ of\ Cl_2$

Group 3A Elements

26. $B_2H_6 + 3\ O_2 \rightarrow 2\ B(OH)_3$

27. a. Thallium(I) hydroxide   b. Indium(III) sulfide   c. Gallium(III) oxide

29. Element 113 would fall below Tl in the periodic table.

Element	AN	r of M^{3+} (Å)
B	5	0.2
Al	13	0.51
Ga	31	0.62
In	49	0.81
Tl	81	0.95
	113	~1.0

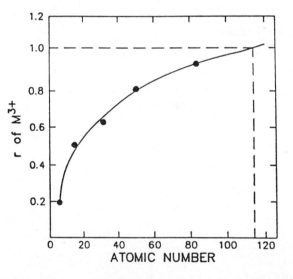

From the graph, we would predict the radius of the 3^+ ion of element 113 to be about 1.0 Å (100 pm). From the data in Table 18.9, we would expect the ionization energy of element 113 to be close to that of Tl. The trend is too erratic to make a more definitive prediction.

31. $In_2O_3(s) + 6\ H^+(aq) \rightarrow 2\ In^{3+}(aq) + 3\ H_2O(l)$

$In_2O_3(s) + OH^-(aq) \rightarrow$ no reaction

$Ga_2O_3(s) + 6 H^+(aq) \rightarrow 2 Ga^{3+}(aq) + 3 H_2O(l)$

$Ga_2O_3(s) + 2 OH^-(aq) + 3 H_2O(l) \rightarrow 2 Ga(OH)_4^-(aq)$

32.   Group 3A elements have one fewer valence electron than Si or Ge. A p-type semiconductor would form.

33.   a.   Out of 100.0 g of compound there are:

$$44.4 \text{ g Ca} \times \frac{1 \text{ mol}}{40.08 \text{ g}} = 1.11 \text{ mol Ca}; \quad 20.0 \text{ g Al} \times \frac{1 \text{ mol}}{26.98 \text{ g}} = 0.741 \text{ mol Al}$$

$$35.6 \text{ g O} \times \frac{1 \text{ mol}}{16.00 \text{ g}} = 2.23 \text{ mol O}$$

$$\frac{1.11}{0.741} = 1.5, \quad \frac{0.741}{0.741} = 1, \quad \frac{2.23}{0.741} = 3; \text{ Empirical formula is } Ca_3Al_2O_6.$$

b. $Ca_9Al_6O_{18}$

c.   There are covalent bonds between Al and O atoms in the $[Al_6O_{18}]^{18-}$ anion; sp^3 hybrid orbitals on aluminum overlap with sp^3 hybrid orbitals on oxygen to form the sigma bonds.

34.   a. $2 In(s) + 3 F_2(g) \rightarrow 2 InF_3(s)$ b. $2 In(s) + 3 Cl_2(g) \rightarrow 2 InCl_3(s)$

c. $4 In(s) + 3 O_2(g) \rightarrow 2 In_2O_3(s)$

d. $2 In(s) + 6 HCl(aq) \rightarrow 3 H_2(g) + 2 InCl_3(aq)$ or $2 In(s) + 6 HCl(g) \rightarrow 3 H_2(g) + 2 InCl_3(s)$

Group 4A Elements

39.   a.   Linear about all carbons;   b.   sp

40.

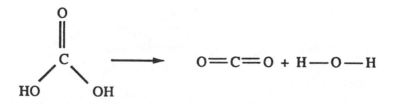

Bonds broken: 2 C – O (358 kJ/mol);   Bonds formed: 1 C = O (799 kJ/mol)

$\Delta H = 2(358) - 799 = -83$ kJ; ΔH is favorable for the decomposition of H_2CO_3 to CO_2 and H_2O. ΔS is also favorable for the decomposition as there is an increase in disorder. Hence, H_2CO_3 will spontaneously decompose to CO_2 and H_2O.

41. CS_2 has $4 + 2(6) = 16$ valence electrons. C_3S_2 has $3(4) + 2(6) = 24$ valence electrons.

$$\ddot{\ddot{S}} = C = \ddot{\ddot{S}} \quad \text{linear};\qquad \ddot{\ddot{S}} = C = C = C = \ddot{\ddot{S}} \quad \text{linear}$$

43.   White tin is stable at normal temperatures. Gray tin is stable at temperatures below 13.2°C. Thus for the phase change: Sn(gray) → Sn(white), ΔG is (-) at $T > 13.2$°C and ΔG is (+) at $T <$ 13.2°C. This is only possible if ΔH is (+) and ΔS is (+). Thus, gray tin has the more ordered structure.

44. $SiCl_4(l) + 2\ H_2O(l) \rightarrow SiO_2(s) + 4\ H^+(aq) + 4\ Cl^-(aq)$

$\Delta H° = 4(-167) + (-911) - [-687 + 2(-286)] = -320.$ kJ

$\Delta S° = 4(57) + (42) - [240 + 2(70)] = -110.$ J/K

$T = \Delta H°/\Delta S° = -320. \times 10^3$ J/-110. J K^{-1} = 2910 K

The reaction is spontaneous at temperatures below 2910 K, due to the favorable $\Delta H°$ term. There are, overall, stronger bonds in SiO_2 and HCl(aq) than in $SiCl_4$ and H_2O.

The corresponding reaction for CCl_4 is:

$CCl_4(l) + 2\ H_2O(l) \rightarrow CO_2(g) + 4\ H^+(aq) + 4\ Cl^-(aq)$

$\Delta H° = 4(-167) + (-393.5) - [-135 + 2(-286)] = -355$ kJ

$\Delta S° = 4(57) + 214 - [216 + 2(70)] = 86$ J/K

Thermodynamics predicts that this reaction would be spontaneous at any temperature.

The answer must lie with kinetics. $SiCl_4$ reacts because an activated complex can form by a water molecule attaching to silicon in $SiCl_4$. The activated complex requires silicon to form a fifth bond. Silicon has low energy 3d orbitals available to expand the octet. Carbon will not break the octet rule, therefore, CCl_4 cannot form this activated complex. CCl_4 and H_2O require a different pathway to get to products. The different pathway has a higher activation energy and, in turn, the reaction is much slower. (See Exercise 18.65.)

46.   SiC would have a covalent network structure similar to diamond.

47. $SiO_2(s) + 4\ HF(aq) \rightarrow SiF_4(g) + 2\ H_2O(l)$

49.
$$
\begin{array}{ll}
(Pb + 2\ OH^- \rightarrow Pb(OH)_2 + 2\ e^-) \times 2 & -E° = +0.57\ V \\
4\ e^- + 2\ H_2O + O_2 \rightarrow 4\ OH^- & E° = +0.40\ V \\
\hline
2\ Pb + 2\ H_2O + O_2 \rightarrow 2\ Pb(OH)_2 & E°_{cell} = +0.97\ V
\end{array}
$$

Comparing cell potentials, Fe pipes corrode more easily than Pb pipes. However, the corrosion of Pb pipes is still spontaneous and Pb(II) is very toxic. Pb pipes were extensively used by the Romans and it has been proposed that chronic lead poisoning is one of the factors leading to the decline and fall of the Roman Empire.

50. $Pb(OH)_2(s) \rightleftharpoons Pb^{2+} + 2\ OH^- \quad K_{sp} = 1.2 \times 10^{-15} = [Pb^{2+}]\ [OH^-]^2$

   s = solubility
   in mol/L $\rightarrow$ s   2s   (Ignore OH$^-$ from H$_2$O)

   $K_{sp} = (s)(2s)^2 = 1.2 \times 10^{-15}$, $4s^3 = 1.2 \times 10^{-15}$, $s = 6.7 \times 10^{-6}$ mol/L; Assumption good.

51.   Sn and Pb can reduce H$^+$ to H$_2$.

   $Sn(s) + 2\ H^+(aq) \rightarrow Sn^{2+}(aq) + H_2(g)$; $Pb(s) + 2\ H^+(aq) \rightarrow Pb^{2+}(aq) + H_2(g)$

Additional Exercises

52.   a.   Na$^+$ can oxidize Na$^-$ to Na. The purpose of the cryptand is to encapsulate the Na$^+$ ion so that
         it does not come in contact with the Na$^-$ ion and oxidize it to sodium metal.

55. $Be + 4\ OH^- \rightarrow Be(OH)_4^{2-} + 2\ e^-$
                       $2\ H_2O + 2\ e^- \rightarrow H_2 + 2\ OH^-$
   _____

   $Be(s) + 2\ H_2O(l) + 2\ OH^-(aq) \rightarrow Be(OH)_4^{2-}(aq) + H_2(g)$

   Be is the reducing agent. H$_2$O is the oxidizing agent.

57.   The Be^{2+} ion is a Lewis acid and has a strong affinity for the lone pairs of electrons on oxygen in
   water. The ion in solution is Be(H$_2$O)$_4^{2+}$. The acidic solution results from the reaction:
   $Be(H_2O)_4^{2+}(aq) \rightleftharpoons Be(H_2O)_3(OH)^+(aq) + H^+(aq)$

59. $Tl^{3+} + 2\ e^- \rightarrow Tl^+$ $E° = +1.25$ V
            $3\ I^- \rightarrow I_3^- + 2\ e^-$ $-E° = -0.55$ V
   _____

   $Tl^{3+} + 3\ I^- \rightarrow Tl^+ + I_3^-$ $E_{cell}^° = +0.70$ V

   In solution, Tl^{3+}can oxidize I$^-$ to I$_3^-$. Thus, we expect TlI$_3$ to be thallium(I) triiodide.

60.   Ga(I):   [Ar]3d^{10}4s^2, no unpaired e$^-$;   Ga(III):   [Ar]3d^{10}, no unpaired e$^-$

   Ga(II):   [Ar]3d^{10}4s^1, 1 unpaired e$^-$

   If the compound contained Ga(II) it would be paramagnetic and if the compound contained Ga(I)
   and Ga(III) it would be diamagnetic. This can easily be determined by measuring the mass of a
   sample in the presence and in the absence of a magnetic field. Paramagnetic compounds will
   have an apparent greater mass in a magnetic field.

63.   a. $K_2SiF_6(s) + 4 K(l) \rightarrow 6 KF(s) + Si(s)$

        b. K_2SiF_6 is an ionic compound, composed of K^+ cations and SiF_6^{2-} anions. The SiF_6^{2-} anion is held together by covalent bonds. The structure is:

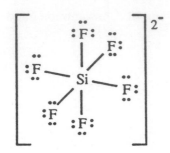

                                                The anion is octahedral.

64.

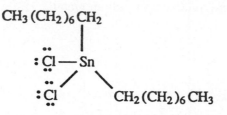

        The compound is held together by covalent bonds. The structure is tetrahedral about the central Sn.

65.   Carbon cannot form the fifth bond necessary for the transition state since carbon doesn't have low energy d orbitals available to expand the octet.

67.   Size decreases from left to right and increases going down the periodic table. So going one element right and one element down would result in a similar size for the two elements diagonal to each other. The ionization energies will be similar for the diagonal elements since the periodic trends also oppose each other. Electron affinities are harder to predict, but atoms with similar size and ionization energy will also have similar electron affinities.

CHAPTER NINETEEN

THE REPRESENTATIVE ELEMENTS: GROUPS 5A THROUGH 8A

Group 5A Elements

2. $\Delta H° = 2(90 \text{ kJ}) - [0] = 180. \text{ kJ}; \ \Delta S° = 2(211 \text{ J/K}) - [192 + 205] = 25 \text{ J/K}$

$\Delta G° = 2(87 \text{ kJ}) - [0] = 174 \text{ kJ}$

At high temperature the reaction $N_2 + O_2 \rightarrow 2 \text{ NO}$ becomes spontaneous. In the atmosphere, even though $2 \text{ NO} \rightarrow N_2 + O_2$ is spontaneous, it doesn't occur because the rate is slow.

3. NH_3: sp^3; N_2H_4: sp^3; NH_2OH: sp^3; N_2: sp; N_2O: central N, sp

NO: sp^2; N_2O_3: both Ns are sp^2; NO_2: sp^2; HNO_3: sp^2

4.   Resonance is possible for N_2O, NO, N_2O_3, NO_2, and HNO_3.

N_2O   dinitrogen monoxide (nitrous oxide)

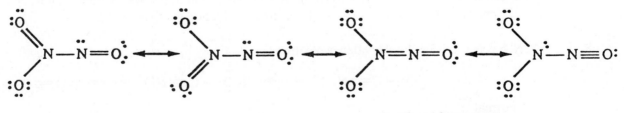

NO   nitrogen monoxide (nitric oxide)

N_2O_3   dinitrogen trioxide

last 2 not important

253

NO_2 nitrogen dioxide

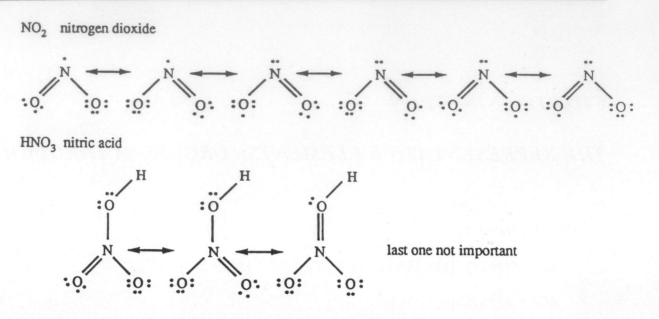

HNO_3 nitric acid

last one not important

5. For the reaction:

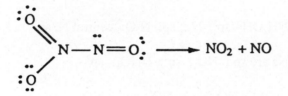

the activation energy must in some way involve the breaking of a nitrogen-nitrogen single bond.

For the reaction:

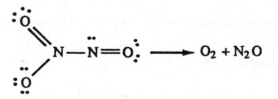

at some point nitrogen-oxygen bonds must be broken. N – N single bonds (160 kJ/mol) are weaker than N – O single bonds (201 kJ/mol). In addition, resonance structures indicate that there is more double bond character in the N – O bonds than in the N— N bond. Thus, NO_2 and NO are preferred by kinetics because of the lower activation energy.

8. OCN⁻ has $6 + 4 + 5 + 1 = 16$ valence electrons.

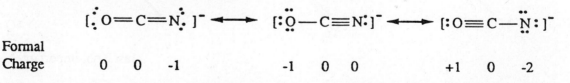

| Formal Charge | 0 | 0 | -1 | | -1 | 0 | 0 | | +1 | 0 | -2 |

Only the first two resonance structures should be important. The third places a positive formal charge on the most electronegative atom in the ion and a -2 formal charge on N.

CNO^-:

$$[\,:\!C\!=\!N\!=\!O\,]^- \longleftrightarrow [:C\!\equiv\!N\!-\!\ddot{O}\!:]^- \longleftrightarrow [:\ddot{C}\!-\!N\!\equiv\!O:]^-$$

Formal
Charge   -2   +1   0   -1   +1   -1   -3   +1   +1

All of the resonance structures for fulminate involve greater formal charges than in cyanate, making fulminate more reactive (less stable).

10.   a. $8\,H^+(aq) + 2\,NO_3^-(aq) + 3\,Cu(s) \rightarrow 3\,Cu^{2+}(aq) + 4\,H_2O(l) + 2\,NO(g)$

       b. $NH_4NO_3(s) \xrightarrow{Heat} N_2O(g) + 2\,H_2O(g)$

       c. $NO(g) + NO_2(g) + 2\,KOH(aq) \rightarrow 2\,KNO_2(aq) + H_2O(l)$

12.   Production of antimony:

            $2\,Sb_2S_3(s) + 9\,O_2(g) \rightarrow 2\,Sb_2O_3(s) + 6\,SO_2(g)$

            $2\,Sb_2O_3(s) + 3\,C(s) \rightarrow 4\,Sb(s) + 3\,CO_2(g)$

       Production of bismuth:

            $2\,Bi_2S_3(s) + 9\,O_2(g) \rightarrow 2\,Bi_2O_3(s) + 6\,SO_2(g)$

            $2\,Bi_2O_3(s) + 3\,C(s) \rightarrow 4\,Bi(s) + 3\,CO_2(g)$

13.   a. $H_3PO_4 > H_3PO_3$; The strongest acid has the most oxygen atoms.

       b. $H_3PO_4 > H_2PO_4^- > HPO_4^{2-}$; Acid strength decreases as protons are removed.

14.   The acidic protons are attached to oxygen.

$H_4P_2O_6$: $H_4P_2O_5$:

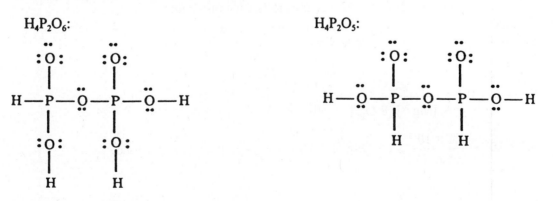

18.

			Bond order	# unpaired e⁻
M.O model:	NO:		2.5	1
	NO⁺:		3	0
	NO⁻:		2	2

Lewis structures: NO⁺: $[:N\equiv O:]^{+}$

NO: $\cdot\ddot{N}=\ddot{O}\cdot \longleftrightarrow :\ddot{N}=\ddot{O}\cdot \longleftrightarrow \cdot\ddot{N}=\ddot{O}\colon$

NO⁻: $\left[:\ddot{N}=\ddot{O}:\right]^{-}$

Lewis structure are not adequate for NO and NO⁻. M.O. model gives correct results for all three species. For NO, Lewis structures are poor for odd electron species. For NO⁻, Lewis structures fail to predict that NO⁻ is paramagnetic.

19. $Mg^{2+} + P_3O_{10}^{5-} \rightleftharpoons MgP_3O_{10}^{3-}$; $[Mg^{2+}]_o = \dfrac{50. \times 10^{-3} \text{ g}}{L} \times \dfrac{1 \text{ mol}}{24.3 \text{ g}} = 2.1 \times 10^{-3} \ M$

$[P_3O_{10}^{5-}]_o = \dfrac{40. \text{ g Na}_5P_3O_{10}}{L} \times \dfrac{1 \text{ mol}}{367.9 \text{ g}} = 0.11 \ M$

Assume the reaction goes to completion since K is large ($10^{8.60} = 4.0 \times 10^8$).

$$Mg^{2+} \quad + \quad P_3O_{10}^{5-} \quad \rightleftharpoons \quad MgP_3O_{10}^{3-}$$

Before	$2.1 \times 10^{-3} \ M$	$0.11 \ M$	0	
Change	-2.1×10^{-3}	-2.1×10^{-3} $\rightarrow$	$+2.1 \times 10^{-3}$	React completely
After	0	0.11	2.1×10^{-3}	New initial

x mol/L $MgP_3O_{10}^{3-}$ dissociates to reach equilibrium

Change	$+x$	$+x$ $\leftarrow$	$-x$	
Equil.	x	$0.11 + x$	$2.1 \times 10^{-3} - x$	

$K = 4.0 \times 10^8 = \dfrac{[MgP_3O_{10}^{3-}]}{[Mg^{2+}][P_3O_{10}^{5-}]} = \dfrac{2.1 \times 10^{-3} - x}{x(0.11 + x)}$

$4.0 \times 10^8 \approx \dfrac{2.1 \times 10^{-3}}{x(0.11)}$, $x = [Mg^{2+}] = 4.8 \times 10^{-11} \ M$;   Assumptions good.

20.   a.

$$(4\ H_2O + Mn^{2+} \rightarrow MnO_4^- + 8\ H^+ + 5e^-) \times 2$$
$$(2e^- + NaBiO_3 \rightarrow BiO_3^{3-} + Na^+) \times 5$$

$$8\ H_2O(l) + 2\ Mn^{2+}(aq) + 5\ NaBiO_3(s) \rightarrow 2\ MnO_4^-(aq) + 16\ H^+(aq) + 5\ BiO_3^{3-}(aq) + 5\ Na^+(aq)$$

b.   Bismuthate exists as a covalent network solid: $(BiO_3^-)_x$.

23.   a. $P_4O_6(s) + 2\ O_2(g) \rightarrow P_4O_{10}(s)$

b. $P_4O_{10}(s) + 6\ H_2O(l) \rightarrow 4\ H_3PO_4(aq)$

c. $PCl_5(l) + 4\ H_2O(l) \rightarrow H_3PO_4(aq) + 5\ HCl(aq)$

Group 6A Elements

26. $OTeF_5^-$ has $6 + 6 + 5(7) + 1 = 48$ valence electrons.

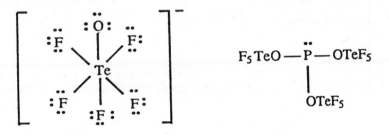

27.   a.   As we go down the family, K_a increases. This is consistent with the bond to hydrogen getting weaker.

b.   Po is below Te, so K_a should be larger. The K_a for H_2Po should be on the order of 10^{-2}.

29.   Sulfur forms polysulfide ions, S_n^{2-}, which are soluble, e.g., $S_8 + S^{2-} \rightleftharpoons S_9^{2-}$. Nitric acid oxidizes S^{2-} to S, which then precipitates out of solution.

32.   Light from violet to green will work.

Group 7A Elements

35.   a. ClF_5, $7 + 5(7) = 42\ e^-$ b. IF_3, $7 + 3(7) = 28\ e^-$

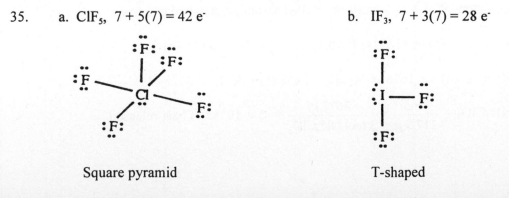

Square pyramid   T-shaped

c. Cl_2O_7, $2(7) + 7(6) = 56$ e-

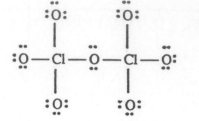

The four O atoms are tetra-
hedrally arranged about each
Cl. The Cl – O – Cl bond angle
is close to the tetrahedral angle.

36.   a. $F_2 + H_2O \rightarrow HOF + HF$; $2\ HOF \rightarrow 2\ HF + O_2$; $HOF + H_2O \rightarrow HF + H_2O_2$ (acid)

In dilute base, HOF exists as OF^- and HF exists as F^-.

$$(2e^- + H_2O + OF^- \rightarrow F^- + 2\ OH^-) \times 2$$
$$4\ OH^- \rightarrow O_2 + 2\ H_2O + 4e^-$$

_____

$$2\ OF^- \rightarrow O_2 + 2\ F^-$$

b.   HOF: Assign +1 to H and -1 to F. The oxidation number of oxygen is then zero. Oxygen is
very electronegative. A zero oxidation state is not very stable since oxygen is a very good
oxidizing agent.

37.

$$:F \!—\! O \!—\! O \!—\! F:$$

Formal Charge	0	0	0	0
Oxid. Number	-1	+1	+1	-1

Oxidation numbers are more useful. We are forced to assign +1 as the oxidation number for
oxygen. Oxygen is very electronegative and +1 is not a stable oxidation state for this element.

41.   a. $ClO_3^- + H_2O \rightarrow ClO_4^- + 2\ H^+ + 2e^-$ $-E° = -1.19$ V
               $2\ H^+ + 2\ e^- \rightarrow H_2$ $E° = \ \ 0.0$ V

_____

       $ClO_3^- + H_2O \rightarrow ClO_4^- + H_2$ $E°_{cell} = -1.19$ V

A minimum potential of 1.19 V must be applied assuming standard conditions.

b. $3\ Al(s) + 3\ NH_4ClO_4(s) \rightarrow Al_2O_3(s) + AlCl_3(s) + 3\ NO(g) + 6\ H_2O(g)$

$\Delta H° = 3(90) + (-704) + (-1676) + 6(-242) - [3(-295) + 3(0)] = -2677$ kJ

$$7 \times 10^8 \text{ g } NH_4ClO_4 \times \frac{1 \text{ mol}}{117.5 \text{ g}} \times \frac{-2677 \text{ kJ}}{3 \text{ mol } NH_4ClO_4} = -5 \times 10^9 \text{ kJ of heat released}$$

42. a. AgCl(s) $\xrightarrow{h\nu}$ Ag(s) + Cl; The reactive chlorine atom is trapped in the crystal. When light is removed, Cl reacts with silver atoms to reform AgCl, i.e., the reverse reaction occurs. In pure AgCl, the Cl atoms escape, making the reverse reaction impossible.

b. Over time chlorine is lost and the dark silver metal is permanent.

Group 8A Elements

44. Helium is unreactive and doesn't combine with any other elements. It is a very light gas and would easily escape the earth's gravitational pull as the planet was formed.

45. The heavier members are not really inert. Xe and Kr have been shown to react and form compounds with other elements.

46. $10.0 \text{ m} \times 5.0 \text{ m} \times 3.0 \text{ m} = 1.5 \times 10^2 \text{ m}^3$; From Table 19.12, volume % Xe = 9×10^{-6}.

$$1.5 \times 10^2 \text{ m}^3 \times \left(\frac{10 \text{ dm}}{\text{m}}\right)^3 \times \frac{1 \text{ L}}{\text{dm}^3} \times \frac{9 \times 10^{-6} \text{ L Xe}}{100 \text{ L air}} = 1 \times 10^{-2} \text{ L of Xe in the room}$$

$$PV = nRT, \quad n = \frac{PV}{RT} = \frac{(1.0 \text{ atm}) (1 \times 10^{-2} \text{ L})}{(0.08206 \text{ L atm mol}^{-1} \text{ K}^{-1}) (298 \text{ K})} = 4 \times 10^{-4} \text{ mol Xe}$$

$$4 \times 10^{-4} \text{ mol Xe} \times \frac{131.3 \text{ g}}{\text{mol}} = 5 \times 10^{-2} \text{ g Xe in the room}$$

$$4 \times 10^{-4} \text{ mol Xe} \times \frac{6.022 \times 10^{23} \text{ atoms}}{\text{mol}} = 2 \times 10^{20} \text{ atoms Xe in the room}$$

A 2 L breath contains: $2 \text{ L air} \times \frac{9 \times 10^{-6} \text{ L Xe}}{100 \text{ L air}} = 2 \times 10^{-7} \text{ L Xe}$

$$n = \frac{PV}{RT} = \frac{(1.0 \text{ atm}) (2 \times 10^{-7} \text{ L})}{(0.08206 \text{ L atm mol}^{-1} \text{ K}^{-1}) (298 \text{ K})} = 8 \times 10^{-9} \text{ mol Xe}$$

$$8 \times 10^{-9} \text{ mol Xe} \times \frac{6.022 \times 10^{23} \text{ atoms}}{\text{mol}} = 5 \times 10^{15} \text{ atoms of Xe in a 2 L breath}$$

47. a. XeO_3, $8 + 3(6) = 26 \text{ e}^-$ b. XeO_4, $8 + 4(6) = 32 \text{ e}^-$

trigonal pyramid   tetrahedral

c. $XeOF_4$, $8 + 6 + 4(7) = 42$ e^-

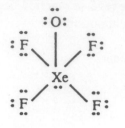

square pyramid

d. $XeOF_2$, $8 + 6 + 2(7) = 28$ e^-

T-shaped

e. XeO_3F_2 has $8 + 3(6) + 2(7) = 40$ valence electrons.

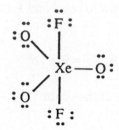

trigonal bipyramid

Additional Exercises

49.   As the halogen atoms get larger, it becomes more difficult to fit three halogen atoms around the small N, and the NX_3 molecule becomes less stable.

51.   Xe has one more valence electron than I. Thus, the isoelectric species will have I plus one extra electron substituted for Xe, giving a species with a net minus one charge.

        a. IO_4^- b. IO_3^- c. IF_2^- d. IF_4^- e. IF_6^- f. IOF_3^-

52.   For $NCl_3 \rightarrow NCl_2 + Cl$, only the $N - Cl$ bond is broken. For $O = N - Cl \rightarrow NO + Cl$, the NO bond gets stronger (bond order increases from 2.0 to 2.5) when the $N - Cl$ bond is broken. This makes ΔH for the reaction smaller than just the energy necessary to break the $N - Cl$ bond.

54.   Plastic sulfur consists of long S_n chains of sulfur atoms. As plastic sulfur becomes brittle, the long chains break down into S_8 rings.

55.   The pollution provides nitrogen and phosphorous nutrients so the algae can grow. The algae consume oxygen, causing fish to die.

56.
$$H_2O + BrO_3^- \rightarrow BrO_4^- + 2\ H^+ + 2\ e^-$$
$$2\ e^- + 2\ H^+ + XeF_2 \rightarrow Xe + 2\ HF$$

$$H_2O(l) + BrO_3^-(aq) + XeF_2(aq) \rightarrow BrO_4^-(aq) + Xe(g) + 2\ HF(aq)$$

CHAPTER TWENTY

TRANSITION METALS AND COORDINATION CHEMISTRY

Transition Metals

1. a. Co: $[Ar]4s^23d^7$

    Co^{2+}: $[Ar]3d^7$

    Co^{3+}: $[Ar]3d^6$

    b. Pt: $[Xe]6s^14f^{14}5d^9$

    Pt^{2+}: $[Xe]4f^{14}5d^8$

    Pt^{4+}: $[Xe]4f^{14}5d^6$

    c. Fe: $[Ar]4s^23d^6$

    Fe^{2+}: $[Ar]3d^6$

    Fe^{3+}: $[Ar]3d^5$

2.
$$Fe^{2+} \rightarrow Fe^{3+} + e^- \qquad \Delta H = 2.957 \times 10^6 \text{ J}$$
$$e^- + Ti^{4+} \rightarrow Ti^{3+} \qquad \Delta H = -4.175 \times 10^6 \text{ J}$$

$$Fe^{2+} + Ti^{4+} \rightarrow Fe^{3+} + Ti^{3+} \qquad \Delta H = -1.218 \times 10^6 \text{ J}$$

From this, we would predict that Fe^{3+} and Ti^{3+} is more stable than Fe^{2+} and Ti^{4+}.

$$Fe^{3+} + e^- \rightarrow Fe^{2+} \qquad E° = 0.77 \text{ V}$$
$$Ti^{3+} + H_2O \rightarrow TiO^{2+} + 2 H^+ + e^- \qquad -E° = -0.099 \text{ V}$$

$$Fe^{3+} + Ti^{3+} + H_2O \rightarrow Fe^{2+} + TiO^{2+} + 2 H^+ \qquad E°_{cell} = 0.67 \text{ V}$$

From E° values, we would predict Fe(II) and Ti(IV) to be more stable. The electrochemical data are consistent with the information in the text. These data are for solutions while ionization energies are for gas phase reactions. Solution data are more representative of the conditions from which ilmenite was initially formed.

4. a. 4 O atoms on faces × 1/2 O/face = 2 O atoms, 2 O atoms inside body, Total: 4 O atoms

    8 Ti atoms on corners × 1/8 Ti/corner + 1 Ti atom/body center = 2 Ti atoms

    Formula of the unit cell is Ti$_2$O$_4$. The empirical formula is TiO$_2$.

    b.
    $$\overset{+4\ -2}{2 \text{ TiO}_2} + \overset{0}{3 \text{ C}} + \overset{0}{4 \text{ Cl}_2} \rightarrow \overset{+4\ -1}{2 \text{ TiCl}_4} + \overset{+4\ -2}{\text{CO}_2} + \overset{+2\ -2}{2 \text{ CO}}$$

    Cl is reduced and C is oxidized. Cl$_2$ is the oxidizing agent and C is the reducing agent.

$$\overset{+4\ \ -1}{\text{TiCl}_4} + \overset{0}{\text{O}_2} \rightarrow \overset{+4\ -2}{\text{TiO}_2} + \overset{0}{2\ \text{Cl}_2}$$

O is reduced and Cl is oxidized. O_2 is the oxidizing agent and $TiCl_4$ is the reducing agent.

5. TiF_4: Ionic compound containing Ti^{4+} ions and F^- ions. $TiCl_4$, $TiBr_4$, and TiI_4: Covalent compounds containing discrete, tetrahedral TiX_4 molecules. As these molecules get larger, the bp and mp increase because the London dispersion forces increase.

6.   pyrolusite, manganese(IV)oxide; rhodochrosite, manganese(II)carbonate

7.   a. $2\ CoAs_2(s) + 4\ O_2(g) \rightarrow 2\ CoO(s) + As_4O_6(s)$

As_4O_6, tetraarsenic hexoxide; As_4O_6 has a cage structure similar to P_4O_6.

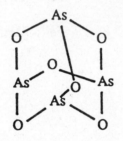

   b. $(Co^{2+} + 3\ OH^- \rightarrow Co(OH)_3 + e^-) \times 2$
                              $2\ e^- + H_2O + OCl^- \rightarrow Cl^- + 2\ OH^-$
_____

$2\ Co^{2+}(aq) + 4\ OH^-(aq) + H_2O(l) + OCl^-(aq) \rightarrow 2\ Co(OH)_3(s) + Cl^-(aq)$

   c. $Co(OH)_3(s) \rightleftharpoons Co^{3+}(aq) + 3\ OH^-(aq)$

Initial   0   0 $1.0 \times 10^{-7}\ M$
                s mol/L $Co(OH)_3$ dissolves to reach equilibrium
Change   -s $\rightarrow$ +s   +3s
Equil.   s $1.0 \times 10^{-7} + 3s$

$2.5 \times 10^{-43} = [Co^{3+}][OH^-]^3 = s(1.0 \times 10^{-7} + 3s)^3 \approx s(1.0 \times 10^{-21})$

$s = [Co^{3+}] = 2.5 \times 10^{-22}\ mol/L$;   Assumptions good.

   d. $Co(OH)_3 \rightleftharpoons Co^{3+} + 3\ OH^-$; pH = 10.00, pOH = 4.00, $[OH^-] = 1.0 \times 10^{-4}\ M$

$2.5 \times 10^{-43} = [Co^{3+}][OH^-]^3 = [Co^{3+}](1.0 \times 10^{-4})^3$, $[Co^{3+}] = 2.5 \times 10^{-31}\ M$

Coordination Compounds

9.   a. ligand: Species that donates a pair of electrons to form a covalent bond to a metal ion (a Lewis base).

     b. chelate: Ligand that can form more than one bond.

     c. bidentate: Ligand that can form two bonds.

     d. complex ion: Metal ion plus ligands.

10. a. hexaamminecobalt(II) chloride   b. hexaaquacobalt(III) iodide

11. a. pentaamminechlororuthenium(III) ion   b. hexacyanoferrate(II) ion

12. a. sodium tris(oxalato)nickelate(II)   b. potassium tetrachlorocobaltate(II)

13. a. $[Co(C_5H_5N)_6]Cl_3$ b. $[Cr(NH_3)_5I]I_2$ c. $[Ni(NH_2CH_2CH_2NH_2)_3]Br_2$

14. a. $FeCl_4^-$ b. $[Ru(NH_3)_5H_2O]^{3+}$

15. a. 2; Forms bonds through the lone pairs on the two oxygen atoms.

     b. 3; Forms bonds through the lone pairs on the three nitrogen atoms.

     c. 4; Forms bonds through the two nitrogen atoms and the two oxygen atoms.

     d. 4; Forms bonds through the four nitrogen atoms.

17. a.

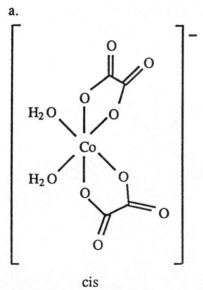

cis

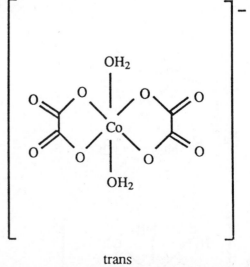

trans

b.

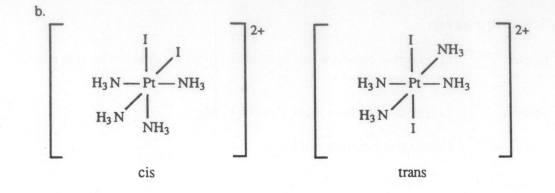

cis   trans

18.   Linkage isomers differ in the way the ligand bonds to the metal. SCN⁻ can bond through the sulfur or through the nitrogen atom. NO$_2^-$ can bond through the nitrogen or through the oxygen atom. OCN⁻ can bond through the oxygen or through the nitrogen atom. N$_3^-$, en, and I⁻ are not capable of linkage isomerism.

19.

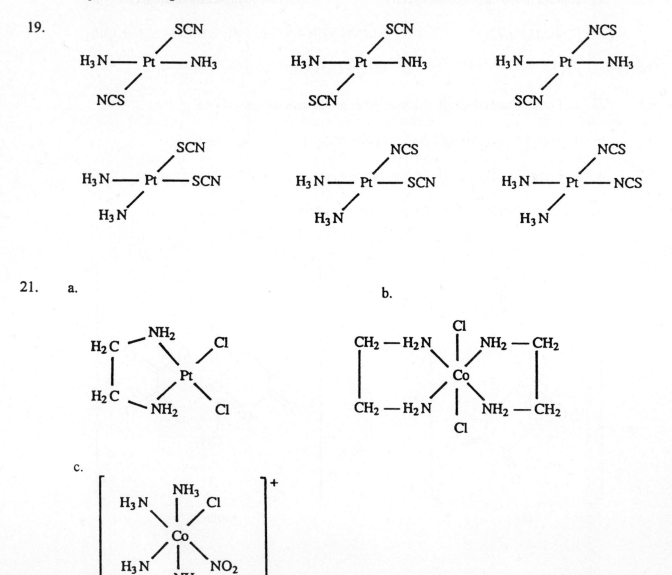

21.   a.   b.

c.

23. $BaCl_2$ gives no precipitate so SO_4^{2-} must be in the coordination sphere. A precipitate with $AgNO_3$ means that the Cl^- is not in the coordination sphere. Since there are only four ammonia molecules in the coordination sphere, then the SO_4^{2-} must be acting as a bidentate ligand. The structure is:

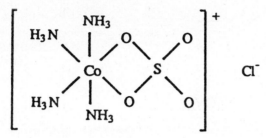

Bonding, Color, and Magnetism in Coordination Compounds

26.   a.   Ligand that will give complex ions with the maximum number of unpaired electrons.

       b.   Ligand that will give complex ions with the minimum number of unpaired electrons.

30.   a. Ru^{2+}: $[Kr]4d^6$, no unpaired e^- b. Fe^{3+}: $[Ar]3d^5$, 1 unpaired e^-

       c. Ni^{2+}: $[Ar]3d^8$, 2 unpaired e^- d. V^{3+}: $[Ar]3d^2$, 2 unpaired e^-

       e. Co^{2+}: $[Ar]3d^7$, 3 unpaired e^- (tetrahedral splitting)

32. $NiCl_4^{2-}$ is tetrahedral and $Ni(CN)_4^{2-}$ is square planar. The corresponding d-orbital splitting diagrams for the d^8 Ni^{2+} are:

$\underline{\uparrow\downarrow}$ $\underline{\uparrow}$ $\underline{\uparrow}$ $\underline{\quad}$

$\underline{\uparrow\downarrow}$ $\underline{\uparrow\downarrow}$ $\underline{\uparrow\downarrow}$

$\underline{\uparrow\downarrow}$

$\underline{\uparrow\downarrow}$ $\underline{\uparrow\downarrow}$

NiCl$_4^{2-}$ Ni(CN)$_4^{2-}$

34.   a. Fe^{2+} (d^6):

$\underline{\uparrow}$ $\underline{\uparrow}$ $\underline{\quad}$ $\underline{\quad}$

$\underline{\uparrow\downarrow}$ $\underline{\uparrow}$ $\underline{\uparrow}$ $\underline{\uparrow\downarrow}$ $\underline{\uparrow\downarrow}$ $\underline{\uparrow\downarrow}$

High spin   Low spin

b. Fe^{3+} (d^5):   c. Ni^{2+} (d^8):

$\underline{\uparrow}$ $\underline{\uparrow}$ $\underline{\uparrow}$ $\underline{\uparrow}$

$\underline{\uparrow}$ $\underline{\uparrow}$ $\underline{\uparrow}$ $\underline{\uparrow\downarrow}$ $\underline{\uparrow\downarrow}$ $\underline{\uparrow\downarrow}$

High spin

35.   Transition compounds exhibit the color compementary to that absorbed. Using Table 20.16, $Ni(H_2O)_6Cl_2$ absorbs red light and $Ni(NH_3)Cl_2$ absorbs yellow-green light. $Ni(NH_3)_6Cl_2$ absorbs the shorter wavelength light which is the higher energy light. Therefore, Δ is larger for $Ni(NH_3)_6Cl_2$. NH_3 is a stronger field ligand than H_2O, consistent with the spectrochemical series.

36. Fe^{3+} complexes have one unpaired electron when a strong-field case and five unpaired electrons when a weak-field case. $Fe(CN)_6^{2-}$ is a strong-field case and $Fe(SCN)_6^{3-}$ is a weak-field case. Therefore, cyanide, CN^-, is a stronger field ligand than thiocyanate, SCN^-.

Additional Exercises

38. $Ni(CO)_4$ is composed of 4 CO molecules and Ni. Thus, nickel has an oxidation state of zero.

39.   Since transition metals form bonds to species with lone pairs of electrons, they are Lewis acids (electron pair acceptors).

42.   i. $0.0203 \text{ g CrO}_3 \times \dfrac{52.00 \text{ g Cr}}{100.0 \text{ g CrO}_3} = 0.0106 \text{ g Cr}; \quad \% \text{ Cr} = \dfrac{0.0106}{0.105} \times 100 = 10.1\% \text{ Cr}$

       ii. $32.93 \text{ mL HCl} \times \dfrac{0.100 \text{ mmol HCl}}{\text{mL}} \times \dfrac{1 \text{ mmol NH}_3}{\text{mmol HCl}} \times \dfrac{17.03 \text{ mg NH}_3}{\text{mmol}} = 56.1 \text{ mg NH}_3$

             $\% \text{ NH}_3 = \dfrac{56.1 \text{ mg}}{341 \text{ mg}} \times 100 = 16.5\% \text{ NH}_3$

       iii. $75.53 + 16.5 + 10.1 = 100.1$;   The compound is composed of only Cr, NH_3, and I.

             Out of 100.00 of compound:

             $10.1 \text{ g Cr} \times \dfrac{1 \text{ mol}}{52.00 \text{ g}} = 0.194 \qquad\qquad \dfrac{0.194}{0.194} = 1.00$

             $16.5 \text{ g NH}_3 \times \dfrac{1 \text{ mol}}{17.03 \text{ g}} = 0.969 \qquad\qquad \dfrac{0.969}{0.194} = 4.99$

             $73.53 \text{ g I} \times \dfrac{1 \text{ mol}}{126.9 \text{ g}} = 0.5794 \qquad\qquad \dfrac{0.5794}{0.194} = 2.99$

             $Cr(NH_3)_5I_3$ is the empirical formula. Cr(III) forms octahedral complexes. So compound A is made of $[Cr(NH_3)_5I]^{2+}$ and two I^- ions or $[Cr(NH_3)_5I]I_2$.

       iv. $\Delta T_f = iK_f m$; For $[Cr(NH_3)_5I]I_2$, $i = 3$ ions.

             $m = \dfrac{0.601 \text{ g complex}}{10.0 \text{ g H}_2\text{O}} \times \dfrac{1 \text{ mol complex}}{517.9 \text{ g complex}} \times \dfrac{1000 \text{ g H}_2\text{O}}{\text{kg}} = 0.116 \text{ molal}$

             $\Delta T_f = 3 \times 1.86 \text{°C/molal} \times 0.116 \text{ molal} = 0.65 \text{°C}$

             Since ΔT_f is close to the measured value, then this is consistent with the formula $[Cr(NH_3)_5I]I_2$.

44. $Fe_2O_3(s) + 6 \text{ H}_2\text{C}_2\text{O}_4(aq) \rightarrow 2 \text{ Fe}(\text{C}_2\text{O}_4)_3^{3-}(aq) + 3 \text{ H}_2\text{O}(l) + 6 \text{ H}^+(aq)$

       The oxalate anion forms a soluble complex ion with iron in rust.

47.   No; In all three cases, six bonds are formed between Ni^{2+} and nitrogen, so ΔH values should be similar. $\Delta S°$ for formation of the complex ion is most negative for 6 NH_3 molecules reacting with a metal ion (7 independent species become 1). For penten reacting with a metal ion, 2 independent species become 1, so $\Delta S°$ is less negative. Thus, the chelate effect occurs because the more bonds a chelating agent can form to the metal, the more favorable $\Delta S°$ is for the formation of the complex ion and the larger the formation constant.

51.   There is no plane symmetry in the complex, thus it is optically active.

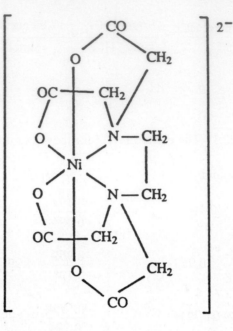

52.

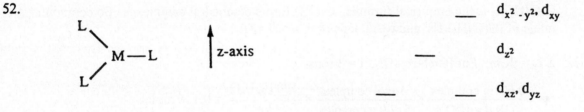

The $d_{x^2-y^2}$ and d_{xy} are in the plane of the three ligands and should be destabilized the most. The d_{z^2} has some electron density in the xy plane (the doughnut) and should be destabilized a lesser amount. The d_{xz} and d_{yz} have no electron density in the plane and should be lowest in energy.

CHAPTER TWENTY-ONE

THE NUCLEUS: A CHEMIST'S VIEW

Radioactive Decay and Nuclear Transformations

1. a. $^{3}_{1}H \rightarrow ^{0}_{-1}e + ^{3}_{2}He$ c. $^{7}_{4}Be + ^{0}_{-1}e \rightarrow ^{7}_{3}Li$

    b. $^{8}_{3}Li \rightarrow ^{8}_{4}Be + ^{0}_{-1}e$

    $^{8}_{4}Be \rightarrow 2\ ^{4}_{2}He$
    _____
    $^{8}_{3}Li \rightarrow 2\ ^{4}_{2}He + ^{0}_{-1}e$

2. a. $^{60}_{27}Co \rightarrow ^{60}_{28}Ni + ^{0}_{-1}e$ b. $^{97}_{43}Tc + ^{0}_{-1}e \rightarrow ^{97}_{42}Mo$

3. ^{8}B and ^{9}B contain too many protons or too few neutrons. Electron capture or positron production are both possible decay mechanisms that increase the neutron to proton ratio. ^{12}B and ^{13}B contain too many neutrons or too few protons. Beta production lowers the neutron to proton ratio, so we expect ^{12}B and ^{13}B to be β-emitters.

4. a. $^{1}_{1}H + ^{14}_{7}N \rightarrow ^{11}_{6}C + ^{4}_{2}He$ b. $2\ ^{3}_{2}He \rightarrow ^{4}_{2}He + 2\ ^{1}_{1}H$

5. a. $^{240}_{95}Am + ^{4}_{2}He \rightarrow ^{243}_{97}Bk + ^{1}_{0}n$ b. $^{238}_{92}U + ^{12}_{6}C \rightarrow ^{244}_{98}Cf + 6\ ^{1}_{0}n$

9. a. $^{207}_{82}Pb$; Complete decay is 7α and 4β: $^{235}_{92}U \rightarrow ^{207}_{82}Pb + 7\ ^{4}_{2}He + 4\ ^{0}_{-1}e$

b. $^{235}_{92}U \rightarrow {}^{231}_{90}Th + {}^{4}_{2}He \rightarrow {}^{231}_{91}Pa + {}^{0}_{-1}e \rightarrow {}^{227}_{89}Ac + {}^{4}_{2}He$

$^{215}_{84}Po + {}^{4}_{2}He \leftarrow {}^{219}_{86}Rn + {}^{4}_{2}He \leftarrow {}^{223}_{88}Ra + {}^{4}_{2}He \leftarrow {}^{227}_{90}Th + {}^{0}_{-1}e$

$^{4}_{2}He + {}^{211}_{82}Pb \rightarrow {}^{211}_{83}Bi + {}^{0}_{-1}e \rightarrow {}^{207}_{81}Tl + {}^{4}_{2}He \rightarrow {}^{207}_{82}Pb + {}^{0}_{-1}e$

11. The most abundant isotope is generally the most stable isotope. The periodic table predicts that the most stable isotopes for exercises a - d are ^{39}K, ^{56}Fe, ^{23}Na and ^{204}Tl.

a. Unstable; ^{45}K has too many neutrons and will undergo beta particle production.

b. Stable

c. Unstable; ^{20}Na has too few neutrons and will most likely undergo electron capture or positron production.

d. Unstable; ^{194}Tl has too few neutrons and will undergo electron capture, positron production and/or alpha particle production.

Kinetics of Radioactive Decay

13. For $t_{1/2}$ = 12,000 yr:

$$k = \frac{\ln 2}{t_{1/2}} = \frac{0.693}{t_{1/2}} = \frac{0.693}{12,000 \text{ yr}} \times \frac{1 \text{ yr}}{365 \text{ d}} \times \frac{1 \text{ d}}{24 \text{ h}} \times \frac{1 \text{ h}}{3600 \text{ s}} = 1.8 \times 10^{-12} \text{ s}^{-1}$$

$$\text{Rate} = kN = 1.8 \times 10^{-12} \text{ s}^{-1} \times 6.02 \times 10^{23} \text{ nuclei} = \frac{1.1 \times 10^{12} \text{ disintegrations}}{s}$$

For $t_{1/2}$ = 12 h:

$$k = \frac{0.693}{t_{1/2}} = \frac{0.693}{12 \text{ h}} \times \frac{1 \text{ h}}{3600 \text{ s}} = 1.6 \times 10^{-5} \text{ s}^{-1}$$

$$\text{Rate} = 1.6 \times 10^{-5} \text{ s}^{-1} \times 6.02 \times 10^{23} \text{ nuclei} = \frac{9.6 \times 10^{18} \text{ disintegrations}}{s}$$

For $t_{1/2}$ = 12 min:

$$\text{Rate} = \frac{0.693}{12 \text{ min}} \times \frac{1 \text{ min}}{60 \text{ s}} \times 6.02 \times 10^{23} \text{ nuclei} = \frac{5.8 \times 10^{20} \text{ disintegrations}}{s}$$

For $t_{1/2}$ = 12 s:

$$\text{Rate} = \frac{0.693}{12 \text{ s}} \times 6.02 \times 10^{23} \text{ nuclei} = \frac{3.5 \times 10^{22} \text{ disintegrations}}{s}$$

14. $t_{1/2} = 5730$ yr; $k = (\ln 2)/t_{1/2}$; $\ln (N/N_o) = -kt$

$$\ln \left(\frac{N}{N_o} \right) = \frac{-0.6931\, t}{t_{1/2}} = \frac{-0.6931\, (2200\text{ yr})}{5730\text{ yr}} = -0.27, \quad \frac{N}{N_o} = e^{-0.27} = 0.76 = 76\% \text{ of } {}^{14}\text{C remains}$$

18. $k = (\ln 2)/t_{1/2}$; $\ln \left(\dfrac{N}{N_o} \right) = -kt = \dfrac{-0.6931\, t}{t_{1/2}}$, $\ln \left(\dfrac{N}{15.3} \right) = \dfrac{-0.6931\, (15{,}000\text{ yr})}{5730\text{ yr}}$

$\ln N = -1.81 + \ln 15.3 = -1.81 + 2.728 = 0.92$, $N = 2.5$ disintegrations per minute per g of C

If we had 10. mg C, we would see:

$$10.\text{ mg} \times \frac{1\text{ g}}{1000\text{ mg}} \times \frac{2.5\text{ disintegrations}}{\min \text{ g}} = \frac{0.025\text{ disintegrations}}{\min}$$

It would take roughly 40 min to see a single disintegration. This is too long to wait and the background radiation would probably be much greater than the ^{14}C activity. Thus, ^{14}C dating is not practical for small samples.

19.   Since 4.5×10^9 years is equal to the half-life, one-half of the ^{238}U atoms will have been converted to ^{206}Pb. The numbers of atoms of ^{206}Pb and ^{238}U will be equal. Thus, the mass ratio is equal to the molar mass ratio:

$$\frac{206}{238} = 0.866$$

20.   a.   The decay of ^{40}K is not the sole source of ^{40}Ca.

b.   Decay of ^{40}K is the sole source of ^{40}Ar and that no ^{40}Ar is lost over the years.

c. $\dfrac{0.95\text{ g } {}^{40}\text{Ar}}{1.00\text{ g } {}^{40}\text{K}} = $ current mass ratio

0.95 g of ^{40}K decayed to ^{40}Ar. 0.95 g of ^{40}K is only 10.7% of the total ^{40}K that decayed, or:

0.107 (m) = 0.95 g, m = 8.9 g = total mass of ^{40}K that decayed

Mass of ^{40}K when the rock was formed was 1.00 g + 8.9 g = 9.9 g.

$$\ln \left(\frac{1.00\text{ g } {}^{40}\text{K}}{9.9\text{ g } {}^{40}\text{K}} \right) = -kt = \frac{-(\ln 2)\, t}{t_{1/2}} = \frac{-0.6931\, t}{1.27 \times 10^9 \text{ yr}}, \quad t = 4.2 \times 10^9 \text{ years old}$$

d.   If some ^{40}Ar escaped then the measured ratio of ^{40}Ar/^{40}K is less than it should be. We would calculate the age of the rocks to be less than it actually is.

22.   a. In 175 mg $Na_3^{32}PO_4$ there are 33.9 mg ^{32}P (see Exercise 21.21).

$$33.9 \times 10^{-3} \text{ g} \times \frac{1 \text{ mol}}{32.0 \text{ g}} \times \frac{6.022 \times 10^{23} \text{ atoms}}{\text{mol}} = 6.38 \times 10^{20} \text{ atoms } ^{32}P; \quad k = (\ln 2)/t_{1/2}$$

$$\text{Rate} = kN = \frac{0.6931}{14.3 \text{ d}} \times \frac{1 \text{ d}}{24 \text{ h}} \times \frac{1 \text{ h}}{3600 \text{ s}} \times 6.38 \times 10^{20} \text{ atoms} = 3.58 \times 10^{14} \text{ disintegrations/s}$$

$$\text{Rate} = \frac{3.58 \times 10^{14} \text{ disint.}}{\text{s}} \times \frac{1 \text{ Ci}}{3.7 \times 10^{10} \frac{\text{disint.}}{\text{s}}} \times \frac{1000 \text{ mCi}}{\text{Ci}} = 9.7 \times 10^6 \text{ mCi}$$

b. $$\text{Rate} = kN = \frac{0.693}{24,000 \text{ yr}} \times \frac{1 \text{ yr}}{365 \text{ d}} \times \frac{1 \text{ d}}{24 \text{ h}} \times \frac{1 \text{ h}}{3600 \text{ s}} \times 6.0 \times 10^{23} \text{ nuclei} = 5.5 \times 10^{11} \text{ disint./s}$$

$$\text{Rate} = \frac{5.5 \times 10^{11} \text{ disint.}}{\text{s}} \times \frac{1 \text{ Ci}}{3.7 \times 10^{10} \frac{\text{disint.}}{\text{s}}} \times \frac{1000 \text{ mCi}}{\text{Ci}} = 1.5 \times 10^4 \text{ mCi}$$

Energy Changes in Nuclear Reactions

26. $\Delta E = \Delta mc^2$, $\Delta m = \dfrac{\Delta E}{c^2} = \dfrac{3.9 \times 10^{23} \text{ kg m}^2/\text{s}^2}{(3.00 \times 10^8 \text{ m/s})^2} = 4.3 \times 10^6 \text{ kg}$

The sun loses 4.3×10^6 kg of mass each second.

27. $\dfrac{1.8 \times 10^{14} \text{ kJ}}{\text{s}} \times \dfrac{1000 \text{ J}}{\text{kJ}} \times \dfrac{3600 \text{ s}}{\text{h}} \times \dfrac{24 \text{ h}}{\text{day}} = 1.6 \times 10^{22} \text{ J}$

$\Delta E = \Delta mc^2$, $\Delta m = \dfrac{\Delta E}{c^2} = \dfrac{1.6 \times 10^{22} \text{ J}}{(3.00 \times 10^8 \text{ m/s})^2} = 1.8 \times 10^5$ kg of solar material provides 1 day of solar energy to the earth.

$1.6 \times 10^{22} \text{ J} \times \dfrac{1 \text{ kJ}}{1000 \text{ J}} \times \dfrac{1 \text{ g}}{32 \text{ kJ}} \times \dfrac{1 \text{ kg}}{1000 \text{ g}} = 5.0 \times 10^{14}$ kg of coal is needed to provide the same amount of energy.

28. $12 \, _1^1H + 12 \, _0^1n + 12 \, _{-1}^{\;0}e \rightarrow \, _{12}^{24}Mg$; mass of proton = 1.00728 amu

$\Delta m = 23.9850$ amu $-[12(1.00728) + 12(1.00866) + 12(5.49 \times 10^{-4})]$amu $= -0.2129$ amu

$\Delta E = \Delta mc^2 = -0.2129$ amu $\times \dfrac{1 \text{ g}}{6.0221 \times 10^{23} \text{ amu}} \times \dfrac{1 \text{ kg}}{1000 \text{ g}} \times (2.9979 \times 10^8 \text{ m/s})^2 = -3.177 \times 10^{-11} \text{ J}$

$\dfrac{\text{BE}}{\text{nucleon}} = \dfrac{-3.177 \times 10^{-11} \text{ J}}{24} = \dfrac{-1.324 \times 10^{-12} \text{ J}}{\text{nucleon}}$

For ^{27}Mg: $12\ {}^{1}_{1}\text{H} + 15\ {}^{1}_{0}\text{n} + 12\ {}^{0}_{-1}\text{e} \rightarrow {}^{27}_{12}\text{Mg}$

$\Delta m = 26.9843$ amu $- [12(1.00728) + 15(1.00866) + 12(5.49 \times 10^{-4})]$ amu $= -0.2395$ amu

$\Delta E = \Delta mc^2 = -0.2395$ amu $\times \dfrac{1\ \text{g}}{6.0221 \times 10^{23}\ \text{amu}} \times \dfrac{1\ \text{kg}}{1000\ \text{g}} \times (2.9979 \times 10^8\ \text{m/s})^2 = -3.574 \times 10^{-11}$ J

$\dfrac{\text{BE}}{\text{nucleon}} = \dfrac{-3.574 \times 10^{-11}\ \text{J}}{27\ \text{nucleons}} = \dfrac{-1.324 \times 10^{-12}\ \text{J}}{\text{nucleon}}$

32. $\Delta m = -2(5.486 \times 10^{-4}\ \text{amu}) = -10.97 \times 10^{-4}$ amu

$\Delta E = \Delta mc^2 = -10.97 \times 10^{-4}$ amu $\times \dfrac{1 \times 10^{-3}\ \text{kg}}{6.0221 \times 10^{23}\ \text{amu}} \times (2.9979 \times 10^8\ \text{m/s})^2 = -1.637 \times 10^{-13}$ J

$E_{\text{photon}} = 1/2(1.637 \times 10^{-13}\ \text{J}) = 8.185 \times 10^{-14}\ \text{J} = hc/\lambda$

$\lambda = \dfrac{hc}{E} = \dfrac{6.6261 \times 10^{-34}\ \text{J s} \times (2.9979 \times 10^8\ \text{m/s})}{8.185 \times 10^{-14}\ \text{J}} = 2.427 \times 10^{-12}\ \text{m} = 2.427 \times 10^{-3}$ nm

35. ${}^{1}_{1}\text{H} + {}^{1}_{1}\text{H} \rightarrow {}^{2}_{1}\text{H} + {}^{1}_{+1}\text{e};\ \ \Delta m = (2.01410\ \text{amu} - m_e + m_e) - 2(1.00782\ \text{amu} - m_e)$

$\Delta m = 2.01410 - 2(1.00782) + 2(0.000549) = -4.4 \times 10^{-4}$ amu for two protons reacting

When two mol of protons undergo fusion, $\Delta m = -4.4 \times 10^{-4}$ g.

$\Delta E = \Delta mc^2 = -4.4 \times 10^{-7}\ \text{kg} \times (3.00 \times 10^8\ \text{m/s})^2 = -4.0 \times 10^{10}$ J

$\dfrac{-4.0 \times 10^{10}\ \text{J}}{2\ \text{mol protons}} \times \dfrac{1\ \text{mol}}{1.01\ \text{g}} = -2.0 \times 10^{10}$ J/g of hydrogen nuclei

36. ${}^{2}_{1}\text{H} + {}^{3}_{1}\text{H} \rightarrow {}^{4}_{2}\text{He} + {}^{1}_{0}\text{n};$ Mass of electrons cancel when determining Δm for the nuclear reaction.

$\Delta m = [4.00260 + 1.00866 - (2.01410 + 3.01605)]$ amu $= -1.889 \times 10^{-2}$ amu

For production of 1.0 mol of ${}^{4}_{2}\text{He}$: $\Delta m = -1.889 \times 10^{-2}\ \text{g} = -1.889 \times 10^{-5}$ kg

$\Delta E = \Delta mc^2 = -1.889 \times 10^{-5}\ \text{kg} \times (2.9979 \times 10^8\ \text{m/s})^2 = -1.698 \times 10^{12}$ J/mol

For 1 nuclei of ${}^{4}_{2}\text{He}$:

$-1.698 \times 10^{12}\ \text{J/mol} \times \dfrac{1\ \text{mol}}{6.0221 \times 10^{23}\ \text{nuclei}} = -2.820 \times 10^{-12}$ J/nuclei

Detection, Uses, and Health Effects of Radiation

37.   The chemical properties determine where a radioactive material may be concentrated in the body or how easily it may be excreted. The length of time of exposure and what is exposed to radiation significantly affects the health hazard. (See exercise 21.46 for a specific example.)

38.   Not all of the emitted radiation enters the Geiger-Müller tube. The fraction of radiation entering the tube must be constant.

39.   The Geiger-Müller tube has a certain response time. After the gas in the tube ionizes to produce a "count," some time must elapse for the gas to return to an electrically neutral state. The response of the tube levels because at high activities radioactive particles are entering the tube faster than the tube can respond to them.

40.   All evolved O_2 comes from water.

41.   A nonradioactive substance can be put in equilibrium with a radioactive substance. The two materials can then be checked to see if all the radioactivity remains in the original material or if it has been scrambled by the equilibrium.

43.   Assuming that the radionuclide is long lived enough such that no significant decay occurs during the time of the experiment, the total counts of radioactivity injected are:

$$0.10 \text{ mL} \times \frac{5.0 \times 10^3 \text{ cpm}}{\text{mL}} = 5.0 \times 10^2 \text{ cpm}$$

Assuming that the total activity is uniformly distributed only in the rats blood, the blood volume is:

$$\frac{48 \text{ cpm}}{\text{mL}} \times V = 5.0 \times 10^2 \text{ cpm}, \quad V = 10.4 \text{ mL} = 10. \text{ mL}$$

Additional Exercises

45. $\Delta x \cdot \Delta(mv) \geq h/4\pi; \quad \Delta(mv) = v\Delta m; \quad \text{Assume } \Delta x(v\Delta m) = h/4\pi$

$$\Delta m = \frac{h}{4\pi(\Delta x)(v)} = \frac{6.63 \times 10^{-34} \text{ J s}}{4(3.14)(1 \times 10^{-35} \text{ m})(3.0 \times 10^7 \text{ m/s})} = 2 \times 10^{-7} \text{ kg}$$

mass of electron, $m_e = 9 \times 10^{-31}$ kg; mass of proton, $m_p = 1.7 \times 10^{-27}$ kg

$$\frac{\Delta m}{m_e} = \frac{2 \times 10^{-7}}{9 \times 10^{-31}} = 2 \times 10^{23}; \quad \frac{\Delta m}{m_p} = \frac{2 \times 10^{-7}}{1.7 \times 10^{-27}} = 1 \times 10^{20}$$

The uncertainty in the superstring mass is 2×10^{23} times the electron mass and 1×10^{20} times the proton mass.

46.   i) and ii) mean that Pu is not a significant threat outside the body. Our skin is sufficient to keep out the α particles. If Pu gets inside the body, it is easily oxidized to Pu^{4+} (iv), which is chemically similar to Fe^{3+} (iii). Thus, Pu^{4+} will concentrate in tissues where Fe^{3+} is found. One of these is the bone marrow where red blood cells are produced. Once inside the body, α particles cause considerable damage.

48.   For fusion reactions, a collision of sufficient energy must occur between two positively charged particles to initiate the reaction. This requires high temperatures. In fission, an electrically neutral neutron collides with the positively charged nucleus. This has a much lower activation energy.

49.   The temperatures of fusion reactions are so high that all physical containers would be destroyed. At these high temperatures most of the electrons are stripped from the atoms. A plasma of gaseous ions is formed which can be controlled by magnetic fields.

51.   Moderator: Slows the neutrons.

        Control rods: Absorbs neutrons to slow or halt the fission reaction.

54.   a. ^{12}C; It takes part in the first step of the reaction but is regenerated in the last step. ^{12}C is not consumed.

        b. ^{13}N, ^{13}C, ^{14}N, ^{15}O, and ^{15}N are intermediates.

        c.   Since protons are reacting in this fusion process, we will calculate the energy released per mole of hydrogen nuclei (^{1}H).

        $$4\,^{1}_{1}H \rightarrow \,^{4}_{2}He + 2\,^{0}_{+1}e; \;\; \Delta m = 4.00260 \text{ amu} - 2\,m_e + 2\,m_e - 4(1.00782 \text{ amu} - m_e)$$

        $\Delta m = 4.00260 - 4(1.00782) + 4(0.000549) = -0.02648$ amu for 4 protons reacting

        For 4 mol of protons, $\Delta m = -0.02648$ g.

        $\Delta E = \Delta mc^2 = -2.648 \times 10^{-5}$ kg $(2.9979 \times 10^8$ m/s$)^2 = -2.380 \times 10^{12}$ J

        $$\frac{-2.380 \times 10^{12} \text{ J}}{4 \text{ mol }^{1}H} = \frac{-5.950 \times 10^{11} \text{ J}}{\text{mol }^{1}H}$$

CHAPTER TWENTY-TWO

ORGANIC CHEMISTRY

Hydrocarbons

1. $CH_3-CH_2-CH_2-CH_2-CH_2-CH_3$ hexane or n-hexane (highest b.p., least branched)

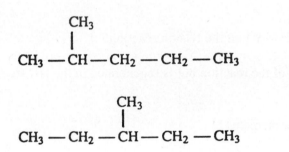

2-methylpentane

3-methylpentane

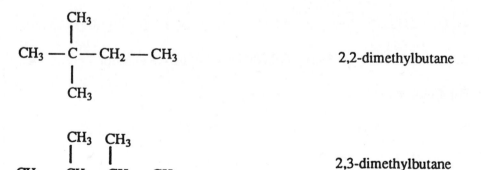

2,2-dimethylbutane

2,3-dimethylbutane

n-Hexane would have the highest boiling point. It is the least branched and, therefore, will have the strongest London dispersion forces between molecules.

2.   a. 2,3,3-trimethylhexane   b. 8-ethyl-2,5,5-trimethyldecane

    c. 3-methylhexane

3.   There is only one consecutive chain of C-atoms. They are not all in a true straight line since the bond angle at each carbon is a tetrahedral angle of 109.5°.

4.   a. $CH_3 - CH - CH_2 - CH_2 CH_3$
           $\quad\quad\quad |$
           $\quad\quad\quad CH_3$

      b.
           $\quad\quad\quad\quad CH_3$
           $\quad\quad\quad\quad |$
           $CH_3 - C - CH_2 - CH - CH_3$
           $\quad\quad\quad\quad |\quad\quad\quad\quad |$
           $\quad\quad\quad\quad CH_3\quad\quad CH_3$

      c. $CH_3 - CH - CH_2 CH_2 CH_3$
           $\quad\quad\quad\quad |$
           $CH_3 - C - CH_3$
           $\quad\quad\quad\quad |$
           $\quad\quad\quad\quad CH_3$

      d.   The longest chain is 6 carbons long.
           $$\overset{\;}{CH_3} - \overset{3}{CH} - \overset{4}{CH_2} - \overset{5}{CH_2} - \overset{6}{CH_3}$$
           $\quad\quad\quad\quad |2$
           $CH_3 - C - CH_3$
           $\quad\quad\quad\quad |1$
           $\quad\quad\quad\quad CH_3 \quad\quad$ 2,2,3-trimethylhexane

5.   a.   1-butene   b.   2-methyl-2-butene   c.   2,5-dimethyl-3-heptene

6.   a. $CH_3 - CH_2 - CH = CH - CH_2 - CH_3$ b. $CH_3CH = CHCH = CHCH_2CH_3$

      c. CH_3
                $|$
           $CH_3 - CH - CH = CHCH_2 CH_2 CH_2 CH_3$

7.   a. CH_3
           $\quad CH_3$
           (benzene ring)

      b.
           $\quad\quad CH_3 \quad\quad\quad\quad CH_3$
           $\quad\quad |\quad\quad\quad\quad\quad\quad |$
           $H_3C - C - (ring) - C - CH_3$
           $\quad\quad |\quad\quad\quad\quad\quad\quad |$
           $\quad\quad CH_3 \quad\quad\quad\quad CH_3$

      c. $CH_2 CH_3$
           (benzene ring)
           $\quad\quad CH_2 CH_3$

8.   a.   1,3-dichlorobutane   b.   1,1,1-trichlorobutane

      e.   chlorobenzene   f.   chlorocyclohexane

      g.   3-chlorocyclohexene (double bond assumed between C_1 and C_2)

9.   a. methylcyclopropane   b. t-butylcyclohexane

      c. 3,4-dimethylcyclopentene

10.   isopropylbenzene or 2-phenylpropane

12.   **a.**   b.

```
        F                              Br   H   H
        |                              |    |   |
   H — C — F                      H — C — C — C — H
        |                              |    |   |
        H                              Cl   Cl  H
```

Isomerism

13.   Structural isomers: Differ in bonding, either the kinds of bonds present or the way in which
                               the bonds connect atoms to each other.

      Geometrical isomers: Same bonds but differ in arrangement in space about a rigid bond or
                               ring.

14.   Resonance: All atoms are in the same position. Only the position of π electrons are different.

      Isomerism: Atoms are in different locations in space.

      Isomers are distinctly different substances. Resonance is the use of more than one Lewis
      structure to describe the bonding in a single compound. Resonance structures are <u>not</u> isomers.

15.

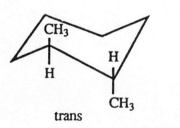

trans

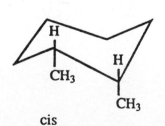

cis

16.

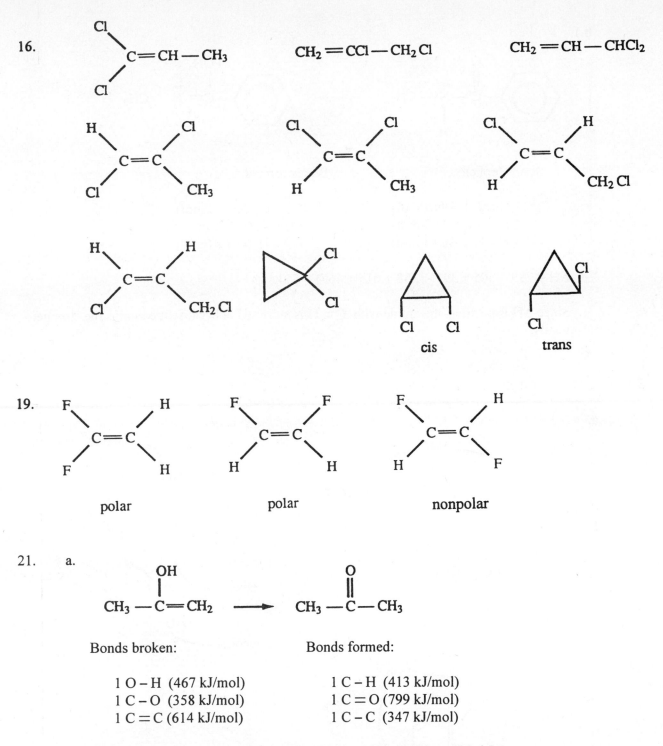

19.

polar   polar   nonpolar

21.   a.

Bonds broken: Bonds formed:

1 O – H (467 kJ/mol)   1 C – H (413 kJ/mol)
1 C – O (358 kJ/mol)   1 C = O (799 kJ/mol)
1 C = C (614 kJ/mol)   1 C – C (347 kJ/mol)

ΔH = 467 + 358 + 614 - (413 + 799 + 347) = 1439 - 1559 = -120. kJ

Since ΔH is negative, the ketone is more stable because it contains the stronger bonds.

b.

Bonds broken:

1 C＝O (799 kJ/mol)
1 C－N (305 kJ/mol)
1 N－H (391 kJ/mol)

Bonds formed:

1 C－O (358 kJ/mol)
1 C＝N (615 kJ/mol)
1 O－H (467 kJ/mol)

ΔH = 799 + 305 + 391 − (358 + 615 + 467) = 55 kJ

Since ΔH is positive, the amide with C＝O is more stable because it contains the stronger bonds.

Functional Groups

23.   **a.**

b.

c.

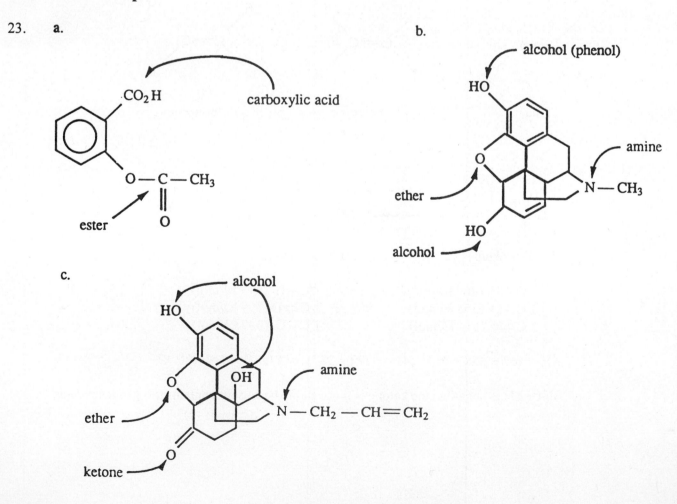

24.

$$HC\equiv\underset{13}{C}-\underset{12}{C}\equiv\underset{11}{C}-\underset{10}{CH}=\underset{9}{C}=\underset{8}{CH}-\underset{7}{CH}=\underset{6}{CH}-\underset{5}{CH}=\underset{4}{CH}-\underset{3}{CH}=\underset{2}{CH}-\underset{2}{CH_2}-\underset{1}{\overset{\overset{\displaystyle O}{\|}}{C}}-OH$$

26.   a.

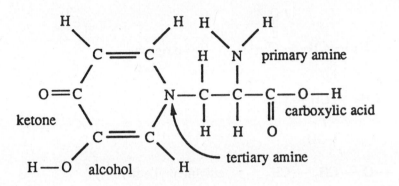

b.   5 carbons in ring and in –CO$_2$H: sp^2; the other two carbons: sp^3

c.   24 sigma bonds; 4 pi bonds

29.   Out of 100.00 g:

$$71.89\ g\ C \times \frac{1\ mol\ C}{12.011\ g\ C} = 5.985\ mol \approx 6\ mol\ C$$

$$12.13\ g\ H \times \frac{1\ mol\ H}{1.0079\ g\ H} = 12.03\ mol \approx 12\ mol\ H \qquad \text{The empirical formula is } C_6H_{12}O.$$

$$15.98\ g\ O \times \frac{1\ mol\ O}{15.999\ g\ O} = 0.9988\ mol \approx 1\ mol\ O$$

$$R_1-\overset{\overset{\displaystyle O}{\|}}{C}-O-R_2 + H_2O \longrightarrow R_1\overset{\overset{\displaystyle O}{\|}}{C}-OH + HOCH_2CH_3$$

R$_2$ must be CH$_3$CH$_2$ since CH$_3$CH$_2$OH is one of the products. The molar mass of –CO$_2$H is
≈ 45 g/mol, so the mass of R$_1$ is 172 - 45 = 127. If R$_1$ is CH$_3$–(CH$_2$)$_n$–, then 15 + n(14) = 127 and
n = 112/14 = 8. Ethyl caprate is:

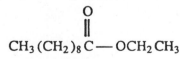

$$CH_3(CH_2)_8\overset{\overset{\displaystyle O}{\|}}{C}-OCH_2CH_3$$

The molecular formula of C$_{12}$H$_{24}$O$_2$
agrees with the empirical formula.

30.   a.   acetone:

$$CH_3 — \overset{\overset{\displaystyle O}{\|}}{C} — CH_3$$

aldehyde that is an isomer of acetone:

$$CH_3 — CH_2 — \overset{\overset{\displaystyle O}{\|}}{C} — H \qquad propanal$$

b.   2-propanol:

$$CH_3 — \underset{\underset{\displaystyle OH}{|}}{CH} — CH_3$$

ether: $CH_3 — O — CH_2 — CH_3$ ethylmethyl ether

c.   cis-2-butene:

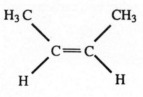

geometrical isomer:

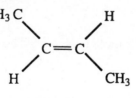

trans-2-butene

d.   trimethylamine:

$$H_3C — \underset{\underset{\displaystyle CH_3}{|}}{N} — CH_3$$

primary amine: $CH_3CH_2CH_2NH_2$ propylamine or 1-aminopropane

31.   a. ketone   b. aldehyde   c. ketone   d. amine

Reactions of Organic Compounds

33.   Substitution: An atom or group is replaced by another atom or group.

e.g., H in benzene is replaced by Cl. $C_6H_6 + Cl_2 \xrightarrow{\text{catalyst}} C_6H_5Cl + HCl$

Addition: Atoms or groups are added to a molecule.

e.g., Cl_2 adds to ethylene. $CH_2 = CH_2 + Cl_2 \rightarrow CH_2Cl - CH_2Cl$

34.   a.   Two monochloro products are formed: $CH_2ClCH_2CH_3$ and $CH_3CHClCH_3$

       b.   Four dichloro products are formed:

             $CHCl_2CH_2CH_3$, $CH_3CCl_2CH_3$, $CH_2ClCHClCH_3$ and $CH_2ClCH_2CH_2Cl$

35.   a. $CH_2 = CH_2 + Br_2 \rightarrow CH_2Br - CH_2Br$

       b. $C_6H_6 + Br_2 \xrightarrow{Fe} C_6H_5Br + HBr$

       c. $CH_3CO_2H + CH_3OH \rightarrow CH_3CO_2CH_3 + H_2O$

36.   a. $CH_3CH = CH_2 + HCl \rightarrow CH_3CHClCH_3$

       b. $CH_3CH = CH_2 + H_2O \rightarrow CH_3CHCH_3$
                                                    |
                                                   OH

       c.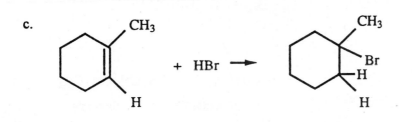

37.   a.   b.

             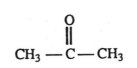

38.   **a.**

i.

$$CH_3 - \overset{\displaystyle O}{\overset{\|}{C}} - OH$$

ii.

$$\text{(ring)} - \overset{\displaystyle O}{\overset{\|}{C}} - OH$$

iii.

$$(CH_3)_2 CH\overset{\displaystyle O}{\overset{\|}{C}} - OH$$

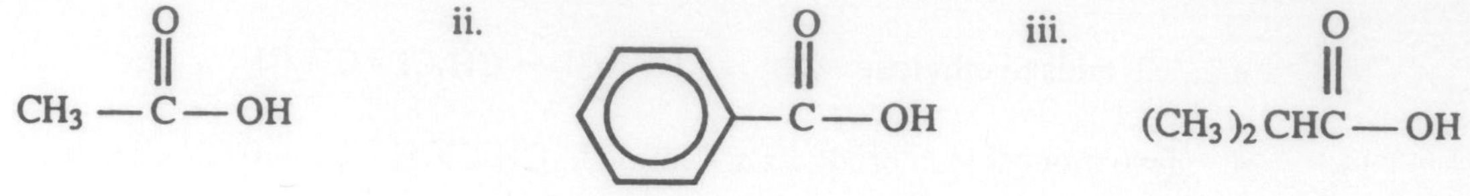

b.

$$CH_3 CH_2 OH \xrightarrow{[Ox]} CH_3 \overset{\displaystyle O}{\overset{\|}{CH}} + CH_3 \overset{\displaystyle O}{\overset{\|}{C}}OH$$

$$(CH_3)_3 C - CH_2 OH \xrightarrow{[Ox]} (CH_3)_3 C - \overset{\displaystyle O}{\overset{\|}{CH}} + (CH_3)_3 C - \overset{\displaystyle O}{\overset{\|}{C}} - OH$$

39.   **a.** $CH_3 CH = CH_2 + Br_2 \rightarrow CH_3 CHBrCH_2 Br$

b. $CH_3 C \equiv CH + H_2 \xrightarrow{\text{catalyst}} CH_3 CH = CH_2 + Br_2 \rightarrow CH_3 CHBrCH_2 Br$

c. $CH_3 CO_2 H + HOCH_2 CH_2 CH_2 CH_3 \longrightarrow CH_3 \overset{\displaystyle O}{\overset{\|}{C}} - O - CH_2 CH_2 CH_2 CH_3 + H_2 O$

ethanoic acid   butanol   butyl acetate or butylethanoate

Polymers

40.   **a.** Addition polymer: Polymer formed by adding monomer units to a double bond. Teflon, polyvinyl chloride and polyethylene are examples of addition polymers.

b. Condensation polymer: Polymer that forms when two monomers combine, eliminating a small molecule. Nylon and dacron are examples of condensation polymers.

c. Copolymer: Polymer formed from more than one type of monomer. Nylon and dacron are also copolymers.

42.

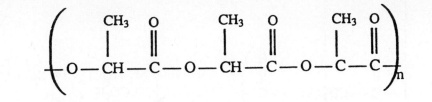

44.

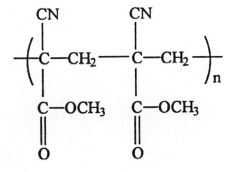

46.

a.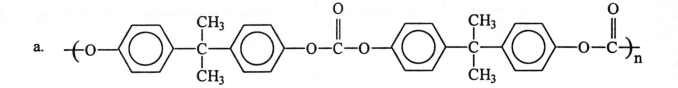

b.   Condensation; HCl is eliminated when the polymer bonds form.

47.   Divinylbenzene crosslinks different chains to each other. The chains cannot move past each other because of the crosslinks making the polymer more rigid.

48.   The stronger interparticle forces would be found in polyvinyl chloride since there are also dipole-dipole forces in PVC that are not present in polyethylene.

49.   a.   repeating unit: $\leftarrow$CHF — CH$_2\rightarrow_n$ monomer: CHF $=$ CH$_2$

   b.   repeating unit: monomer: HO – CH$_2$CH$_2$ – CO$_2$H

$$\left(-OCH_2\,CH_2\,\overset{\displaystyle O}{\overset{\|}{C}} - \right)_n$$

c.   repeating unit:

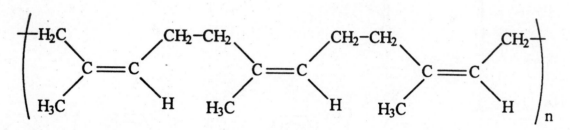

copolymer of: $HOCH_2CH_2OH$ and
$HO_2CCH_2CH_2CO_2H$

Additional Exercises

51.   a.   **2-methyl-1,3-butadiene**

      b.

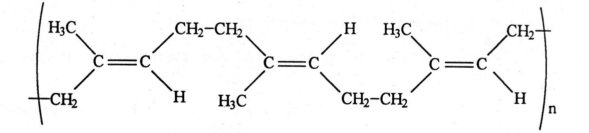

cis-polyisoprene (natural rubber)

trans-polyisoprene (gutta percha)

52.   a.

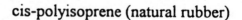

b.

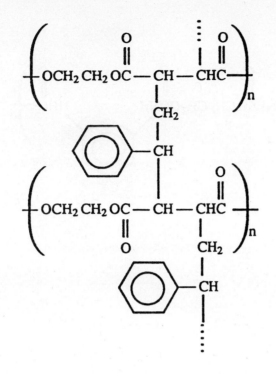

54.   For the reaction: $3\,CH_2 = CH_2(g) + 3\,H-H(g) \rightarrow 3\,CH_3-CH_3(g)$

   Bonds broken: Bonds formed:

   3 C$=$C (614 kJ/mol)   3 C$-$C (347 kJ/mol)
   3 H$-$H (432 kJ/mol)   6 C$-$H (413 kJ/mol)

$\Delta H = 3(614) + 3(432) - [3(347) + 6(413)] = -381\ kJ$

From enthalpies of formation: $\Delta H° = 3\,\Delta H_f°\,(C_2H_6) - 3\,\Delta H_f°\,(C_2H_4)$

$\Delta H° = 3\ mol(-84.7\ kJ/mol) - 3\ mol(52\ kJ/mol) = -410.\ kJ$

The two values agree fairly well.

For $C_6H_6(g) + 3\,H_2(g) \rightarrow C_6H_{12}(g),$ we would get the same ΔH from bond energies as the first reaction since the same number and type of bonds are broken and formed. $\Delta H = -381\ kJ$.

From enthalpies of formation: $\Delta H° = -90.3\ kJ - (82.9\ kJ) = -173.2\ kJ$

There is about a 208 kJ discrepancy. Benzene is more stable by about 208 kJ/mol (lower in energy) than we expect from bond energies. This extra stability is evidence for resonance stabilization.

56.

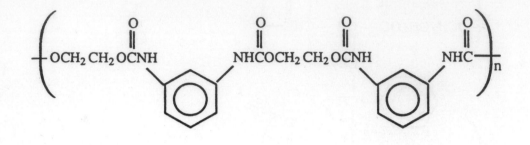

CHAPTER TWENTY-THREE

BIOCHEMISTRY

Proteins and Amino Acids

1.   a. $H_2NCH_2CO_2H \rightleftharpoons H^+ + H_2NCH_2CO_2^-$ $K_a = 4.3 \times 10^{-3}$

          $H_2NCH_2CO_2^- + H^+ \rightleftharpoons {}^+H_3NCH_2CO_2^-$ $K_2 = 1/K_a(\text{amino}) = K_b/K_w$

                                              $K_2 = 6.0 \times 10^{-3}/10^{-14} = 6.0 \times 10^{11}$

          $H_2NCH_2CO_2H \rightleftharpoons {}^+H_3NCH_2CO_2^-$ $K = K_aK_2 = 2.6 \times 10^9$

       Equilibrium lies far to the right since $K \gg 1$.

    b. ${}^+H_3NCH_2CO_2H$, $1.0\ M\ H^+$; $H_2NCH_2CO_2^-$, $1.0\ M\ OH^-$

2.   a.   Aspartic acid and phenylalanine

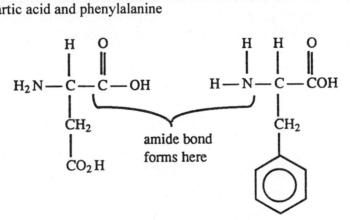

    b.   Aspartame contains the methyl ester of phenylalanine. This ester can hydrolyze to form methanol:

        $R\text{–}CO_2CH_3 + H_2O \rightleftharpoons RCO_2H + CH_3OH$

                                            R
                                            |

3.   Crystalline amino acids exist as zwitterions, ${}^+H_3N\text{–}CH\text{–}CO_2^-$. The ionic interparticle forces are strong. Before the temperature gets high enough to break the ionic bonds, the amino acid decomposes.

4.   They are both hydrophilic amino acids because both contain highly polar R groups.

7.   Glutamic acid: R = -CH₂CH₂CO₂H; Valine: R = -CH-(CH₃)₂

Glutamic acid: $R = -CH_2CH_2CO_2H$; Valine: $R = -CH\text{-}(CH_3)_2$

A polar side chain of the amino acid is replaced by a nonpolar group. This could affect the tertiary structure and the ability to bind oxygen.

10.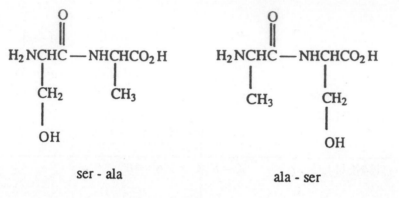

ser - ala   ala - ser

11.   Writing peptides from amino to carboxyl ends: ala-ala-gly, ala-gly-ala, gly-ala-ala
        Three peptides are possible.

13.   Both denaturation and inhibition reduce the catalytic activity of an enzyme. Denaturation changes the structure of an enzyme. Inhibition involves the attachment of an incorrect molecule at the active site, preventing the substrate from interacting with the enzyme.

14.   The initial increase in rate is a result of the effect of temperature on the rate constant. At higher temperatures the enzyme begins to denature, losing its activity and the rate decreases.

15.   All amino acids can act as both a weak acid and a weak base; this is the requirement for a buffer.

Carbohydrates

18.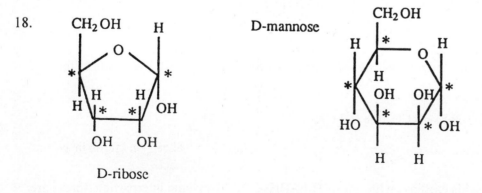

D-mannose

D-ribose

19.   Chiral carbons are marked with an asterisk in Exercise 23.18.

Optical Isomerism and Chiral Carbon Atoms

22.   Structural isomers: Same formula, different functional groups or chain lengths (different bonds).

       Geometrical isomers: Same functional groups (same bonds), but different arrangement of some groups in space.

       Optical isomers: Compounds that are nonsuperimposable mirror images of each other.

23.   A chiral carbon has four different groups attached to it. A compound with a chiral carbon is optically active. Isoleucine and threonine contain more than the one chiral carbon atom (see asterisks).

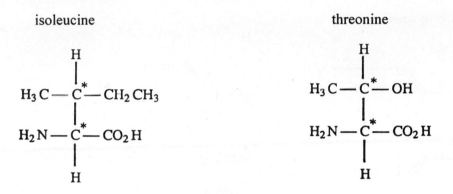

25.

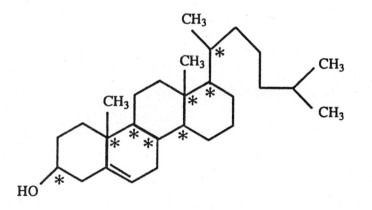

Each chiral carbon atoms (marked with *).

28.   A chiral carbon has four different groups attached to it. The two chiral carbon atoms in α-pinene are marked with a *. Since it has chiral carbons, α-pinene is optically active.

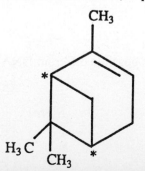

Nucleic Acids

30.   Nitrogen atoms with lone pairs of electrons.

31. $5 \times 10^9 \text{ pairs} \times \dfrac{340 \times 10^{-12} \text{ m}}{\text{pair}} = 1.7 \text{ m} \approx 2\text{m}$

       1.7 m corresponds to 5' 7".

33.   T-A-C-G-C-C-G-T-A

34.   For each letter, there are 4 choices; A, T, G, or C. Hence, the total number of codons is
       $4 \times 4 \times 4 = 64$.

35.   Uracil will H-bond to adenine.

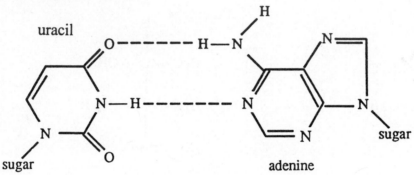

36.   Base pair: a. Glu: CTT, CTC

           RNA   DNA   Val: CAA, CAG, CAT, CAC

           A . . . . T   Met: TAC

           G C   Trp: ACC

           C . . . . G   Phe: AAA, AAG

           U . . . . A   Asp: CTA, CTG

       b. DNA sequence for Met - Met - Phe - Asp - Trp:

                   TAC - TAC - AAA - CTA - ACC
                              or   or
                             AAG   CTG

       c. Due to phe and asp, there are four possible different DNA sequences.

d.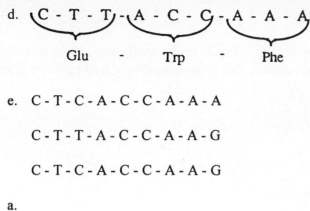

Glu - Trp - Phe

e. C - T - C - A - C - C - A - A - A

C - T - T - A - C - C - A - A - G

C - T - C - A - C - C - A - A - G

40.   a.

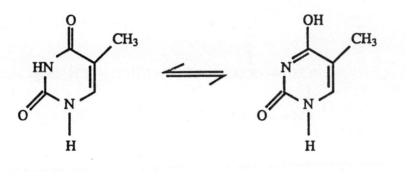

Bonds broken: Bonds formed:

   1 C = O (799 kJ/mol)   1 C - O (358 kJ/mol)
   1 N - C (305 kJ/mol)   1 N = C (615 kJ/mol)
   1 N - H (391 kJ/mol)   1 O - H (467 kJ/mol)

ΔH = 799 + 305 + 391 - (358 + 615 + 467) = +55 kJ

Since ΔH is positive, the structure with two C = O bonds is more stable.

b.   The tautomer could hydrogen bond to guanine, forming a G–T base pair instead of A–T.

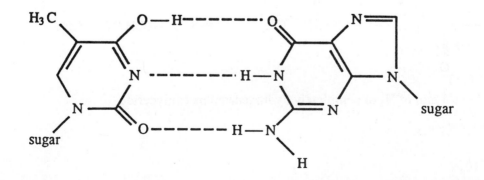

Lipids and Steroids

41.   Organic solvents are generally nonpolar solvents. Lipids are nonpolar and will be soluble in organic solvents. Carbohydrates contain several -OH groups capable of hydrogen bonding and are soluble in polar solvents (water).

42.

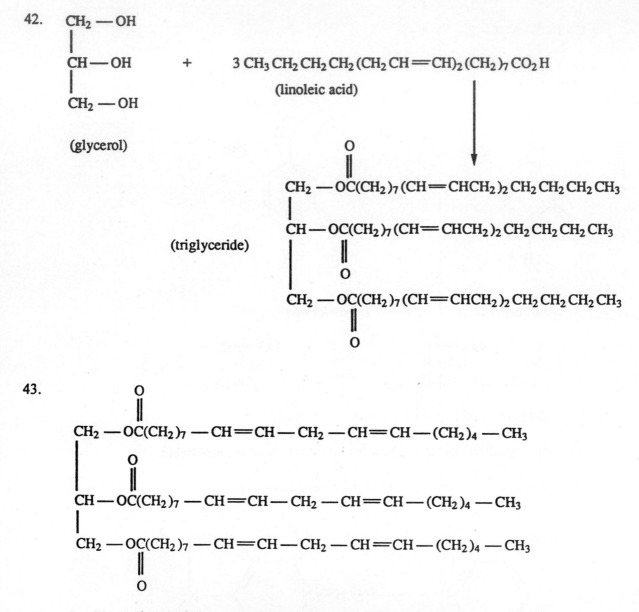

It will take 6 mol of H_2 to completely hydrogenate this triglyceride.

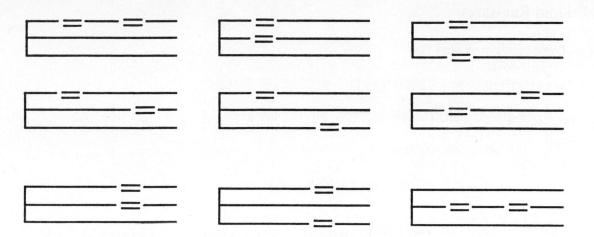

Nine products with 2 double bonds are possible as illustrated above.

47.   The R groups are all hydrophobic, alkyl chains from fatty acids.

Lecithin:

$$CH_2 - O - \overset{\overset{\displaystyle O}{\|}}{C} - R$$

$$CH - O - \underset{\underset{\displaystyle O}{\|}}{C} - R$$

hydrophobic

$$CH_2 - O - \underset{\underset{\displaystyle O}{\|}}{\overset{\overset{\displaystyle O\ \ominus}{|}}{P}} - OCH_2CH_2\overset{\oplus}{N}(CH_3)_3$$

hydrophilic

Sphingomyelin:

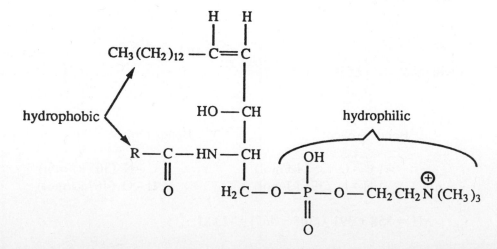

Additional Exercises

50.   From $-NH_2$ to $-CO_2H$ end:

phe-phe-gly-gly, gly-gly-phe-phe, gly-phe-phe-gly,

phe-gly-gly-phe, phe-gly-phe-gly, gly-phe-gly-phe

Six tetrapeptides are possible.

52.   a. $^+H_3N-CH_2-CO_2H + H_2O \rightleftharpoons H_2CH_2CO_2H + H_3O^+$

$$K_{eq} = K_a\,(-NH_3^+) = \frac{K_w}{K_b\,(NH_2)} = \frac{1.0 \times 10^{-14}}{6.0 \times 10^{-3}} = 1.7 \times 10^{-12}$$

b. $H_2NCH_2CO_2^- + H_2O \rightleftharpoons H_2NCH_2CO_2H + OH^-$

$$K_{eq} = K_b\,(-CO_2^-) = \frac{K_w}{K_a\,(CO_2H)} = \frac{1.0 \times 10^{-14}}{4.3 \times 10^{-3}} = 2.3 \times 10^{-12}$$

c. $^+H_3NCH_2CO_2H \rightleftharpoons 2\,H^+ + H_2NCH_2CO_2^-$

$$K_{eq} = K_a(-CO_2H) \times K_a(-NH_3^+) = (4.3 \times 10^{-3})(1.7 \times 10^{-12}) = 7.3 \times 10^{-15}$$

53.   For the reaction:

$^+H_3NCH_2CO_2H \rightleftharpoons 2\,H^+ + H_2NCH_2CO_2^- \qquad K_{eq} = 7.3 \times 10^{-15}$

$$7.3 \times 10^{-15} = \frac{[H^+]^2[H_2NCH_2CO_2^-]}{[^+H_3NCH_2CO_2H]} = [H^+]^2, \; [H^+] = (7.3 \times 10^{-15})^{1/2}$$

$[H^+] = 8.5 \times 10^{-8}; \quad pH = -\log\,[H^+] = 7.07 = \text{isoelectric point}$

55.   **a.**

$$H_2N-CH_2-CO_2H + H_2N-CH_2-CO_2H \rightleftharpoons$$

$$H_2N-CH_2-\overset{\overset{\displaystyle O}{\|}}{C}-\underset{\underset{\displaystyle H}{|}}{N}-CH_2-CO_2H + H-O-H$$

Bonds broken: Bonds formed:

1 C – O (358 kJ/mol)   1 C – N (305 kJ/mol)
1 H – N (391 kJ/mol)   1 H – O (467 kJ/mol)

$\Delta H = 358 + 391 - (305 + 467) = -23$ kJ

b. ΔS for this process is negative (unfavorable) since order increases.

c. $\Delta G = \Delta H - T\Delta S$; ΔG is positive because of the unfavorable entropy change. The reaction is not spontaneous.

56. $\Delta G = \Delta H - T\Delta S$; For the reaction, we break a P–O and O–H bond and form a P–O and O–H bond. Thus, $\Delta H \approx 0$. $\Delta S < 0$, since 2 molecules are going to form one molecule (order increases). Thus, $\Delta G > 0$ and the reaction is not spontaneous.

57.   Both proteins and nucleic acids must form for life to exist. From the simple analysis, it looks as if life can't exist, an obviously incorrect assumption. A cell is not an isolated system. There is an external source of energy to drive the reaction. A photosynthetic plant uses sunlight and animals use the carbohydrates produced by plants as sources of energy. For a cell, $\Delta S_{sys} < 0$, but $\Delta S_{surr} > 0$ and $\Delta S_{surr} > |\Delta S_{sys}|$. Therefore, ΔS_{univ} increases (the second law of thermodynamics).